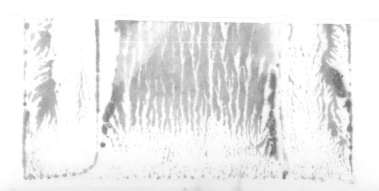

READINGS ON RACE

Edited by

STANLEY M. GARN, Ph.D.

Chairman, Physical Growth Department
Fels Research Institute
Associate Professor of Anthropology
Antioch College
Yellow Springs, Ohio

READINGS

ON

RACE

CHARLES C THOMAS • PUBLISHER
Springfield · Illinois · U.S.A.

CHARLES C THOMAS · PUBLISHER

BANNERSTONE HOUSE

301-327 East Lawrence Avenue, Springfield, Illinois, U.S.A.

Published simultaneously in the British Commonwealth of Nations by

BLACKWELL SCIENTIFIC PUBLICATIONS, LTD., OXFORD, ENGLAND

Published simultaneously in Canada by

THE RYERSON PRESS, TORONTO

Library of Congress Catalog Card Number: 59-14196

With THOMAS BOOKS careful attention is given to all details of
manufacturing and design. It is the Publisher's desire to present books
that are satisfactory as to their physical qualities and artistic possibilities
and appropriate for their particular use. THOMAS BOOKS will be true
to those laws of quality that assure a good name and good will.

Printed in the United States of America

PREFACE

During the past ten years the study of race in man has taken many new and exciting turns. In place of the comparative and historical directions characteristic of the century past, contemporary investigators are concerned with race as a part of human evolution. In this work, physicians, physiologists, population geneticists, serologists and biochemists are joined with physical anthropologists.

Up to now we have no textbook that portrays this new panorama. Moreover, any text written now would be premature: it would become obsolete almost as soon as it were published. What is needed is more a case-book than a text-book, a book that includes the theorists' own words and the investigators' plans of action. This is the purpose of *Readings on Race*.

In selecting the articles and papers that appear here a few of the more technical were deliberately omitted. Many publications relating to selection within A-B-O and Rh systems have been deferred until the direction of selection within particular race-populations becomes clear. Papers on preferential mating and other culturally-determined restrictions on gene-flow similarly have been held in abeyance, despite their obvious theoretical importance.

Intentionally, the index is not exhaustive. Each of the readings must be read as a unit, and the very nature of this work precludes its use as a textbook. However, the bibliographies accompanying each article are reprinted, with one exception, *in extenso*, and selected additional readings are suggested at the end of each introductory statement.

In this work the editor is indebted to many individuals, first among them the authors who have consented to be represented here. He further wishes to thank the editors of the journals who have given permission to reprint articles and the publishers of the various journals. He is grateful to Demarest L. Polacheck, who redrew the many figures in this book and to Joan A. Haskell and Lois A. Conklin for their very arduous editorial assistance. The librarians of the Fels Research Institute and Antioch College were most helpful throughout. The encouragement of Dr. Lester W. Sontag, Director of the Fels Research Institute, is again noted.

Needless to say, the editor accepts credit for including the fine work of others, and he also accepts responsibility for omitting or overlooking key articles and pivotal contributions.

STANLEY M. GARN

CONTENTS

READINGS ON RACE

I. INTRODUCTION

Up to 1950, the study of race in man consisted primarily of detailed descriptions of different races and populations, made for strictly comparative purposes. After 1950, the study of human races became a part of the study of evolution, and particular attention was paid to the evolutionary mechanisms operating in race formation. Thus, within a very few years a major field of investigation changed its sights, and to a lesser extent, its methods.

The men who studied race between 1850 and 1950 had two purposes in view. Whether they used anthropometry, ratings and descriptions, or whether they adopted the techniques of blood group genetics, their purposes were either taxonomic or historical. Quite correctly they realized that a satisfactory taxonomy, that is a classification, could be accomplished only if data on a great many human populations were collected and compared. And again, they realized that historical relationships could only be uncovered by the meticulous and detailed comparison of population differences and population similarities.

We might say now that the great bulk of the earlier studies on race were atheoretical, and lacked a sense of problem. Such a generalization is neither fair to the men whose travels brought them to the ends of the earth, nor does it do justice to the information they brought back, frequently at the risk of their lives. The multitude of earlier comparative studies on race lacked a theoretical matrix because there were few generally accepted theories to build on. Many studies lacked a sense of problem, as we see it now, because the problems of today were not recognized as problems even a few short years ago.

In the classic period of racial investigation, in the years when most of the descriptive studies were completed, the idea that races can change, scarcely was considered. Races, it was firmly believed, were fixed and immutable hereditary groupings, reaching back into dimmest antiquity. Investigating the mech-

3

anisms responsible for change, was therefore held as unnecessary. The notion that human races were the product of evolution had been denied by such an authority as Darwin himself, in his *Descent of Man*. Therefore, the causes of change (except for admixture or hybridization) or the rates of change, were not subjects for investigation.

Contemporary studies of race, however, are primarily concerned with change, and the emphasis on change constitutes a tremendous departure from the thinking of even a decade ago. Add to this the fact that today's students of race are actively exploring the mechanisms of evolution, the how, why and what of raciation and speciation, and the magnitude of the difference in approach to race becomes evident.

What accounts for the dramatic divergence between the racial studies of today, with their strong evolutionary undercurrent, and the earlier, primarily descriptive studies of race in man? Fortunately, we have the historical record to draw upon. We can point to the advent of evolutionary genetics effectively beginning with Fisher's *The Genetical Theory of Natural Selection* (1930). For years Darwinian evolution seemed incompatible with genetical theory. It was Fisher, and workers like Darlington, Mather and Wright who showed that evolution could be and should be comprehended in strictly genetical terms.

Following *The Genetical Theory of Natural Selection* by a decade there came the *New Systematics* (1942), and the organization of such groups as the Society for the Study of Evolution. Students of race in man gradually became aware of the important new genetical approach to speciation and raciation in other living forms. Simpson's work, especially his *Tempo and Mode in Evolution* (1944, 1947), and Dobzhansky's *Genetics and the Origin of Species* (1937, 1941 . . .) had obvious bearing on race-study in man. No one could read about the geographical and climatic factors that created races and even species of *Drosophila* without becoming aware of their implications to our own species.

Again, much credit should be given to the Cold Spring Harbor Symposium on Quantitative Biology held in 1950. There, overlooking Long Island Sound, over one hundred geneticists and physical anthropologists met, and though suspicious of each other at first, they came away cognizant of each other's problems, and each sharing the language of the other. No longer could physical anthropologists isolate themselves from the genetical approach to race. And, by the same token, human geneticists could no longer remain oblivious of the historical and comparative problems that physical anthropologists have to face as part of their work.

At first, the legacy of 1950, and the Cold Spring Harbor Symposium seemed overwhelming. While it was obvious that the mechanisms of evolution were the subjects to investigate, there was the very real problem of investigating natural selection, mutation and drift in modern man. How do you demonstrate natural selection operating within a contemporary race-population? Where and how do you investigate the evolutionary significance of polymorphism when human polymorphism had traditionally been explained in terms of admixture and trait-survivals, and not something important in its own right?

As is evident in the readings that follow, these methodological considerations have been both met and, in many cases, solved. Partially through luck and partially through sweat, the operation of natural selection within particular race-populations has been both documented and demonstrated. Genetic drift, the "Sewall Wright effect," has been sawed down to operational size and studied. Increasingly, experimental studies on human adaptations are replacing the purely speculative approaches. Inevitably, the study of race in man has moved out of the armchair and into the laboratory.

And yet we are still as far as ever from a reasonably adequate taxonomy for man. Most of Asia is now inaccessible to scientists from the western world: some compensation is offered by the endeavors of Indian scientists now mapping out their own subcontinent. Hopes of solving many of the complex interrelationships between populations were raised by the serologists, but these hopes appear dimmer now that we know that the serological traits too, are subject to natural selection.

The studies on race in man conducted since 1950, and others now in process, differ tremendously from the whole accumulation of studies in the century past. It is not enough to say that they are newly set in a theoretical matrix, that their direction is the direction of evolutionary biology, or that they are primarily concerned with the mechanisms of evolution that apply to races and race formation in man. These studies must be sampled to be appreciated, hence the reason for the present collection.

II. A CONTEMPORARY DEFINITION OF RACE

The term "race" has been used in various ways, not only by biologists, but also by politicians with little interest in the biological meaning of race. Even biologists, working in a pre-Darwinian and pre-genetical context, encountered difficulties in delineating the exact limits of a race. Further confusion was added in the twentieth century, when euphemisms for race were suggested, as a means of avoiding the word yet retaining its meaning.

At the present time there is general agreement that a race is a breeding population, largely if not entirely isolated reproductively from other breeding populations. The measure of race is thus reproductive isolation, arising commonly but not exclusively from geographical isolation. The extent of differentiation between any two races is therefore of subordinate importance to the fact of comparative isolation.

However, the one term "race" is inadequate to delineate the different taxonomic levels that can be seen and described in man. At one level there are *collections* of races including a number of natural populations, all contained within a particular geographical area. At a second level there are the identifiable, isolated local populations themselves. And, at a third level there are areas of the world, lacking truly isolated populations, but where clear-cut genetic differences distinguish one micro-race from another.

For taxonomic purposes, it is useful to describe the geographically-delimited collections of races as *geographical races,* following Rensch. Similarly, it is operational to distinguish the natural units or race-populations as *local races.* Lastly, in such areas as Europe or Southeast Asia, the widespread population, though not divisable into natural isolates, obviously constitutes a series of *micro-races.*

In 1950 Coon, Garn and Birdsell described a system of 30 races, all *local races* in the present terminology. In the same year, Boyd described a system of 6 races, all *geographical races*

7

as defined here. Since that time Boyd had enlarged his system, and consequently reduced the size of the taxonomic units considered. Despite inevitable differences in conceptualization and approach, the two systems are obviously drawing closer, as is evident in the two papers that are reprinted in this section.

ADDITIONAL READINGS

Count, E. W.: *This is Race*, New York, Shuman, 1950.

Washburn, S. L.: Thinking about race, *Science Education, 28*:65-76, 1944.

Dobzhansky, Th.: *Genetics and the Origin of Species*, Chapter VI, pp. 135-178, New York, Columbia University Press, 1951.

Coon, C. S., Garn, S. M. and Birdsell, J. B.: *Races: A Study of the Problems of Race Formation in Man*, Springfield, Thomas, 1950.

Boyd, W. C.: *Genetics and the Races of Man*, Boston, Little, Brown, 1950.

Garn, S. M.: The races of mankind, in *The Book of Popular Science*, New York, Grolier Society, Inc., 1958, Vol. 8, pp. 213-220.

Hunt, Jr., E. E.: Anthropometry, genetics and racial history, *Am. Anthropol., 61*:64-87, 1959.

On the Number of Races of Mankind

Reprinted from *American Anthropologist*, Vol. 57, No. 5, pp. 996-1001 (1955).

By STANLEY M. GARN *and* CARLETON S. COON

INTRODUCTION

Physical anthropologists, taxonomists, and geneticists are, with few exceptions, agreed that the genus *Homo* is represented by but one polytypic species to which all living races belong (Wiedenreich '46; Mayr '50; Dobzhansky '44). They are also agreed that there are races or equivalent taxonomic units sometimes designated by other names (Kalmus '50; Montagu '51). But there is considerable seeming disagreement as to how many races there are. Different taxonomies have listed as few as two races and as many as two hundred. Of two books on race that appeared in 1950, one distinguished six races, including a hypothetical Early European race (Boyd '50), while another described thirty races (Coon, Garn and Birdsell '50). Such divergences have not simplified the problem of teaching about race, nor have the reasons for the discrepancies always been made clear.

Actually, what seems to be a disagreement of considerable magnitude narrows down to a lack of agreement on just what taxonomic unit is properly designated as a race in man. What Boyd calls a race is a geographical unit, and Boyd's system of races admittedly resembles the "stocks" or "divisions" recognized by other workers. On the other hand, the populations listed as races by Coon, Garn, and Birdsell merit no special label in Boyd's system. Inescapably, applying the term "race" to the larger taxonomic unit results in a smaller number of "races," while restricting the term "race" to the smaller unit yields a larger number of races. There, and in a nutshell, lies the gap between four and forty races.

Agreement as to which taxonomic unit properly constitutes race in man is not easily achieved at this time. Carolus von

9

Linnaeus, the great classifier, and Blumenbach (whose taxonomy is most famous of all) both distinguished a small number of geographically delimited races. The rule of priority, therefore, favors the larger geographically defined taxonomic unit. But usage—the usage of the last century and, particularly, the usage of population genetics—favors restricting the term "race" to the breeding or Mendelian population (Dobzhansky '53:140). Thus we are confronted with two somewhat different concepts of race and no acceptable rule to resolve the conflict in favor of one or the other.

Fortunately, however, it is possible to retain both meanings while moving in the direction of simplicity and clarity. For there are collections of human populations having an obvious similarity and contained within particular geographical limits. Such a collection is properly a *geographical race,* as the term has been used by Rensch ('29), Mayr, and others. And there are the populations themselves, or *local races,* corresponding to the units that are subject to investigation. If we simply state whether we are referring to geographical races, of which there are a small number, or local races, of which there are many, the discrepancies mentioned above largely cease to exist.

GEOGRAPHICAL RACES

A geographical race is, in simplest terms, a collection of (race) populations having features in common, such as a high gene frequency for blood group B, and extending over a geographically definable area. In man, as in other widely ranging mammals, the geographical limits often correspond to continental areas. This is due to the fact that seas, oceans, and major mountain chains are more effective barriers to migration and "gene-flow" than are rivers and smaller land elevations.

The human stocks or divisions, recognized by many anthropologists, and the races of Linnaeus, Blumenbach, and Boyd are equivalent to geographical races as defined here. They include for the most part numbers of populations, the populations have many features in common, and the geographical areas correspond to the continents or to major island groups. There is much similarity between the areas inhabited by the different geographical races of man and the geographical regions drawn up by Wallace (1876) for other mammals. It is especially instructive to note that those human populations whose taxonomic status has been most in doubt inhabit areas where, following Wallace, we might expect separate geographical races. Examples are the Bushmen-Hottentot, who have been classified in and out of the Negro category, the non-Negrito Australian aborigines, and the Eskimo of panarctic or circumpolar distribution. However, we need not expect precise accord between geographical areas and geographical races in such an adaptable and footloose species as man. Rather we mean to stress the fact that the taxonomic unit immediately below the species is best defined as a geographical race. As Mayr ('50:110) put it: "The adoption of these intermediate categories facilitates classification without encumbering nomenclature."

LOCAL AND MICROGEOGRAPHICAL RACES

In contrast to geographical races, which are assemblages or collections of local race-populations and whose marginal members may be somewhat in dispute, there are also the populations called local races in the present terminology. These are units that can be subjected to study (*cf.* Thieme '52), and these are the units that change most in evolutionary time. In many cases such local races can be identified, not so much by average differences, but by their nearly complete isolation.

Yet, in more densely populated areas, neatly circumscribed and reproductively isolated populations may be hard to find. Europe, in contrast to the Americas in early colonial times, consists of a single sheet of humanity. And yet there are systematic differences as we proceed in any direction, and there are human islands where particular morphological or serological traits are especially common or unusually rare. Sheer weight of numbers, like distance and geographic barriers, serves to effect partial isolation and to preserve longstanding genetical differences. What we find in Europe, in particular, is not neatly defined local races but rather microgeographical races which differ only qualitatively from local races (*cf.* Dobzhansky '53).

A note should be added about those local race-populations formed in historic times as a result of admixture between different populations. Despite their recent and known origins, they constitute races just as good as those of greater antiquity and whose origins are shrouded in ignorance. Setting these recently formed races aside as "mixed" races does emphasize the existence of investigative problems peculiar to them, but it is not only an indefensible taxonomic practice but makes us appear more certain than we are about the origins of the older human groupings.

RELATIONSHIP BETWEEN LOCAL AND GEOGRAPHICAL RACES

In an earlier taxonomic day it was the fashion to assign, or to try to assign, every population to an appropriate geographical race. This effort was due in part to a desire for taxonomic neatness—a compulsive trait—and in part to the incorrect assumption that a taxonomy needs also serve as a phylogeny. As a result there have been some blatantly incongruous assignments, such as putting Australian aborigines in the Negro category, and some needlessly complicated categories for groups of presumed hybrid origin.

Europe, to be sure, is a special case. Except perhaps for the migrant gypsies and the formerly isolated Lapps, all local and microgeographical races in Europe do fit into a single European geographical race. The Americas constitute a second area where all purely indigenous local races can be assigned to an American or Amerindian geographical race. But in the rest of the world there are numerous populations that cannot be contained in a tidy system of three to seven geographical races. And, apart from compulsiveness, there is no compelling need to do so.

The aboriginal Australians constitute one such example. Sometimes granted a geographical race of their own, they have been assigned to the Negro category (on the basis of skin color) and again to the White category (on the basis of facial form and, occasionally, light hair color). These men of the bush have been shuttled between Negro and White in different taxonomies, upon the didactic assumption that they must be one or the other. Likewise, the hunters of the Kalahari, often placed in the Negro category, occasionally have been assigned to the Mongoloid group on the basis of an assumed yellow skin pigment that has never been demonstrated! In similar fashion other populations, such as the Ainu, have rested uneasily, being out of place in their present geographical area yet not acceptable candidates for membership in a European geographical race.

In addition to these rather isolated, small, and scattered populations, it is in India that the either-or system of assignment has led to the most serious problem. The millions in India do have a rather high gene frequency for B, yet (as Boyd now accedes [Boyd and Boyd '54]!) they are not Mongoloid. They are not Negroid either, despite a generally high skin melanin concentration, nor are they Caucasian in Blumenbach's sense. While India does merit a geographical race of her own, the lesson from India is that every population cannot be tagged in a simple system of but a few "major races" or "stocks."

ON THE NUMBER OF RACES OF MANKIND

Returning to the central theme of this paper, it is possible to achieve agreement on the number of races of mankind, once we distinguish between geographical races and local and microgeographical races. If a geographical race is defined as a collection of similar populations inhabiting a broad continental area or island chain, then the number of geographical races of man is approximately six or seven. And, if the local race is equated with the Mendelian population, then the number of local and microgeographical races is upwards of thirty.

Clearly one can recognize a European and Western Asiatic geographical race conforming to Blumenbach's category "Caucasian." There is a Northern and Eastern Asiatic geographical race, encompassing a very large number of local races. That there is an African geographical race goes without saying, as does the existence of an Indian geographical race. Micronesia and Melanesia merit a separate category, and the same is true for Polynesia. But the Americas constitute a particular problem. Anatomically the aboriginal Americans resemble Asiatics closely; serologically the dissimilarities are many. Since a taxonomy need not solve the complicated problem of origins, granting the twin Americas separate status seems advisable, and the number of geographical races here listed is thus raised to seven.

As to the smaller taxonomic unit, our enumeration depends on the minimum size of the population units we wish to consider (in the case of local races) and on the minimum degree of difference we choose to emphasize (in respect to microgeographical races). Regarding the Pitcairn Islanders and the inhabitants of Tristan da Cunha, though their numbers are small and their origins recent and "hybrid," both constitute happily breeding and effectively isolated local races. There are other local populations, like the Cowrie-shell Miao and the Lolos, the now extinct Tasmanians, or the British Colored (chiefly located in Liverpool), that may not be listed as races in an elementary textbook yet constitute perfectly good biological races. In fact it is rather shocking to see that American anthropologists, familiar with the large number of American populations, have failed to support the claims of these to racial status. For a realistic census of local races, starting at Point Barrow and ending in the Fire Islands, would come close to exhausting our minimum race list of thirty.

Microgeographical races pose the problem they always have —a problem long antedating the term. For in a large continuously inhabited continental area, where individual mobility is small relative to the size of the total population, there may be distinct regional differences without either geographical barriers or group endogamy to help in delimiting the "population." Thus for Europe various taxonomies have ranged from a simple dichotomous system, involving a Northern or "Nordic" and a Southern or "Latin" race, to systems utilizing all of the permutations of the Van Eikstadt taxonomy. To the extent that local differences within large populations are considered, rather than abstracted or idealized types, there is equal justification for finer or coarser divisions when dealing with microgeographical races.

Counting up the number of geographical races is comparatively simple, because there are a limited number of continents and islandic chains, and different human groups have radiated through and exploited each of them. A count of local and microgeographical races, however, is a more difficult procedure. Not only are we currently unable to enter into a very large section of the world, where many populations remain unstudied, but we have been remiss in investigating race-populations within our own national borders. These observations, plus the foregoing, should make it clear that in regard to the number of local and microgeographical races of man, the count is thirty *plus*. And the "plus" represents an indeterminate number at least as large as the thirty.

CONCLUSION

It has been the purpose of this paper to point out that no major discrepancy exists between one taxonomic system listing only six human races and a second system enumerating thirty, once the taxonomic units are adequately defined. Taking first the larger taxonomic unit, the geographical race, well under ten such geographical races seem sufficient in the present state of knowledge. The smaller taxonomic units, the local and microgeographical races, are of necessity more numerous. Local or microgeographical races, isolated by distance or by numbers and corresponding more nearly to Mendelian populations, are but barely represented by a taxonomy listing as few as thirty such "races."

Since adequate data are in many cases lacking, every local race cannot be assigned to an appropriate geographical race. While this frustrates attempts at a nicely tidy taxonomy, functioning as a phylogeny as well, the study of race and the investigation of ongoing evolution in man are in no way hampered. Rather it centers attention on the fact that geographical races are to a large extent collections of convenience, useful more for pedagogic purposes than as units for empirical investigation.

Local and microgeographical races, on the other hand, not only
are susceptible to direct study but also afford insight into the
evolutionary mechanisms still at work in shaping man.   For
such purposes a complete enumeration of the number of races
of man is needless.   A numerically small, out-of-the-way population of recent and hybrid origin may prove more informative
than a large Western population extending backward to the
dawn of European civilization.

REFERENCES

Boyd, W. C. and Boyd, L. G.:   The blood groups in Pakistan, *Am. J. Phys. Anthropol., N. S. 12*:393-405, 1954.

Boyd, W. C.:   *Genetics and the Races of Man,* Boston, Little, Brown and Company, 1950.

Coon, C. S., Garn, S. M. and Birdsell, J. B.:   *Races,* Springfield, Thomas, 1950.

Dobzhansky, Th.:   On species and races of living and fossil man, *Am. J. Phys. Anthropol., N. S. 7*:251-265, 1944.

Dobzhansky, Th.:   *Genetics and the Origin of Species,* New York, Columbia University Press, 1953.

Kalmus, H.:   *Genetics,* Harmondsworth, England, Penguin Books, 1950.

Mayr, E.:   Taxonomic categories in fossil hominids, *Cold Spring Harbor Symposia on Quantitative Biology, 15*:109-118, Cold Spring Harbor, The Biological Laboratory, 1950.

Montagu, M. F. A.:   *An Introduction to Physical Anthropology,* Springfield, Thomas, 1951.

Rensch, B.:   *Das Prinzip geographischer Rassenkreise und das Problem der Artbildung,* Berlin, Boentraeger, 1929.

Thieme, F.:   The population as a unit of study, *Am. Anthropol., 54*: 504-509, 1952.

Wallace, A. K.:   *The Geographical Distribution of Animals,* New York, Harper, 1876.

Weidenreich, F.:   Genetic, specific and subspecific characters in human evolution, *Am. J. Phys. Anthropol., N. S. 4*:413-431, 1946.

Genetics and the Races of Man

Reprinted in part from Boston University Lecture. December 11, 1957, pp. 1-12, Boston, Boston University Press (1958).

By WILLIAM C. BOYD

INTRODUCTION

Man is a curious animal, interested in many things. One of the things that interests him most is mankind itself, and he has devoted much thought, especially in the last few centuries, to the recording and interpretation of observations on the peculiarities of mankind. One of the features that impresses the common man and the scientist alike are the differences in customs, languages, skin color, and physique between human beings from different parts of the earth. It may be that we all have the makings of a taxonomist in us, for long ago people began, on the basis of such differences, to classify individuals from other nations and countries into races. The scientists who are most concerned with setting up such classifications are called anthropologists.

The first classifications were not very scientific. Originally people tended to confuse cultural traits, which are simply learned differences, with physical differences which are inherited and are not much influenced by environment. Thus the layman and early students of man attempted to classify mankind into races, for example, on the basis of language, and one heard of the Latin races, the Germanic races, the Slavic races, the Greek race, and even the Anglo-Saxon race. It is true that in some cases language is a guide to racial origins, as in the case of the French Canadians of Québec or the Pennsylvania "Dutch" of the United States, but languages can be, and are, forgotten by their original speakers and/or acquired by people of unrelated stocks, as the American melting pot shows us every day, so that the differences in the world's languages, fascinating and useful as they are to the linguist, are very shaky foundations for racial classification. Later skin color was utilized. One heard of a "white" race, a "yellow" race, a "red," "brown," and "black" race. The terms used are poor descriptions of actual human skin colors, but this method did have the advantage that color of the skin is only partly determined by the environment, being mostly an inherited characteristic. But it is too broad and vague a classification to be of much scientific value. Not all "black" races, for example, are closely related, as shown by the many differences between African Negroes, southern Indians of India, Australian aboriginals and Pacific Negritos. The color of the skin is evidently subject to fairly rapid change by natural selection, and the inhabitants of hot sunny regions all tend to develop high pigmentation because in this environment a dark skin is an advantage.

About a hundred years ago the Swedish anatomist, Anders Retzius, thought he had discovered a really scientific basis for racial classification, which was the shape of the head, in particular the ratio of the breadth of the head to its length. This is called the cephalic index, and has been much used by anthropologists. It has the agreeable feature that it can be applied to the skulls of ancient populations as well as to the heads of the living peoples of today.

It is true that the inhabitants of a given area tend to have similar cephalic indices, but it has not proved possible to erect a very satisfactory classification into races on the basis of this criterion alone, and we are now beginning to realize that no one criterion, even though based on an inherited character which is not influenced by the environment, can be enough for a good classification. The cephalic index, moreover, does not seem to be immune to changes which are presumably due to environmental influences and, although it is no doubt inherited, is determined by a genetic mechanism which we are as yet far from understanding. These and other considerations have led physical anthropologists in the last few decades to make more and more use, in racial classification, of characteristics inherited in a way which is completely understood. Instead of measurements of the proportions of the skull and other bones, we tend to make more use of the frequencies of certain genes in the population. For the present audience it is surely unnecessary to define a gene; let us say merely that the gene is the unit of heredity. The frequency of a gene can range from 1.00 (all members of the population have the gene) to zero (no member of the population has it). The use of gene frequencies has a number of advantages, of which I may mention three:

(1) The method of gene frequencies is completely objective. No element of subjective judgment enters into the determination of the frequency of a gene in a population, although the value of a frequency which divides two races is a man-made and arbitrary decision, as we shall see in a moment. (2) Tables of gene frequencies are more compact than tables of morphological and other features which may result from the action of the genes. In the Rh blood group system, for example, the frequencies of just 8 genes will summarize the variations in 27 possible blood types. (3) The gene method is quantitative rather than qualitative, so that the estimated gene frequencies give us an idea *how much* different races differ from each other, and enable us to predict the consequences of race mixture accurately.

This advantage in making quantitative comparisons is seen for example when we are dealing with a mixed race and wish to ascertain the proportions of the component races which went to make it up. Glass and Li were able to calculate from blood group data that North American Negroes have about 31 per cent white ancestry. From the rate at which race mixture has been progressing in this population Glass and Li were able to calculate that the American Negro will have become indistinguishable from the American white (in other words, be assimilated), *assuming mixture continues at the same rate as it has been going on in the past,* in some 1000 to 1100 years. In a later paper, Glass, using similar methods, was able to show that the common belief that North American Negroes have considerable amounts of American Indian ancestry is erroneous.* Such results could not have been obtained by morphological and metrical methods, or by studies of skin color.

---

*Reprinted in Section IX.

As another example of point (2), we may mention the Australian aborigines and the Ainu. Both these peoples have been called by some authors "basic white." However, in the present state of our knowledge of the inheritance of skin color, we cannot state how much the very dark skin of the Australian marks him off from the European. But a glance at his blood group frequencies tells us at once that he is pretty similar in regard to the original absence of B, but different in regard to M and Rh negative. We can probably account for the acquisition of the Rh negative gene by the Europeans on the hypothesis of mixture, and the peculiar M frequencies of the Australian by the selection of random genetic drift, which I shall discuss later. Thus it is not impossible to imagine a common origin for these diverse peoples, although they have by this time differentiated into separate races.

It is only when characteristics are inherited in a completely understood manner that gene frequencies can be calculated. The best methods of estimating gene frequencies, a subject which has interested me, are too mathematical for presentation here, however. In man there seem to be two classes of characteristics whose mode of inheritance is understood: (1) rare abnormalities such as Huntington's chorea, Marfan's syndrome, color blindness, and hemophilia, and (2) common normal characteristics, mainly blood groups.

Very rare characteristics are not satisfactory as a basis of comparison of different races and ethnic groups because the amount of data which would have to be collected is prohibitive. This rules out practically all the characteristics of type (1), and we are left with type (2).

It is presumably only an accident that the majority of characteristics of type (2) are blood groups, although there may be some feature of the blood groups which makes them peculiarly susceptible to genetic analysis. In any case, there is certainly no reason to suppose that other physical characteristics, if fully analyzed genetically, would be in any way inferior to blood groups as a basis for race classification, and I should not like my audience to think that my use of blood groups for this purpose is just a desire to use only the characters I have studied so long and understand relatively well, or in other words just an attempt to blow my own horn. When the genetic mechanisms of other physical characteristics such as head shape have been worked out, I propose to use them also.

It is surely unnecessary here to give much account of the human blood groups. They were discovered in 1900 by Karl Landsteiner. You all know that for purposes of blood transfusion human beings may be classified into four groups depending on the kind of blood they possess, and that it is important that donor and recipient belong if possible to the same blood group. The details of the separation into four groups may be a little more hazy in your minds, but that is not important for our present purposes. What is more important is to know that these four blood groups can be considered as resulting from the action of three genes, which we designate as A, B, and O, each gene capable of occupying a particular point (locus) of the appropriate gene-carrying structure. Such structures are called chromosomes. Since we all have two chromosomes of any particular sort, one from our father and one from our mother, it follows that six combinations of these genes exist, namely OO, OA, AA, OB, BB, and AB. When the O gene is accompanied by A or B, it does not exert any perceptible action, and OA and OB are not distinguishable in the laboratory from AA and BB respectively, thus giving us the four basic kinds of blood.

Most of you probably know that this is a rather oversimplified version of the actual situation, and that more genes are actually involved. You doubtless also know that another blood group system, the Rh system, is important in some transfusions and sometimes responsible for a disease of infants known as erythroblastosis fetalis, and that there are other blood groups in addition to these. In fact there are nine well-studied blood group systems, all independent (probably) in their inheritance, and a number of systems more recently discovered which have not been so well studied. It is mainly on the basis of the data concerning the nine best-known systems that our racial classification must be erected.

BLOOD GROUP SYSTEMS

The *ABO* blood group system has been known the longest and is consequently the best studied. Thousands of populations have now been tested.

The ABO system is not the most useful, anthropologically, but the availability of much more extensive data than for any other blood group system partially compensates for this, and even before such extensive information was available preliminary racial classifications based on the ABO system alone had been proposed.

The only populations having no A and no B are certain tribes of American Indians, although some American Indians possess moderate to large amounts of A. The Australian aborigines agree with the latter in possessing a high frequency of A. Nowhere besides North America is A so high, but on the other hand hardly anywhere else is it zero. The populations of the rest of the world differ mainly in the amount of B they possess; frequencies range from 0.04-0.05 in Western Europe and the Caucasus to nearly 0.30 in parts of Asia. The Basques, long thought to be an isolated remnant of a very early European people, have virtually no B.

The ABO data alone do not enable us to separate the peoples of the world into clear-cut races which make much sense geographically; they would for example force us to put some of the American Indians, the Australian aborigines, and the Baffin Land Eskimos into the same race, which hardly makes sense.

However, in view of the processes by which races are formed, we should not really expect to be able to make a satisfactory classification on the basis of any *one* series of genes. Also, the gradations (clines) between existing human populations are too gradual for sharp separation, and distant populations seem in some cases to have altered in the same direction.

The fact that blood antigen A can be divided into two main sorts of A, A_1, and A_2, probably determined by two corresponding genes, greatly increases the anthropological value of the ABO system. For it turns out that the A_2 gene is unknown in Eastern Asia, Australia, the Pacific and the American aborigines, being found only in the peoples of Europe, the Middle East, and Africa. The *proportion* of A_2 to A_1 is higher in Africa than in Europe, and the Middle East is in this respect as in others a transition area between Europe and Eastern Asia.

The second oldest blood group system, in order of discovery, is the *MN* system. The frequencies of M and N show less geographical variation than do the ABO frequencies, but two of the world's populations do differ sharply from the rest of the world (and from each other). These are the American Indians on the one hand and the Australian aborigines and Melanesians on the other. High frequencies of N, and consequently low M, are found throughout the Pacific area, with the highest N in New Guinea. In American Indians N is very low.

The anthropological value of the MN system has been increased very much by the discovery of a pair of antigens, S and s, which are closely associated with it. As a result we now postulate that 4 genes (or chromosomes), Ms, MS, Ns, and NS are involved instead of merely 2. Use of anti-S enables us to distinguish sharply between the natives of New Guinea, and the Australian aborigines, for antigen S is present in New Guinea and absent in Australia.

The *Rh system* is anthropologically the most useful blood group system, although fewer data are available than for ABO or MN. The 12 or more phenotypes distinguishable with the usual serums depend upon the action of more than 8 genes or chromosomes, and these genes, as I shall call them, vary significantly in frequency in different parts of the world.

May I note the high frequency of r (the Rh negative gene) in the Basques, the absence of this gene in Asians, American Indians, and Pacific populations, and the intermediate values of the black Africans? And finally the very high frequencies of R^o in black Africans, as opposed to its very low frequencies in the other populations (it seems to be actually absent in American Indians), make it practically an African gene.

More recently a new factor, V, has been found to belong to the Rh system. It is rare in whites but common in Negroes.

Time will not permit a discussion of the more recently discovered blood group systems, often identified by the name of the patient in whom they were first identified. I may mention one of them, however.

The *Duffy* blood groups promise to be among the most interesting of the new blood groups. In Europeans two genes, Fy^a and Fy^b are involved; in England the frequency of Fy^a is about 0.40. It is much higher than this in Lapland and Asia. In Africans there is another gene, which has been designated merely as *Fy*. This gene, unknown in Europeans save in rare individuals, is actually in Negroes the most frequent at this locus, having a frequency of over 0.8. Fy therefore, constitutes another "African" gene.

Aside from R^0, Fy and V, blood group genes which are virtually restricted to one race are mostly conspicuous by their absence, as would be expected from the way in which races originate. That still others may exist, however, is suggested by the recent discovery that a blood antigen called *Diego* was not found at all in 200 white Americans, but individuals positive for Diego constitute over 30 per cent of certain American Indian tribes and all American Indians so far tested possess at least a moderate amount of this antigen. This may constitute the discovery of an "American Indian" or Asian gene.

THE RACES DEFINED BY THESE DATA

Definition of Race. Everybody knows what races are, he supposes, yet people constantly use the word in different senses. Even our later discussion of the mechanisms of race formation, although it should make the general meaning of the concept clear, does not provide us with a definition. The reason for this is partly that race is a more subjective unit than is species, and classifications into races depend to a large extent upon the purpose and even the whim of the classifier. Until the differentiation of different populations has reached the stage of making them different species, it is often almost a matter of taste whether we separate them into different races, or lump them together as members of the same race. In particular the amount of difference demanded by classifiers for a basis of classification of two populations as two different races will vary. Some will be satisfied merely with a difference in skin color, others will demand that the two populations differ in a number of ways. In a book published in 1950 I defined 6 races on the basis of blood group data. In the same year Coon, Garn, and Birdsell published a book on race formation in which, using mainly morphological data, they defined 30 (possibly equally valid) human races, no one of which was identical with any of mine. Our points of view were actually not so different. It simply suited the purpose of Coon, Garn, and Birdsell to divide mankind up into 30 races, and it suited my purpose, at that time, to divide the human species into 6 races. Even if we had both been using only blood group data, there is the possibility that considerable differences in the number of races defined would still have been seen.

I have previously suggested a definition of a human race which I propose to use here: "a population which differs significantly from other human populations in regard to the frequency of one or more of the genes it possesses."

There are clear-cut differences in blood group gene frequencies which distinguish a number of human populations one from the other, and we may accordingly call these populations races. Since these differences are generally merely quantitative, that is, one population has more of one gene and less of another, it is not easy to present such distinctions without recourse to tables which it would not be easy to show under the present circumstances. I shall try to show you the general procedure by presenting the basis for the distinction between *Northwest Europeans,* to which race many of the present audience will belong, at least by descent, and *Lapps,* a small but very distinctive European race in northern Scandinavia.

The Northwest Europeans have fairly high percentages of blood group gene A and relatively low B (gene frequency of B less than 0.1). The frequencies of M and N are "normal," meaning that M is roughly equal to N, but perhaps a little higher. The frequency of A_2 is higher than in Africa (A_2 is absent in most of the rest of the world). The Rh negative gene has the highest frequency in the world except for the values found in the Basques. Fy^a about 0.4.

The Lapps have the highest N frequencies in Europe, a high value of the Duffy gene Fy^a, a very low B frequency (B is present everywhere in Europe except possibly in the Basques), and the A$_2$ frequencies are 3 times those found anywhere else in the world. The Rh negative gene (r) is relatively infrequent, another of the Rh genes, R^1, is somewhat above the usual European values, and another, R^2, is high.

Thus we see that the Lapps, a small and at present minor European group, are sharply distinguished from the group we think of as the principal European race. The distinction is so clear that the location of the Lapps is visible on a map of Europe on which virtually any of the blood group frequencies have been plotted. The distinctions between the other racial groups proposed below are mostly equally clear, and many subdivisions of these will undoubtedly become possible as more data accumulate.

At present I propose the following 13 races:

A. *European Group*: (1) Early Europeans, (2) Lapps, (3) Northwest Europeans, (4) Eastern and Central Europeans, (5) Mediterraneans.

B. *Africa*: I consider the Egyptians and North Africans to be predominantly European, and put only Africans south of the Sahara into (6) The African Race.

C. *In Asia* we have a very great diversity, but one can easily distinguish (7) The Asian Race, and (8) The Indo-Dravidian Race.

D. There are indications that the American Indians will prove to be separable into North American and South American types, at least, but at present I distinguish only (9) the American Indian Race. (I include the Eskimo in this race, although there are some differences.)

E. *Pacific Group*: The vast Pacific area still needs further investigation but the extensive studies of Simmons, Graydon, and associates have been largely summarized in papers dealing respectively with Micronesia, Indonesia, Melanesia with Australia, and Polynesia. Birdsell in the U. S. A., sometimes working in collaboration with the Australian investigators, has also done a great deal of fine work. Although it may be too soon to set up any definitive classification, it is tempting to classify the main Pacific populations (leaving Australia aside) into 3 races: (10) Indonesian Race, (11) Melanesian Race, (12) Polynesian Race.

F. *The Australian Aborigines* fall into the (13) Australian (aboriginal) Race.

III. EVOLUTION AND RACE

In a century dominated by the idea of evolution, surprisingly little attention was given to the evolution of human races. Although Blumenbach (1752-1840), Buffon (1707-1788) and Kant (1724-1804) were all evolutionists with respect to race in man, post-Darwinians steadfastly adhered to non-evolutionary explanations for racial diversity.

Understandably, there was a reluctance to apply natural selection to contemporary human beings. Some Darwinists felt that evolution stopped short of *Homo*. Others drew the line at *Homo sapiens*. Still others tried to juggle Genesis and the *Origin,* holding that the Hebrews were created by God, but that all other peoples were the product of organic evolution!

Moreover, the notion of evolving races was clearly antithetical to the doctrine of racial fixity. If, for the purpose of historical reconstructions, static and unchanging races were a necessary assumption, the idea of racial evolution could hardly be accepted. To paraphrase Aggasiz' famous letter, if races change how can there be races? Fixed, unchanging and static races fitted the nineteenth-century assumptions better, and were therefore accepted as fact.

The realization that race was a part of evolution was slow in coming, yet it was inevitable. If any date is to be associated with the revived interest in human racial evolution, 1946 is the date. Prior to that time the notion of changing race was largely untenable. Thereafter, and especially after 1950, evolution within human races was accepted, first on theoretical and later on experimental grounds. Today, it is a rare student of race who holds to the contrary opinion.

ADDITIONAL READINGS

Hall, T. S.: *A Source Book in Animal Biology,* New York, McGraw-Hill, 1951, pp. 38-51, 565-570.

Dobzhansky, Th.: *Genetics and the Origin of Species,* New York, Columbia University Press, 1951, or later edition.

Dobzhansky, Th.: Races, nature and origin of, in *Encyclopedia Americana,* Chicago, Americana Corporation, 1950, Vol. 23, pp. 107-111.

Race and Evolution

Reprinted from *American Anthropologist*, Vol. 59, No. 2, pp. 218-224 (1957).

By Stanley M. Garn

INTRODUCTION

Until rather recently race in man was held to be fixed, unchanging, and static, stable over long periods of time, except in the event of "admixture." And in similar fashion the criteria of race, the natural characteristics that distinguish one race from another, were also considered as constants, neither adaptive nor inadaptive, but adaptively neutral.

Franz Boas opened a new chapter in physical anthropology by demonstrating the plastic nature of those metric traits once extensively used as taxonomic criteria. But to Boas, race itself was fixed, a race being "a stable type reaching into deep antiquity" (Herskovits '43:43).

Earnest Hooton did more than anyone else to spur popular interest in human evolution. Yet in the first edition of *Up from the Ape,* and for some years afterward, he insisted upon nonadaptive bodily characters as racial criteria (*cf.* Hooton '46:452).

It is not surprising, therefore, that the blood groups were first extolled as of particular taxonomic value on the basis of supposed adaptive neutrality. Blood groups were hereditary, free from environmental modification, and there was no reason to suppose that A had any advantage over B, or disadvantage compared to O. Seemingly, blood groups were the answer to the taxonomist's prayer.

Now the concept of static race and of stable racial criteria had, on the surface, much to recommend it. In particular, the reconstruction of racial history and the analysis of race-mixture appeared quite simple, if race itself did not change. To trace a race you merely had to find similar skeletons further back in time. And to compute racial admixture, simple mathematics answered

30

how much p and how much q would—in genic matrimony—yield a given proportion of p and q (assuming no exceptions to the Hardy-Weinberg rule).

Yet the notion of stable races and of inadaptive racial criteria led to a logical impasse. If races do not change, how did races come to be? And if skin color, body proportions, hair form, or gene frequencies are not subject to natural selection, how is it that races now differ from each other, often to so great an extent? It is this logical impasse that led Hooton to change his opinions, as described in the revised edition of *Up from the Ape* (Hooton '46).

There is no escape from this impasse, only a devious detour. All that could be done was to place the origin of the geographical races of man as far in the past, and in the most remote areas, as possible. Whites, Blacks, Yellows—all were derived from archeologically inaccessible sections of Asia. Some taxonomists hopefully looked to the Upper Cave at Choukoutien for early Mongoloids and nascent Melanesians, presumably strictly endogamous then. And Gates (following an extreme line of reasoning) assigned to the geographical races of man an antiquity older than mankind itself (Gates '48).

Today, as we investigate evolutionary mechanisms at first hand, as we demonstrate drift and compute rates of selection, we may wonder at the seeming reluctance to admit race as a part of human evolution. Retrospectively, it may seem strange that men who devoted their lives to human evolution at the species level should have balked at accepting evolution at the racial level. Here, perhaps, one may blame Darwin, the father of evolution, himself. For pre-Darwinian evolutionists, like Blumenbach, Buffon, and Kant, readily accepted race as a product of local evolution, while Darwin (in his *Descent of Man*) toyed with the possibility that the differences between human races were due to evolution, and then recoiled from the obvious (Darwin 1871). Not until the evolutionary nature of race was firmly accepted by entomologists, mammologists, and herpetologists, did anthropologists regain the interest in the evolution of human races held by naturalists 250 years ago.

EVIDENCE FOR RECENT EVOLUTION IN MAN

In truth, acceptable evidence for ongoing evolution in man was extraordinarily hard to come by. No trend comparable to the phenomenon of "industrial melanism" in butterflies could be demonstrated. And no human trait had proven adaptive value, comparable to coat color in geographical races of mice. Almost by default the evidence was against recent hominid evolution, and in consequence the notion of static race and neutral taxonomic traits seemed the wiser assumption to follow.

Many evolutionary "trends" have been suggested for recent man. But apparent trends, like agenesis of the third molar and changes in the digital formula, were obtained by sampling different populations and not by following one population through recent time. Nearest to a satisfactory trend is the undoubted shift toward round-headedness exhibited by contemporary populations (Weidenreich '45). Now it is possible that brachycephaly has some adaptive value under modern conditions of life. Yet the trend toward round-headedness may simply reflect a growth response to more adequate nutrition (Abbie '47): in this event brachycephalization cannot be termed an evolutionary trend at all.

Again, there is every reason to believe that many human differences have adaptive value in climatic extremes. Just as the reduced mass and increased peripheries of the desert fox, and the extra insulation of the arctic seal represent genetic adaptations to desert and freezing temperatures respectively, variations in the human surface-mass ratio follow expected climatic lines (Coon, Garn and Birdsell '50; Roberts '53; Newman '53). The degree of melanin deposition in man also bears a statistical relationship to mean ultraviolet intensities (Coon, Garn and Birdsell '50). And desert men tend to small overall size, an expected finding since the smaller man has a better capacity to throw off heat (Morehouse and Miller '53:325). In short, a great many racial differences seem to relate to the geographical histories of the particular races in question.

But it is one thing to prove either logically or experimentally that a given trait may be beneficial, and another thing to demonstrate survival value. Given a sunlamp and a timer one can easily show that the Negro is slower to reach erythema and subsequent discomfort. Given a tank of cold water and a thermocouple it is no trick to show that Eskimo skin temperatures remain higher and that peripheral blood flow is twice that of whites (Brown, Hatcher and Page '53). But to clinch the argument, selective survival must be demonstrated; the possessors must be differentially represented in the next generation. Such had not been demonstrated for any morphological trait useful in distinguishing one race-population from another.

The first break came in 1940 with the discovery of the "Rhesus factor"—the Rh series of alleles. Here for the first time one could demonstrate a common gene having adaptive value, and its relatively inadaptive alleles. For our purposes, the implications to neonatal mortality and the medical aspects of the problem are dwarfed by the simple realization that the present Rh gene frequencies need not have obtained in the past. There must have been a time when the Rh+ and Rh— alleles for whites more nearly approached 50-50 than the present 85-15. And for some future time, unless replacement transfusions can brake this line of evolution, we might predict an American white population nearly homozygous for the more common (Rh positive) alleles.

More recently, evidence has accumulated that incompatibilities in the classical A-B-O system may also result in fetal deaths and neonatal loss (Race and Sanger '54). One can see, for the first time, possible advantages of population homozygosity as far as successful reproduction is concerned, even though heterozygosity may be desirable from the standpoint of species survival (Lerner '54). The important conclusion is that the blood group genes, once extolled as particularly neutral, have proven to be far from neutral. And more important, blood group gene frequencies as we know them now may be purely temporary, no accurate indications of past conditions.

Counteracting or reinforcing these selective trends may be the relationships between the A-O-B blood groups and some common organic diseases. Though O is differentially favored at or before birth, the apparent linkage between O and ulcers suggests that O may be relatively inadaptive later in life (Aird, Bentall and Fraser-Roberts '53; Buckwalter *et al.* '56). On the other hand the dominant alleles, represented by the genes p and q, seem to be associated with other noninfectious disorders such as gastric carcinoma (*cf.* Buckwalter *et al.* '56). Taken as a whole, we can visualize one human population moving rapidly toward an excess of O, and another building up in the B factor year after year. Maternal-fetal incompatabilities plus differential adult survival could well yield the kind of differences in blood group frequencies we know for the races of man today. The net results of such trends may be (like drift) trivial as far as species evolution is concerned. As Sewall Wright has pointed out, the net effects of "drift" are minimal in the face of even slight selection pressure. For this reason the phenomenon of genetic drift, which provides an attractive explanation for small differences between contiguous isolates, is given minimal attention here. But racial differences are trivial in comparison to species differences, and it is the phenomenon of race we are considering here.

The most dramatic example to date is that of Thallasemia major, the so-called Mediterranean anemia. Here, though the gene is strikingly disadvantageous in the homozygous state, gene loss is more than balanced by relative resistance to malaria exhibited by the heterozygote (Allison '54). As a result, people in malaria zones differ remarkably from their less steamy neighbors in the frequency of this gene (Ceppellini '55). Here is an example of local evolution, proceeding at a very rapid pace. And here, evolution is not unrelated to temperature changes and to the mean annual rainfall. Drop the annual temperature but a few degrees, reduce the rainfall a few inches (or use DDT), and the recessive carrier ceases to be at an advantage. Conversely, there must have been periods in the past when the gene for Thallasemia was more widely distributed in Mediterranean countries than it is now. And the related sickling gene may have been more extensively distributed in Africa during periods of heavier rainfall.

Let it not be assumed that blood-group genes or genes affecting the blood alone have adaptive value in man. Our present sampling of knowledge is an accidental by-product of widespread blood-typing, and of the ease with which some haematological studies can be made. It is quite likely that all of the traits in which peoples differ have adaptive value. It is likely that the recessive carrier of Morquio's syndrome, the genetic diabetic, and the hypertensive and the coronary-prone individual all possess certain unique advantages over their fellows. Were skin color, hair form, and bone lengths regularly recorded in relation to the more common diseases (as is cholesterol level today), the probabilities are great that they too would cease to be considered neutral in regard to human welfare.

There is now excellent evidence that under our noses (and often without outward signs) races have been changing. Evolution has been taking place, often to an appreciable degree, since the *Origin of Species* first appeared on British bookstands. Genes and traits that once seemed as neutral as a Swiss diplomat may now be listed among those having proven adaptive value. In short, we must now acknowledge the fact that races do change, and that the criteria that (temporarily) distinguished one race from another, are only temporarily suited to that purpose. These two conclusions, now demonstrated in fact as well as in theory, have tremendous bearing on our studies of man.

RACE AND EVOLUTION

With what we know now, two conclusions are quite inescapable. First, human races—like higher taxonomic units—are subject to evolutionary change. Second, the particular traits by which races distinguish themselves are subject to natural selection, and therefore do not have eternal taxonomic value. In retrospect, all of the characters used in constructing a classification of man must have been grist in the evolutionary mill.

Now we cannot have change and no change simultaneously. Present frequencies of blood groups or of morphological traits are, at best, interim reports of present conditions. They need not be identical to frequencies in the recent or remote past, and they need not predict gene or trait frequencies in the future. Traits now common may once have been rare, and vice versa. Only a rash worker would care to estimate how common the sickling trait was a few hundred years ago. It would be equally rash to estimate the incidence of shovel-shaped incisors, transitional vertebrae, or suture-bones in the days of the Caesars.

As a consequence, the search for ancestors becomes far more difficult than it once seemed. It is not necessary to assume that ancestral Amerindians were derived from a B-free population (with the implied late appearance of B); they may have lost it in transit. But it is equally likely that B had adaptive value in Asia, but none in America. By the same token, the absence of a sickling-trait among the Veddoids does not prove that there existed no ancient linkage with Africa. As soon as we accept changes in gene frequencies, we can no longer employ present frequencies as certain indications of past events (Hiernaux '55).

While this obvious corollary admittedly pulls the rug from beneath our more cherished reconstructions, evidence for changing race may free us from the burden of prefabricated and hypothetical ancestors. If blondism is adaptive in a particular climatological zone, all-blond *echt*-Nordics need not be invoked to explain blondism in the Baltic. And if Rh⁻ (cde) is adaptive in certain times and places, then the Basques may have attained their serological uniqueness with no help from (still) hypothetical "Early Europeans." Not too long ago local and geographical differences among American Indian populations were explained by a bewildering number of unverifiable migrations. Admitting the possibility of local evolution in the Americas has cleared the air (Newman '53), though demanding a new set of proofs instead.

In the past "intermediate" populations have been attributed, almost exclusively, to hybridization. Without denying this oldest human accomplishment, contemporary evolutionary genetics provides an alternative explanation. Suppose that melanism is adaptive in the tropics, and blondism in the North. In between we would expect, as a result of competing rates of selection, intermediate coloration, a simple example of balanced polymorphism. Then, there are numerous populations whose intermediate status has given them the rank of triple or even quadruple-hybrids. In some cases the explanation of multiple origins can be justified on the basis of historical and archeological evidence. But even where such documentation is complete, balanced polymorphism may be responsible for the continuance of the various parental genes. And in other cases, the triple-hybrids may not be "hybrids" at all.

The fact that a race can change markedly in the course of a few score generations complicates our search for ancestors, especially those more remote. If we cannot be sure that contemporary Ainu, to take an extreme example, really resemble their pre-Neolithic ancestors, how about long-term reconstructions of our phyletic line? Need a trait in Chancelade be ancestral to a similar trait in the Greenland Eskimo? Need shoveling of the incisors in *Pithecanthropus* have any bearing on similar dental formations in contemporary Chinese? And further, admitting rapid change over the centuries, need all so-called "Neanderthals" be peas from the same genetic pod?

Contemporary evolutionary studies have opened wide Pandora's box. Yet the situation need not be disheartening to the adventurous student of man. While some genes may be subject to rapid selection, others may be very close to adaptive neutrality. It may be possible to prepare a list of almost-neutral genes, for the specific purpose of phyletic reconstruction. Yet there will always be doubts. We have no assurance that the neutral gene of today will not prove adaptive tomorrow. Reconstructions of racial history, or the history of our species, may always be marked by uncertainties which even the most complete skeletal record can never totally resolve.

At the same time, if we are confronted with change rather than static conditions, it is change that we must study, considering it a challenge to research rather than an obstacle to progress. There are a whole series of challenges, first documenting change (and this we have scarcely begun to do) and then explaining it (which may require a major excursion into medical genetics). The older, static, unchanging concept of race was essentially self-limiting. Once all the pigeon-holes were filled, there would have been nothing more to do. With changing race and adaptive traits, we have our job cut out for generations to come.

REFERENCES

Abbie, A. A.: Head form and human evolution, *J. Anat., 81*:233-258, 1947.

Aird, I., Bentall, H. H. and Fraser-Roberts, J. A.: Relationship between cancer of stomach and the ABO groups, *Brit. M. J., 1*:799-801, 1953.

Allison, A. C.: Protection afforded by sickle-cell trait against subtertian malarial infection, *Brit. M. J., 1*:290-294, 1954.

Brown, G. M., Hatcher, J. D. and Page, J.: Temperature and blood flow in the forearm of the Eskimo, *J. Appl. Physiol., 5*:410-420, 1953.

Buckwalter, J. A., Wohlend, E. B., Coulter, D. C. and Tidrick, R. T.: Natural selection associated with the ABO blood group, *Science, 123*:840-841, 1956.

Ceppellini, R.: The usefulness of blood factors in racial anthropology, *Am. J. Phys. Anthropol., N. S. 13*:389 (abstract), 1955.

Coon, C. S., Garn, S. M. and Birdsell, J. B.: *Races,* Springfield, Thomas, 1950.

Darwin, C.: *The Descent of Man, and Selection in Relation to Sex,* London, John Murray, 1871.

Gates, R. R.: *Human Ancestry from a Genetical Point of View,* Cambridge, Harvard University Press, 1948.

Herskovits, M. J.: Franz Boas as physical anthropologist, *Memoirs Am. Anthropol. Assoc., 45*:39-51, 1943.

Hiernaux, J.: Physical anthropology and the frequency of genes with a selective value, *Am. J. Phys. Anthropol., N. S. 13*:455-472, 1955.

Hooton, E. A.: *Up from the Ape,* New York, Macmillan, 1946.

Lerner, I. M.: *Genetic Homeostasis,* New York, John Wiley & Sons, 1954.

Morehouse, L. E. and Miller, A. T., Jr.: *Physiology of Exercise,* St. Louis, C. V. Mosby, 1953.

Newman, M. T.: The application of ecological rules to the racial anthropology of the New World, *Am. Anthropol., 55*:311-327, 1953.

Race, R. R. and Sanger, R.: *Blood groups in Man,* Springfield, Thomas, 1954.

Roberts, D. F.: Body weight, race and climate, *Am. J. Phys. Anthro-pol., N. S. 11*:533-558, 1953.

Weidenreich, F.: The brachycephalization of recent mankind, *S. W. J. Anthropol., 1*:1-54, 1945.

IV. PAST AND PRESENT POPULATION SIZES AMONG THE HUMAN RACES

If we look over any listing of contemporary races, great differences in relative size immediately become obvious. There are, for example, approximately 200,000,000 members of the Northwest European local race, now including much of North America, Australia and New Zealand. The Southeast Asiatic local race encompasses an equal or greater number of individuals. In contrast, many local races comprise but a few thousand individuals. The population of Fargo, North Dakota is greater than the number of living Ainu, or the total number of Bushmen.

The existence of such miniscule race-populations has bothered many classifiers aiming at taxonomic simplicity. To them it seemed both neater and more reasonable to incorporate the Ainu or the Australian "blackfellows" into the European geographical race or the Bushmen into the African local race, than to carry groups representing no more than one one-thousandth of one per cent of the world's population on the taxonomic balance sheet.

However, the size of a population should have no bearing on its taxonomic status. Even a few-score individuals, geographically and reproductively isolated, constitute a perfectly valid race. On the other hand, a much larger population extending into the millions may with difficulty be divided into a series of micro-races. Furthermore, the size of race-populations is by no means constant, as we have seen in recent generations.

Present population sizes, in fact, largely reflect three technological advances. The first, of course, was the agricultural revolution, which made large populations practicable. The second was the industrial revolution which resulted in explosive population expansion in Europe. And the third is the revolution in sanitation and medical care which is now allowing unlimited population expansion in Asia, India and Africa. Obviously those race-populations that got in early on these technological advances have expanded to the greatest degree, as F. R. Hulse points out in the following section.

If we turn back the calendar two thousand years, the European geographical race was scarcely larger than the American or Amerindian geographical race. A further flashback in time, to the dawn of the Neolithic in Europe provides an even more startling change in proportions. In all probability there were then as many inhabitants of Australia as there were of Europe! It is not unlikely that the Bushmen were once as numerous as Europeans or Southeast Asiatics. As of 5000 B. C., or even A. D. 1, we could not sweep the Bushmen under the taxonomic rug simply because of their small numbers.

Such a time-oriented perspective warns us against setting up one or another race as "typical" of morphologically modern man. European taxonomists of the past century made this mistake partly out of ethnocentrism and partly because Northwest Europeans were then so numerous. But it was sheer accident that brought rapid population expansion to post-Reformation Europe and not to Australia. Leaving numbers aside, no one group is more typical or less typical of modern man—a point of importance when phylogeny rather than taxonomy is being considered.

ADDITIONAL READINGS

Hulse, F. S.: Some factors influencing the relative proportions of human racial stocks, *Cold Spring Harbor Symposia on Quantitative Biology*, 22:33-45, Cold Spring Harbor, The Biological Laboratory, 1957.

Technological Advance and Major Racial Stocks

Reprinted from Human Biology, Vol. 27, No. 3, pp. 184-192 (1955).

By FREDERICK S. HULSE

We humans are a polytypic species. Both as individuals and as breeding populations, we differ from one another in numerous biological characteristics. The extent to which these differences are due to environmental influences during the growth of each individual has not yet been determined. It remains clear, however, that genetic differences do exist between the various tribes of men, and, naturally enough, attempts have been made to find some order in the variety. Most typically, scholars have attempted a three-fold division of our species: after all, three has long been a sacred number in our culture. So we continue to hear of Mongoloids, Negroids and Caucasoids as basic, primary or original stocks, from whom all of us today, by further evolution or hybridization are derived.

Some authorities, like Howells ('44), insist upon 4 rather than three; some, like Boyd ('50:268-272), speak of 6. Sergi ('11) divided us all into two original varieties, the Eurafrican and the Eurasiatic. Keith ('49:234-244) has written also of two basic groups, one being deeply pigmented or Negroid, the other being rather less pigmented but variable. Three is, however, the more orthodox number, and it must be noted that each is named after a group or type which is very numerous at our stage of history. Average or run-of-the-mill specimens of each stock, as described by the usual authorities, can also be recognized by anyone with our cultural perceptions as being different from either of the others.

Hooton's position with respect to the existence and primacy of the three major stocks is made clear by his statement in *Up From the Ape* ('46:449) : "The differences between the various subgroupings within the three great or primary races are *obvi-*

ously more recent, and quantitatively and qualitatively *less* than exist between the primary races respectively." Kroeber ('48:134) accepts this idea, albeit with some reservations. He refers, for instance, to "remaining minor, aberrant forms which are best kept separate, provisionally. Some, like the Ainu and Australoid, appear to affiliate preponderantly with one of the three great classes." Ashley Montagu ('51:301, 304-306), on the other hand, apologizes for mentioning divisions or major stocks. Yet he goes on, at once, to speak of Nilotes as "probably hybrids between Hamites," whom he classifies as a branch of Whites and "Forest Negroes." He supposes a group whom he labels "Half Hamites" to have arisen in the same manner. Why, therefore, he distinguishes them from Nilotes he does not say.

It is, indeed, the existence of such groups as Nilotes and Ainu, the extraordinary distribution of dark-skinned pygmy types, the accumulation of findings concerning genetic characteristics, and the recent studies of climatic adaptations within the human stock, which lead me, at least, to doubt the existence, past or present, of two, three or 4 major stocks, or even of the 6 listed by Boyd ('50) from his study of blood-type distributions. Coon, Garn and Birdsell ('50:115), indeed, state, that "a stock is not a race, but merely a convenience in classification: It is a lumping of races which seem similar to each other in broad categories." In fact, I wonder if the concept of the major stock does not usually serve to mislead the student of taxonomy, which is an inconvenience rather than a help. From the concept of the major stock flows, perhaps sometimes unconsciously, the assumption of genetic priority, which is explicitly accepted by Hooton.

Is this assumption well based? What is the evidence? Let us take a few cases.

The data of human genetics provides evidence of a remarkable difference in numerous characteristics within each of the major stocks. This is notably demonstrable in comparative serology. Some of the differences in gene-frequency do not correspond with the lines which are supposed to divide stocks. Boyd ('50:268-269), consequently, would separate the Basques from the Caucasoids, and the American Indians from the Mongoloids.

The more we learn of human genetics, the greater the number of genetically distinctive groups we discover.

The data of palaeontology provide far better evidence concerning the regional antiquity, at least, of Bushmen (Galloway '37), Australoids (Weidenreich, '45), Nilotes (Leaky, '35), Ainu (Hooton, '46:402) than of Mongoloids and Negroids. Regional variety within the Caucasoid group appears to be as old as the group itself. The best fossil relics point to what Hooton calls sub-races or composite races rather than to the great primary races which are said to be the ancestral stocks.

The data from ethnology concerning the geographical distribution of living and recently living peoples provides most equivocal evidence. Although the Caucasoid stock appears to have its major center of distribution in Europe and the Middle East, it is alleged to have contributed genes to such groups as Ainu, Polynesians and Hottentots. Negroids are scattered, mostly in tropical areas, from Fiji and Tasmania to Senegal and Capetown, Negritos sporadically distributed among them. There are large gaps, by oceans, deserts, and intervening populations of quite different phenotype and genotype, which separate the dark-skinned tribes. Those who accept, even as a convenience, the prior existence of Negroids or Caucasoids as major stocks have had to exercise much ingenuity to explain these improbable distributions.

Kroeber ('48:125), for instance, in writing of the Ainu, assumes that if they resemble Europeans (as he appears to think they do) they must be a *branch* of the Caucasian stock, they must have come from the West, and that they have no connection with the Mongolian Japanese among whom they now live. Further unstated assumptions which must logically underlie these statements are: that the Europeans are typical Caucasians, that the Japanese are typical Mongolians, that there is some other direction from which to reach Hokkaido and that the Ainu have always been, as they are now, a relatively small population. None of these unstated basic presuppositions can be demonstrated to be true, and, indeed, most of them are rather unlikely. The Ainu resemble native Australians at least as much as they resemble either European or Asiatic Caucasians. Japanese are not especially typical Mongolians. There is no particular reason to believe that the relative proportions now existing between the various racial and tribal groups, in numbers, have existed unaltered throughout prehistory.

Let us look again at the Nilotic tribes. If indeed they are nothing but hybrids between Negroids and Caucasoids one would expect them to be intermediate in genotype between the original stocks. As a matter of fact they possess a notably high incidence of the allele for sickle cells, a low incidence in the allele for blood-group A, and a typically African incidence in the alleles for the Rh subtypes (Mourant, '54). One might expect them to be quite variable in phenotype, at least in skin color, if they are hybrids, but one finds them to be especially dark-skinned, and elongated in body-build far more than either of the presumptive ancestral stocks, Negroid or Caucasoid. In other words, they have numerous characteristics which cannot be explained by the hypothesis of mixed ancestry.

Are they, on the other hand, more closely related to all other very dark skinned tribes, no matter where, than they are to less deeply pigmented peoples to the north, such as Caucasoids of the Mediterranean area? There is positively no indication or even suggestion from genetics that this might be so. We have no record of sicklemia in Melanesia, for instance, but the gene is known among Greeks, Sicilians and some tribes in India. Although blood-group A is very common among Melanesians, the subtype A_2 is unknown: both among Nilotic and Mediterranean peoples the ratio of A_2 to A_1 is high. The allele frequency of N is high in Melanesia, but much lower throughout Europe and Africa. The Melanesians are utterly un-African in Rh subtype distribution (Mourant, '54). Indeed, it seems to be reasonably clear that a considerable variety of very dark-skinned peoples exist, and that they are not necessarily closer cousins to one another than any of them are to less dark-skinned groups.

In fact, there are numerous peoples in the world whose characteristics simply cannot be adequately explained by any of the theories derived from a belief in two, three or 4 original major stocks. Bushmen, Basques, Lapps, even Polynesians and American Indians just don't fit. Nevertheless, there they are, alive and breeding just like the rest of us. If one assumes that the major stocks are original, and the actual people of the world just a later derivation, great difficulties are created.

Now as a matter of fact people don't live, work and breed in racial groups, but in tribes, castes and other culture-bound groupings. Opportunities for spreading one's genes in distant places have, in the past, been limited. Most migrants move in groups, rather than individually. The social group, furthermore, modifies the natural or raw environment to a greater or lesser degree, depending upon its technology and social organization. Some forms of technology and social organization permit and encourage greater population densities than do others.

The invention of Neolithic ways of life was revolutionary in this respect (Childe, '36). With agriculture, the population of a tribe could increase rapidly, and we have ample archaeological evidence to show that population movements followed this increase, as farmers sought new lands to cultivate. Areas previously rather useless to man could now be profitably exploited. Other technological advances have permitted the survival of individuals without climatic adaptation. Indeed, the better the technology, the higher the survival rate, no matter what the bodily form. Members of European royal families can even afford to have hemophilia.

Today the vast bulk of the world's population, although not all, can be squeezed somehow into one or another of the so-called major stocks. In seeking to uncover the story of ancestral relationships within the human stock, however, we should consider, instead, the most likely distribution of population before the Neolithic revolution. After all, that is less than 10,000 years ago, only 1% of the period of man's existence. The population explosions which resulted in the present distribution occurred only in limited areas at first, and, consequently, affected only a limited number of the population groups at the time. Yet these groups gained an initial advantage in numbers, and such an initial advantage is difficult to overcome. The genetic systems of populations which happen to have good tools are not better, in any sense of the word, than are the genetic systems of populations which lack good tools. The former do have a higher survival value than the latter, however, simply because the tools help their owners to survive and to multiply.

Now we cannot, of course, reconstruct with any high degree of precision, the picture of the distribution of the world's population at the end of the Palaeolithic. Nevertheless, the advance of archaeological investigation and of ecological studies do permit us to come to logical conclusions with respect to relative sizes of populations inhabiting certain areas of the world in the days when all were food-collectors.

Before the beginning of the Neolithic, real forests, whether tropical jungle or temperate zone, were not especially desirable places for human habitation. From what we know of hunting and fishing peoples, we have every reason to believe that parklands, savannahs, prairies and the like can support denser populations, because of greater abundance of seeds and game and greater ease of collection and hunting. Consequently, we may be sure that Europe was not thickly inhabited, and the archaeological evidence suggests that, with new technologies, population movements from the Near East repeatedly came into Europe.

On the other hand, East and South Africa, then as now, appear to have been, like the Near East, land fit for hunting and collecting. It also appears to have been until even later, indeed much later, inhabited at least in part by Khoisans, or Boskopoids, presumptive ancestors of Bushmen. There is little or no reason to suppose that East and South Africa, home of the ancestors of Bushmen, were less densely populated than the Near East, home of the ancestors of modern Europeans. In area, the parklands, savannahs and prairies of the Near East, of what is now the Moslem world, from Pakistan to Morocco, do not exceed 2,500,000 square miles. Regions similarly favorable to hunting-collecting peoples, from an ecological standpoint, in East and South Africa cover an approximately equal area. Consequently, there is no reason to suppose that populations with genetic systems similar to those of Europeans were, 10,000 years ago, more numerous

than were populations with genetic systems similar to those of
Bushmen. Yet today the first is regarded as the typical representative of a major, primary stock, the latter as an aberrant
and mysterious racelet.

Are we not fooling ourselves, in a case like this, simply
because of the present day preponderance of numbers?—a preponderance due simply to the fortuitous correlation between
Caucasoid types and the invention of agriculture and the technological developments which later, and doubtless consequently,
ensued in history.

This, of course, is even more true if we consider the blond-
ish varieties of Europeans. Many suspect that really extensive
and widespread depigmentation is an adaptive character suitable
to the climate of northwest Europe (Coon, Garn and Birdsell,
'50:50). It may very well be exceedingly ancient there. But this
region, until only 5,000 years ago, was most sparsely inhabited
by primitive savages. They are quite likely to have numbered
only a few tens of thousands, if we can judge by population densities of peoples of equivalent economies and environments among
today's hunting and fishing groups, such as the Yahgan.

Yet we unconsciously designate such Europeans as the standard Caucasoids, simply because there are now some hundreds
of millions of people with such physical characteristics. Let us
examine how this came about: here is one case concerning which
we have ample historical documentation.

By the end of the Middle Ages, the population of the British
Isles, the Low Countries and Scandinavia was still less than
10,000,000. Because of geographic position and historical cir-
cumstance, the British emigrated in astonishing numbers, settling
in lands previously only scantily occupied. Although in 1600
there were perhaps 3,000,000 there are now at least 150,000,000
of British stock. The world population has increased by 6 times
in these last few centuries, that of British ancestry by 50 times.
This is no sign of superior British virtue, mentality or fecundity,
yet it is an evolutionary fact. Areas in Europe containing a high
per cent of blondism held perhaps 3% of the world's inhabitants
then. People originating from such areas comprise at least 12%

of the world's inhabitants now. If the allele or alleles for blondness have increased proportionately (and, with modern technologies, blonds can survive even in the tropics, especially if they are in the upper class) blondness should now be more than 4 times as common as it was then. Technology, and historical events resulting from technology, have produced a remarkable change in the incidence of this allele. This is evolution in action.

The population explosion in part of the areas inhabited by Caucasians, remarkable though it has been, is not unique. Neolithic techniques, although apparently developed and originated very largely in areas occupied by people of this population group, have not been their unique possession by any means.

In China, for instance, food production took root long ago, with the result that the local population there began to expand also, with respect both to numbers and area occupied. The genetic characteristics of the Chinese, like those of the Europeans, have become much more common than they were in the Palaeolithic. The movement southward of peoples in East Asia is amply documented by ethnological distribution studies, linguistics, archaeology, history and indeed by contemporary events. Extensive hybridization, and migration as well, have followed culture-trait diffusion, so that both phenotypes and genetic systems typical of northeast Asia have spread more and more to the south, even into Indonesia.

As a result of this process, which has almost certainly taken place only since the application of Neolithic, or even Iron Age techniques, we find hundreds of millions of individuals with more or less Mongoloid characteristics spread along the western rim of the Pacific basin, and, scattered among them, in all sorts of refuge areas, populations which are clearly much less Mongoloid. At the end of the Paleolithic, the situation must have been far different, with few Mongoloids living in the open lands to the north, and a great variety of populations with genetic systems quite unlike that of the Mongoloids in Japan, China, Indo-China and Indonesia. This proposition is so widely accepted that it need not be argued here, yet its implications with regard to the question of the genetic priority of major stocks seem to have been neglected.

It seems to me that we can be quite certain that 10,000 years ago the numerical proportions between populations of different genetic characteristics must have been violently different from what they are today. We do not yet have adequate data to postulate the typical characteristics of most of the tribal groups then in existence. But the numbers of tribes with genetic systems similar to the so-called Mongoloid and Caucasoid stocks must have been relatively few. Blonds were probably as rare then as Bushmen are today. The numbers of Bushmen, of Australoids, and perhaps of other populations as well, was relatively great, but probably exceedingly diverse genetically.

Changes in proportion, which have led us to attempt classification into three major stocks, have come about during the last 1% of human existence and have come about entirely because of a fortuitous correlation between more advanced technical skills and certain racial characteristics. Historical circumstances, not racial virtues, determined the expansion of a certain few among the many population groups which existed at the beginning of the Neolithic. When man succeeds in modifying his environment he directs the future course of his own evolution, albeit quite unaware of his direction, his speed, or even of the fact that he is in the driver's seat.

REFERENCES

Boyd, W. C.: *Genetics and the Races of Man,* Boston, Heath, 1950.

Childe, V. G.: *Man makes Himself,* London, Watts, 1936.

Coon, C. S., Garn, S. M. and Birdsell, J. B.: *Races, a Study of the Problems of Race Formation in Man,* Springfield, Thomas, 1950.

Galloway, A.: The characteristics of the skull of the Boskop physical type, *Am. J. Phys. Anthropol., 23*:31-46, 1937.

Hooton, E. A.: *Up from the Ape,* New York, Macmillan, 1946.

Howells, W. W.: *Mankind so Far,* New York, Doubleday, 1944.

Keith, A.: *A New Theory of Human Evolution,* New York, Philosophical Library, 1949.

Kroeber, A. L.: *Anthropology,* New York, Harcourt, Brace, 1948.

Leaky, L. S. B.: *The Stone Age Races of Kenya,* London, Oxford

University Press, 1935.

Montagu, M. F. A.: *An Introduction to Physical Anthropology,* Springfield, Thomas, 1951.

Mourant, A. E.: *The Distribution of Human Blood Groups,* London, Blackwell, 1954.

Sergi, G.: *L'Uomo, secondo le origini, l'antichitá, le variazione e la distribuzione geografica,* Torino, Fratelli Bocca, 1911.

Weidenreich, F.: The Keilor skull: a Wadjak type from southeastern Australia, *Am. J. Phys. Anthropol., N. S. 3*:21-32, 1945.

V. CLIMATE AND RACE

There is considerable reason to believe that climate plays an important role in bringing about racial differentiation in man. Not only are human pigmentary extremes predictably located with respect to the intensity of solar radiation, but the surface/volume ratio follows an orderly path as well.

To appreciate the nature of climatic selection, one must consider not the mean annual temperature, nor the average radiation flux density, but the extremes that push men to the limits of their physiologic adaptation. As with any living form, selection pressure is greatest when the physiologic limits are reached. Such selection need not be continuous, but need only operate once within the individual's life span.

In the absence of experimental studies (see section X) general rules can be established by arranging various measurable parameters with respect to climatic variables. In this way, it can be shown that body size, linearity-laterality, nose form and similar variables bear an orderly relationship to temperature etc. Naturally such arrangements do not explain why the relationships exist, but merely document their existence.

In addition to making orderly arrangements, it is also possible to hazard guesses as to the adaptive value of various morphological traits. The more extensive sweat gland activity of many Negro peoples would seem to be related to heat stress. The reduced peripheries of some arctic peoples would seem to constitute a genetic adaptation to cold. Still other explanations, such as those involving racial differences in the pilous system are often beyond the capacity of the experimental method.

At the present time local races are viewed as the result of natural selection, in which local factors play a predominant part. The particular interest in climatic selection is thus understandable. At the same time it is important that no *single* factor (and this includes climate) be granted a disproportionate role in human racial evolution. Wilber's article, which follows those by Roberts, Baker and Weiner, thus serves as a healthy reminder.

ADDITIONAL READINGS

Baker, P. T.: Racial differences in heat tolerance, *Am. J. Phys. Anthropol. N. S. 16*:287-305, 1958.

Coon, C. S.: Climate and race, in *Climatic Change*, Shapley, H. (ed.), Cambridge, Harvard University Press, 1954.

Weiner, J. S.: Human adaptability to hot conditions of deserts, *Symposium on the Biology and Productivity of Hot and Cold Deserts*, UNESCO Institute of Biology, 1953.

Garn, S. M.: A comment on Wilber's "Origin of human types," *Human Biol., 30*:337-340, 1958.

Hiernaux, J.: Analyse de la variation des caractères physiques humains en une région de l'Afrique centrale: Ruanda-Urundi et Kivu, *Ann. Mus. Congo Belge, 3*: 1956.

Basal Metabolism, Race and Climate

Reprinted, with exception of one figure, from *Man*, Article 251, pp. 169-170 (1952).

By D. F. ROBERTS

As part of an extensive survey of the ecological significance of human physical characteristics, a study was made of the influence of climate and race upon basal metabolism; defined as the minimal heat-production of the body when it is at rest (not asleep), is not engaged in heavy digestive processes (i.e. is in a post-absorptive state) and is not undergoing marked mental activity, etc., basal metabolism represents the total energy utilized in maintaining the body states and processes necessary to life, e.g. body temperature and circulation.

All available literature recording the basal metabolic rate of human samples was examined, and data thus collected relating to over 200 groups of varying race, sex, age, habits, etc., living in different parts of the world. Straightforward comparison was impossible on account of differences in presentation of the material, technical discrepancies and incomparability of samples, so that it was necessary to subdivide the assemblage of data into comparable subgroups.

Initially, all records for adults were considered. Mapping of their geographical distribution revealed a distinct pattern related to environmental temperature but at the same time suggested certain differences among continental groups. Subsequently, this relationship was examined statistically, technically incomparable samples being excluded.

The daily basal calorie-production of adult male samples, examined in the regions in which the races to which they belong are indigenous, was found to be related ($r = - \cdot 736$ significant at 0·1 per cent.) with mean annual temperature, while similar female samples gave a confirmatory result. Further, significant differences appeared among the great varieties (or continental groups) of man, suggesting that levels of mean basal daily calorie-production, for a given mean environmental temperature, decreased in the following order: American Indian, European, East Mongoloid. The correlation was not apparently explicable by differences in diet, immediate temperature or technique.

Examination of heat-production expressed per unit weight apparently confirmed the inter-varietal differences, suggesting that intrinsic differences in basal metabolism exist among the varieties of man, irrespective of the influence of weight and temperature. Although the production of calories per kilogram was also significantly related to temperature, there was reason to believe that variations in weight to a certain extent were coincident with, and possibly represented adjustments to, differences in temperature (a suggestion which has since been made the subject of a further study).

Examination of those results expressed per unit surface area indicated that the supposed relationship of basal metabolism to surface area was not constant, there being a significant association with temperature and, again, marked differences among human varieties. On account of the number of associated factors involved, it appeared necessary to take account of their interrelationships. Analysis by multiple correlation of those 30 male samples in which weight and stature details were furnished as well as the total basal calorie-production produced the total and partial correlation coefficients shown.

Correlation of Daily Basal Calorie-production with	Mean Annual Temp.	Stature	Weight
Total corr. coefficient	−.7725*	−.1730	+.6927*
Partial corr. coefficient	−.679*	−.631*	+.687*

* = significant at 1 per cent.

The partial correlation coefficients indicate the marked relationship of basal metabolism with each of the three factors after account is taken of the association with the other two. The following 'prediction' formula was calculated: $Y = 2873 − 4.29T − 13.23S + 19.22W$, where Y is mean daily basal calorie-production, T is mean annual temperature in degrees Fahrenheit, S is stature in centimetres, and W is weight in kilograms. The multiple correlation coefficient of basal calorie-production, weight, temperature and stature was found to be .902 (a rise, insignificant however, occurred when relative humidity was included) ; it was therefore not surprising that comparison of the observed results with those predicted from the formula showed reasonably close agreement, the East Mongoloid series nevertheless showing a predominance of negative discrepancies, the American Indian series a predominance of positive discrepancies, suggesting that differences in basal metabolism previously demonstrated in this study between these two continental groups exist apart from the influence of weight, temperature and stature.

These results, unfortunately only as clearly as the nature of the still inadequate evidence permits, offer a solution to the question of race and basal metabolism, indicating that while there appear to be intervarietal differences in heat-production after allowing for the influence of body size and environment, racial or intra-varietal differences largely reflect variations in habitat. Perhaps more important for the study of the morphology of the human body, there can be deduced from the relationships outlined the tendency for linearity of form to increase with increased temperatures and to decrease with lower temperatures, the relationship of surface area to weight becoming respectively larger and smaller; thus a mechanism is provided by which variations in body form in response to environmental demands may be understood. The hypothesis may be briefly stated as follows: in order to facilitate the balance of human body-heat exchange, under those conditions in which heat-loss is more difficult, less heat is produced (on account of reduction in the amount of body tissue) and the ratio of surface area to weight (i.e. the ratio of potential heat-loss to potential heat-production) is increased. Thus the functional mechanism underlying Bergmann's and Allen's rules, postulated for the relationship of body size and proportions with environment in warm-blooded species, would appear to be confirmed when applied to man.

It would have been of interest to compare with the foregoing the records of non-indigenous groups (i.e., those groups, for example Europeans in America, who have inhabited a particular re-

gion for too brief a time to allow selective influences to function).
Samples were unfortunately too few for satisfactory statistical
investigation, but a difference was tentatively suggested in European groups between those who were immigrants to particular
extra-European areas and those who were born and grew up there,
the heat-production of the latter tending to approach the conditions observed among indigenous races.

A more comprehensive report of this work will, it is hoped,
appear shortly.

Body Weight, Race and Climate

Reprinted, with deletion of the appendix and five figures, from *American Journal of Physical Anthropology*, N. S., Vol. 11, No. 4, pp. 533-558 (1953).

By D. F. ROBERTS

Examination of heat production in indigenous peoples by reference to the climates of their habitats (Roberts '52a, '52b) suggested that a relationship existed between body weight and mean environmental temperature. Further investigation of this suggestion forms the subject of the present study. The problem may be stated as follows: Does mean body weight vary with mean annual temperature, and is any racial influence evidenced?

Data were obtained from the literature. (I should like to express my thanks to Dr. J. Hiernaux, at the Institut Royal des Sciences Naturelles, Belgium, for making available to me his unpublished figures for weights in Ruanda Urundi; to Mr. J. Harries and Miss D. Hollingsworth of the Ministry of Food, London, for allowing me access to their data; and to Dr. J. S. Weiner for the stimulus of numerous discussions and for his valuable criticism of the text.) The first main source was the large number of papers giving metrical information about human groups. Unfortunately, in these "racial" studies, with their objective of classification and the consequent neglect of the more variable body features, weight data are rarely to be found: for example, to obtain the 28 comparable African samples here used, 4 of which are not yet published, it was necessary to examine nearly 750 series of African measurements, an incidence of slightly more than 3%. However, when weight details are included in anthropometric studies, the sample may usually be regarded as of adequate size and as representative of the population. The second source of data was furnished by reports devoted to the examination of particular physiological problems. These generally refer to smaller numbers of individuals, the samples are rarely drawn at random from the population but include those subjects who are available at the laboratory or hospital, the provenance of the subjects is often omitted, and their racial affinities are but loosely described. Publications of both types were reviewed and, in all, data were collected relating to more than 220 adult male and fewer female samples drawn from indigenous populations in many parts of the world (excluding European residents outside Europe).

From this assemblage of data were obtained series which could be regarded as comparable when due consideration was given to the factors known to influence body weight.

Error due to misprints was minimized by obtaining figures in every instance from original sources. Mean values were used. No sample was included of fewer than 20 individuals, sample size thus varying between 20 and about 3,000; the lower limit was determined after consideration of such data as were available for weight variability, standard deviations in the present series ranging from 3.78 to 9.4 kg and averaging 6.72 kg. All sexually heterogeneous samples were rejected, and samples for each sex dealt with separately. It was obviously necessary to consider carefully the age composition of the samples; the relatively slight rise (*circa* 4 kg) in mean weight between the ages of 20 and 40 in European populations (Kemsley, '50) and its apparent parallel in other human populations (e.g. in Japanese, Indo and Miwa, '13), seemed to justify the selection of these age limits; all samples containing individuals of less than 20 years of age, and samples whose mean age fell above the upper limit, were excluded. The immediate effects of disease may be discounted, since only healthy individuals were included in the groups considered, although it was impossible to estimate the effect of previous diseases. Ensuring that samples were indeed representative of their parent populations was impossible; all that could be done was to reject, where the relevant information was given, those samples socially or occupationally selected (e.g. labor recruits) and thus diminish, not eliminate error on this score. The influence of clothing was almost eliminated by the use in most instances of nude weights. Although variation due to season,

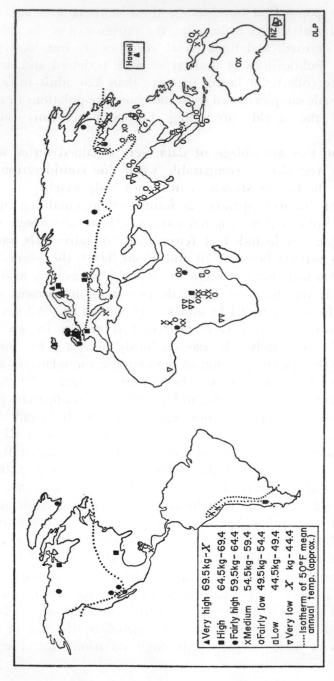

Fig. 1. Distribution of mean body weight in indigenous males (redrawn from Roberts '53, Fig. 2).

the time of day at which the observations were taken, the length of time since the last meal, diet, quality and quantity of the food supply, habits and occupation, could not be eliminated, these factors should be borne in mind.

In short, of the factors known to influence weight, an attempt was made to reduce the number operating upon the data here considered by rejecting all questionable samples; it is unfortunate that so few factors could be eliminated.

Subsequent to this preliminary assessment of the material, there remained 116 male and 33 female samples which seemed sufficiently comparable for statistical examination, and rather more groups whose weight could be mapped, representing populations of many races, of all major human varieties, from many parts of the world.

GEOGRAPHICAL DISTRIBUTION OF BODY WEIGHT

General

The geographical distribution of the series of 116 male mean body weights chosen for statistical examination is shown in the sketch map (Fig. 1). There is apparent a marked tendency for most "very high" weights to occur in cold areas and for "very low" weights in hotter regions. "Medium" weights occur at all latitudes from 0° to 40°, while weights above average preponderate in more temperate and cooler regions, those below average in warmer areas. A temperature relationship is clearly demonstrated by reference to the isotherms of mean annual temperature, one of which (that for 50° F.) is indicated on the diagram; very few of the samples in the categories heavier than medium fall to the warmer side, and only one sample lighter than medium falls on the cooler side, of this isotherm.

A temperature relationship also appears to exist within continental groups. In Europe and eastern Asia weights tend to increase from warmer south to cooler north. In America the gradient of weight from cold to hot areas in somewhat less clear, largely on account of the high figure for the Choctaw. For African groups, the mean environmental temperatures cover a smaller range, some 17° F.; comparison of racially and culturally similar groups, e.g. Ituri Bambuti with Ruanda Batwa, Bahutu at low medium and high altitudes, suggests weight variation either with altitude or concomitantly temperature.

Differences are also suggested among continental groups. In Oceania, Polynesians seem to be characterized by higher weights than Melanesians. Europeans appear to be heavier than East Mongoloids at similar temperatures. It is difficult to identify the effects on body weight of economy (e.g. pastoral Batutsi and cultivating Bahutu are both of medium weight, but pastoral Masai are heavier than the nearby Kikuyu cultivators).

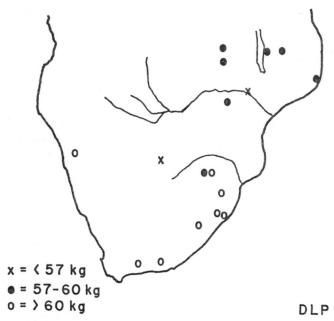

x = ‹ 57 kg
● = 57-60 kg
o = › 60 kg

DLP

Fig. 2. Weights of Bantu mineworkers at Johannesburg according to area of origin (figures of Brodie and Turner). All samples over 25 in number (redrawn from Roberts '53, Fig. 4).

Occupation seems to exert some influence: e.g. when the sample of Chinese at Changsha is subdivided into occupation groups, heavier weights tend to occur in the more laborious occupation groups and among students; samples from Pekin support this suggestion.

In short, examination of the distribution of mean body weight in indigenous male groups suggests that, although minor variations due to occupation and several other factors may occur, there is an underlying inverse relationship between weight and mean environmental temperature discernible not only when all mankind is considered but also within continental groups of man, and that differences in level occur among continental groups.

The same general pattern appeared when weights expressed per unit stature were mapped.

Regional

For a few regions more detailed information is available. There are a number of observations of southern Africans at the mines at which they worked, obtained by Brodie and Turner, both unpublished. The numbers of individuals are large—Brodie measured 3,339, Turner 604—and were drawn from several tribes. These samples were not included in the examination of other African groups living under tribal conditions since they were quite heavily selected by age, physique and several other qualities, besides living conditions and diet. The effect of this selection was assumed to be constant on all groups of mine-workers. The weights of samples containing 25 or more individuals were plotted according to the area from which they were recruited. The sketch (Fig. 2) shows that weights of Bantu mineworkers are in agreement with the findings of the general survey, in that higher weights tend to occur in cooler, and lower in warmer, areas.

As an example from an area with a small range of mean temperature, a representative cross-section of the population of Britain is afforded by the large number of young men, all between the ages of 20 and 21, measured in 1939 (Martin '49). Weights for rural groups, when plotted, show that heaviest people occur in the Scottish highlands and Cornwall, lightest in South Wales, and that otherwise a marked gradient can be perceived which, passing from heavier means in the south and east to lighter in the north and west, is not in accordance with the slight temperature differences. Weights for samples from county boroughs show a similar gradient, but these urban populations are all lighter in weight than their rural neighbors.

The distribution of stature for these samples shows a similar pattern, there being again a diminution northwards and westwards (save for the Scottish highlands), and again a tendency for values to be lower in urban than in rural communities. Hence it is suggested that to variations in stature, whatever their cause, may be attributed a certain proportion of the regional variation in weight in Britain; a similar conclusion is reached from examination of regional variation in weight in Finland (figures are given in Suominen, '29).

That stature is not the only determining factor, however, is shown by comparison of groups of identical height. For example, samples from county boroughs in the Wiltshire/Sussex and Shropshire/Bedfordshire regions both have the same mean height of 67.8″ but the former is 3.3 lb. heavier; county boroughs in the Southwest, East Anglia, and Warwickshire, have average statures of 67.5″ but the first sample is more than 2 lb. heavier than the other two; rural districts both of Glamorgan and the 4 northern counties have mean heights of 76.2″, but the former is 2.7 lb. lighter than the latter; rural districts in Leicestershire/Northamptonshire share with the Scottish highlands a mean stature of 67.8″ but the latter is more than 5 lb. heavier. Clearly, though the last two comparisons may reflect a temperature influence, such may not be postulated for the first two comparisons.

Examination then of series drawn from regions of more limited environmental range shows that the expected small effect of the climatic factor in these instances may be obscured by relatively greater variation in a number of other influences—a possible reason for the overlooking of "large-scale" geographical relationships of weight in the past. Of these other influences, stature would appear to be predominant; the other factors it is difficult at the moment to identify.

STATISTICAL RESULTS

Evaluation of the suggested relationships by statistical methods was accordingly undertaken. The series of samples used is given in the appendix. Mean temperature figures were obtained for each locality from which the samples had been drawn, from local meteorological records where available, but otherwise by interpolation from the nearest stations.

First, the significance of the association between mean weight and mean annual temperature was examined (Fig. 3). When all comparable 116 male samples were considered, the correlation coefficient $r = -.600$ resulted, highly significant at 0.1%; the relationship appearing linear, a regression line of weight on temperature was fitted by the method of least squares with a value for the regression coefficient $b = -.305$ (kilograms per degree Fahrenheit). Thus the inverse relationship between weight and environmental temperature, postulated from examination of the geographical distribution, is supported by statistical analysis.

To clarify further this apparent relationship it was necessary to take into account stature which was obviously responsible for a certain amount of variation. The question was whether the lower weights of tropical, and the higher weights of temperate, dwellers were due to respectively smaller and greater statures, for in the present series of samples a significant relationship appeared between stature and temperature ($r = -.351$, significant at 0.1%) and the correlation coefficient between stature and weight was $r = +.734$, highly significant at 0.1%. The partial correlation coefficients were therefore calculated. The high correlation between weight and stature exclusive of temperature was again highly significant at 0.1% with the value $r_{ws.t} = +.698$; the high correlation between weight and temperature, exclusive of stature remained highly significant at 0.1% ($r_{wt.s} = -.538$); and the correlation between stature and temperature disappeared ($r_{st.w} = +.164$, not significant). The multiple correlation coefficient, $R = .820$, indicates the importance of stature and temperature in affecting the weight of a sample, seven-tenths of the total variance in weight thus being ascribable to these two factors. Both partial regression coefficients being highly significant, the "prediction" formula for mean body weight may be expressed

$$W = .071S - .199T - 48.1$$

where W is the mean body weight in kilograms, S is stature in millimeters, and T is mean annual temperature in degrees Fahrenheit. Mean weight then apparently decreases by a kilogram with an increase in temperature of 5° F., but increases by a kilogram with an increase in stature of approximately 1.4 cm.

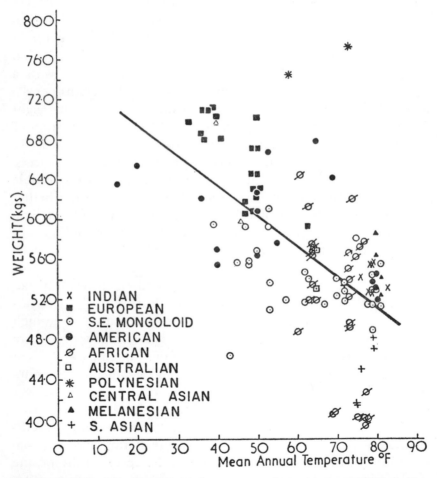

Fig. 3. Relationship of weight and mean annual temperature. Male indigenous groups.

TABLE 1

CORRELATION COEFFICIENTS IN THE FEMALE SERIES

	Total Correlation Coefficient	Signif- icant at	Partial Correlation Coefficient	Signif- icant at
Weight and stature	+.813	0.1%	+.712	0.1%
Weight and temperature	−.809	0.1%	−.704	0.1%
Stature and temperature	−.587	0.1%	+.208	not

The use of a cubic function in the comparison of weight and stature has been advocated by a number of authors, e.g. Livi (1898), and Gavan ('52). Would the relationship have been different if stature had been expressed in terms of its third rather than its first power? Calculation of the total correlation coefficients in these terms produced no significant difference from those stated above; the correlation coefficient between weight and stature cubed was $r= +.742$, between temperature and stature cubed $r= −.360$, and the multiple correlation coefficient $R= .823$. Hence it was not incorrect to use stature to the first power during the present calculations.

By way of confirmation of the foregoing relationships, similar calculations were performed on the short series of female samples available, 33 in all, giving the results shown in Table 1; there is general concordance between the results for the two sexes.

The samples having been drawn from all varieties of man it was necessary to enquire whether any variation in body weight could be associated with or attributed to the fact that a particular sample was drawn from a particular variety of man. For this purpose covariance analysis was applied to the data.

The samples were assigned to the following 10 varieties or geographical groups: American, all samples drawn from native Indian and Eskimo populations of that continent; African, all samples examined in that continent south of the Sahara, including Pygmy and Bushman; East Mongoloid, samples of Mongoloid affinities from east and south Asia, i.e. excluding populations of India and aboriginals of Malaya, but including Indonesian

groups; Central Asian, the samples from that region of Kazak
and Kirghiz; South Asian, non-Mongoloid primitive groups, aboriginals of Malaya and Eastern India; Indian, all samples from
that subcontinent save the aboriginals; European, peoples in that
continent; Australian, aboriginal samples; Polynesian, samples of
Maori and Hawaiians; Melanesian, samples from that region. The
basis of the grouping was geographical, but a tentative anthropological classification was incorporated, the aim being that any sample within a group should possess more features in common with its
companions in that group than with any sample in any other group.
To anticipate criticism of this system, some of the more striking departures may perhaps be commented upon. Bushmen were included in the African group since their exclusion would have necessi-
tated similar treatment of the Sandawe, who, though possessing a
number of traits in common with the Bushmen, also show affinities
with neighboring Bantu-speaking groups. Eskimo were assigned
to the American category since they may not be incorporated in

TABLE 2

ANALYSIS OF VARIANCE

Source	Degrees of Freedom	Sum of Squares	Mean Square	
Total	115	715714		
Within groups	106	275878	2602.6)	F = 18.78
	—	———	———)	significant
Among groups	9	439836	48870.7)	at 0.1%

TABLE 3

ANALYSIS OF COVARIANCE: COMPARISON OF ADJUSTED MEANS.
ERRORS OF ESTIMATE

Source	Degrees of Freedom	Sum of Squares	Mean Square	
Total	113	234809		
Within groups	104	119345	1147.5)	F = 11.18
	——	———	———)	significant
Among groups	9	115464	12829.3)	at 0.1%

any of the others here used, a classification with which known gene frequencies of other Eskimo samples appear to agree. Details of the racial composition of Indian town samples were almost completely lacking so that a continental description distinct from the other groups seemed the obvious solution.

It is when such a classification is attempted that the inadequacy of available material is most realized. Lack of genetic information of the samples precludes accurate genetic classification, an essential preliminary to the assessment of environmental influence. The small number of samples tends to lead to the use of too-inclusive categories, or categories containing too few results, both of which may well render indistinct any existing relationships. It was thought better, however, to err in this direction rather than the contrary.

First, were there significant differences among the weights of the 10 groups? Analysis of variance given in Table 2 showed that such differences were highly significant at 0.1%, indicating that some of the groups possessed greater weights than others.

Were these differences attributable to variations in features shown to be associated with weight, viz. temperature or stature? Covariance analysis, given in Table 3, indicated that differences among adjusted means of the groups were highly significant at 0.1%, i.e. that intrinsic differences in weight existed among the groups after allowance was made for the association with stature and temperature. Calculation of the adjusted means of the groups produced the interesting results shown in Table 4, that the lowest weights occurred among groups thought to have occupied a trop-

TABLE 4

MEAN WEIGHTS OF GROUPS ADJUSTED FOR TEMPERATURE AND STATURE
ARRANGED IN INCREASING ORDER

	kg.		kg.
South Asian	51.79	Melanesian	59.84
Australian	51.90	American	59.92
African	53.92	European	59.93
Indian	54.52	Central Asian	62.20
East Mongoloid	54.69	Polynesian	71.82

ical habitat for a considerable time, South Asian and Australian aboriginal and African populations. The proximity of Indian and East Mongoloid results is worth notice, and so is the position of American, European, and Central Asian groups at the upper end of the scale. For interpretation of Melanesian and Polynesian figures it is necessary to await further evidence since the groups contain respectively 4 and two samples.

Moreover, this analysis demonstrated that the relationship of weight with temperature and stature also occurred within groups, i.e. remained after allowance was made for the differences among groups. Within groups, the total correlation coefficient between weight and temperature remained highly significant (at 0.1%) with the value $r = -.362$; that between weight and stature was again highly significant (at 0.1%) with the value $r = +.711$; but that between stature and temperature disappeared ($r = -.166$, not significant). Calculation of the within group partial correlation coefficients produced similar results; that between weight and temperature exclusive of stature ($r_{wt.s} = -.352$) was highly significant at 0.1%; that between weight and stature exclusive of temperature ($r_{ws.t} = +.712$) was highly significant at 0.1% while there was again no correlation between stature and temperature exclusive of weight ($r_{st.w} = +.160$, not significant). The within group multiple correlation coefficient was calculated to be $R = .753$.

Nor did the use of stature expressed to the third power instead of the first appreciably alter these findings. The total

TABLE 5

ANALYSIS OF COVARIANCE: COMPARISON OF ADJUSTED MEANS.
ERRORS OF ESTIMATE

Source	Degrees of Freedom	Sum of Squares	Mean Square	
Total	113	230388		
Error	104	119069	1144.9)	F = 10.80
	—	———	———)	significant
Between groups	9	111319	12368.8)	at 0.1%

TABLE 6

INTRA-GROUP CORRELATIONS

	No. of Samples	Weight/ Temperature	Significant at	Weight/ Stature	Significant at
African	28	−.395	5%	+.852	0.1%
American	16	−.493	10%	+.818	0.1%
East Mongoloid	29	−.421	5%	+.357	10%
European	20	−.755	0.1%	+.450	5%

correlation coefficient of stature cubed with weight was r = + .716 (significant at 0.1%), with temperature r = − .163 (not significant); the differences between adjusted means were again highly significant at 0.1% as is shown in Table 5.

Only 4 groups contained sufficient samples to allow any attempt at the evaluation of individual within group correlations; total correlation coefficients are shown in Table 6.

DISCUSSION

Statistical examination of the data then appears to confirm the inferences drawn from general geographical considerations. The inverse relationship postulated between the mean weight of human groups and mean temperature is seen to be an actual relationship rather than a pattern due to any chance selection of the data. The depression of mean weights in tropical areas, and their elevation in cooler areas, is seen to be accounted for in part by the affinities of the samples with particular racial or geographical groups, in part by a tendency within such groups. Variation of weight with stature, marked though it be, seems scarcely to affect the temperature relationship; that is to say that the weight of a group is influenced by the temperature of its habitat, stature merely inducing additional variation. Other factors may well be operative, as the sketch maps suggested, but the extent of their influence, including that of chance effects, is not greater than would account for three-tenths of the total variance of the series here examined. It should perhaps be noted that the overall correlation of stature and temperature in the present series, which disappeared in the within-group calculations and hence may be considered due to the differences in stature among the different continental groups here used, was tested on a longer series of samples (between 300 and 400) and found to be absent.

The need for caution in the interpretation of the results, on account of the limitations of the data used, must be stressed. The number of samples included is admittedly small; the blame for this should be laid on those responsible for directing past anthropometric investigations who have overlooked the value of weight as a descriptive character, one moreover not difficult technically to obtain. The use, dictated by the availability of records, of mean annual temperature instead of some physiologically more meaningful climatic measure could doubtless be improved upon. Hence no claim is made to finality, but the results to date seem to be of sufficient interest to be put on record.

What meaning is to be attached to the relationship of weight of indigenous peoples with temperature? Three possibilities may be suggested:

1. It may indicate, for a given stature, a different distribution within the body of the body mass, a different morphology. It can easily be shown that for a given stature a lower weight at increased temperature gives an advantageous ratio of body surface area to mass, thereby facilitating the *maintenance of the body heat balance.*

2. In the course of examination of the relationship of basal heat production with environmental temperature (Roberts 52b), the following interesting fact emerged: there was a high correlation between weight and temperature ($r_{tw} = - .573$) which remained highly significant ($r_{tw.s} = - .584$) when allowance was made for the association of weight with stature, but which disappeared ($r_{tw.sh} = + .155$, not significant) when allowance was made for the influence of stature and heat production. Hence it seems reasonable to infer that the weight/temperature relationship may exist as an aid in the *adjustment of body heat production*

to environmental conditions.

3. It may include a tendency in cold climates for greater amounts of fat to occur subcutaneously which, from its insulating properties, would appreciably affect *body heat loss*.

Each or all of these suggestions may be contributory. It would clearly be of interest to investigate the body composition of indigenous peoples, to enquire whether it is the lean body mass instead of overall weight which is associated with climate. (It is not legitimate at the present stage to extend the prediction formula, obtained by Miller and Blyth ('52) for lean body mass from oxygen consumption, to non-European populations living in different climates; should however the application of this formula to indigenous peoples prove to be valid, it would suggest that lean body mass per unit weight decreases with increased temperature, or in other words that in colder climates the proportion of metabolically active tissue to inert tissue is higher than in warm climates.) Again it would not be difficult to include measurements of skin thickness, and the bodily distribution of its variations, in anthropological surveys. Until data of this type are forthcoming, little more can be said concerning the ecological significance of the weight/temperature relationship, save that possession of lower weights in warmer, and greater in cooler, areas may well be advantageous.

The weight/temperature relationships here demonstrated suggest that Bergmann's rule (that within a polytypic warm-blooded species, the body size of a subspecies usually increases with decreasing mean temperature of its habitat), is applicable to man. Clearer definition of "body size" is, however, necessary. Defined by reference to stature, although from the series here considered Bergmann's rule might seem to be applicable, this suggestion is refuted by more extensive material. Defined by weight, it is not only applicable but needs restatement to incorporate, with the postulated variation in size among subspecies, similar variation within the subspecies.

The present data are not adequate to show whether the relationship between weight and temperature is direct or indirect, in the former case constituting an immediate response to tem-

perature, in the latter acting through the intermediaries of type
and amount of food supply, habits, genetics, etc. If it is indeed
advantageous in warmer areas to possess lower weights, then providing that condition is attained it would appear immaterial
whether achieved directly or indirectly.

If, at the moment, it appears profitless to speculate on the
degree of causality of the relationship, it may be pointed out
that all responsibility should not be attributed to nutrition, for
this would render difficult of explanation a number of features,
e.g. the European correlation, the high non-European cold results,
and the low figures of adequately-fed tropical dwellers. It is
interesting that the lowest weights do not appear in areas of
greatest population pressure, nor do the highest always occur
where living conditions are easiest. Further, if nutrition were
the cause, one might expect a certain nutritional influence during the growing period, affecting for example stature; elimination of the stature factor then should markedly reduce the correlation between weight and temperature, which clearly does
not occur.

The impression received during the course of the present
study is that there is a general weight level for given climatic
conditions about which actual weights vary according to socio-
economic and nutritional standards. Could there be a genetic
factor involved in such a general weight level?

To prove this suggestion, to assess quantitatively the relative importance of genetic and long- and short-term phenotypic
influences, is at the moment impossible. The evidence, however,
at least suggests that some genetic factor is operating:

1. Studies of twins have shown (Newman '42) that more
than 75% of observed variability in weight may be attributed to
genetic influence.

2. In America (Meredith '52), mean weight of viable Negro
infants at birth was about 4% lighter than that of American
White infants living in the same area; further, between Negro
and White infants receiving adequate dietary and medical care,
there was no difference in mean stature at ages of 6 months, 9
months, and 12 months, but White infants were slightly heavier

at each age.

3. As compared with temperate groups, lighter weights for given statures in long-established tropical populations have been reported at all ages, e.g. in West Africa boys from 10 to 18 years (Weiner and Thambipillai '52), in aboriginals of Bihar from 7 to 15 years (Majumdar '52); however the Polynesians (Wissler '30) and Micronesians (Greulich '51) appear to possess greater weights for their stature and age than other tropical dwellers. Each of these facts would be expected were the weights of indigenous groups genetically adjusted over a period of time to their environments.

4. The extent of the short-period phenotypic effects of temperature and calorie intake may be roughly estimated by further analysis of the fluctuations in Britain between 1943 and 1949 of weights (Kemsley '50, '52), of food consumption (Harries and Hollingsworth '53) and of temperature. Regressions of weight on these variables were calculated, and the results were applied to the weight/temperature relationship found in the present study. The short-period temperature effect, exclusive of food intake, appears to account for only one-eighth of the overall world depression in weight with increased temperature; further, the differences in calorie intake, exclusive of temperature, required to account for the remaining seven-eighths are considerably greater than those observed in nutritional studies to date. Although, in view of the crudity of the procedure, no great stress should be laid on these findings, they seem to suggest that effects of differences of food intake and temperature such as operate in short-term weight fluctuations are only partly, if at all, responsible for the geographical pattern of body weight shown in this survey.

As regards the material used in the present study, it is interesting that, wherever an equatorial sample is designated as representing the aboriginal population of an area, its weight is lower than that of later comers, e.g. the aboriginal Orang Balik Papan of Borneo have a mean weight of about 46 kg whereas later immigrants vary about 51 kg, the Senoid peoples of the Malayan interior vary between 45 and 48 kg whereas the Malays vary about 52 to 55 kg, the Santals and Paharias of Bihar vary between 41 to 45 kg while later comers vary about 52 to 55 kg. A certain proportion of this depression may be accounted for by the different way of life and less opportunity to take as full advantage of their surroundings as the newcomers, who would tend to choose the more favorable areas; however, in view of the findings of the present study it may perhaps be suggested that at least part of this depression may be due to the longer period over which any selective advantages conferred by lower weight might have operated. Unfortunately this argument may not yet be supported by application to aboriginal inhabitants of cold areas since there are at present no data. It is moreover possible to interpret the significant differences between adjusted means (Table 4) as being in accordance with genetic influence upon weight; it is however equally possible to interpret them as reflecting some other as yet unanalyzed influence, e.g. habits, or they may in fact be due to a curvilinear relationship between weight and temperature, rather than linear. Final judgment is impossible in view of the lack of genetic, nutritional, and other necessary information.

Whatever the solution to the question of directness of response, which future work alone can decide, there is one implication clearly carried by the present study. There is a relationship between mean weight and environmental temperature. There should therefore no longer be talk of universal "norms" of weight based upon European standards, to be applied indiscriminately in nutrition and growth studies of other races in other parts of the world.

SUMMARY

The geographical distribution of mean body weight in indigenous populations suggests an inverse relationship with mean environmental temperature. Statistical analysis showed this association to be highly significant, both before and after the influences of stature and group affinity were taken into account. There are differences in weight among geographical groups or varieties of man, not attributable to the temperature and stature relationships.

The ecological significance of the results is discussed, and some genetic influence suggested.

REFERENCES

Brodie, Unpublished: Manuscript in the Department of Human Anatomy, Oxford.

Gavan, J. A.: Growth of Guamanian children—some methodological questions, *Am. J. Phys. Anthropol., N. S. 10*:132-135, 1952.

Greulich, W. W.: The growth and developmental status of Guamanian school children in 1947, *Am. J. Phys. Anthropol., N. S. 9*:55-70, 1951.

Harries, J. M. and Hollingsworth, D. F.: Food supply, body weight, and activity in Great Britain, 1943-49, *Brit. M. J., 4801*:75-79, 1953.

Indo (Quoted in T. Kubo): *Beiträge zur physischen Anthropologie der Koreaner,* Tokyo, 1913.

Kemsley, W. F. F.: The weight and height of a population in 1943, *Ann. Eugen., 15*:161-183, 1950.

Kemsley, W. F. F.: Body weight at different ages and heights, *Ann. Eugen., 16*:316-334, 1951-52.

Livi, R.: L'indice ponderale o rapporto tra la statura e il peso, *Atti della Soc. Romana di Antropologia, 5*:125-153, 1898.

Majumdar, D. N.: Growth trends among aboriginal boys of Kolhan, Bihar, *Eastern Anthropol., 2*:201-205, 1948-49.

Martin, W. J.: *Physique of Young Adult Males,* London, H. M. Stationary Office, 1949.

Meredith, H. V.: North American Negro Infants: size at birth and growth during the first postnatal year, *Human Biol., 24*:290-308, 1952.

Miller, A. T. and Blyth, C. S.: Estimation of lean body mass and body fat from basal oxygen consumption, *J. Appl. Physiol., 5*:73-78, 1952.

Miwa (quoted in T. Kubo): *Beiträge zur physichen Anthropologie der Koreaner,* Tokyo, 1913.

Newman, H. H.: *Twins and Supertwins,* London, Hutchinson, 1942.

Roberts, D. F.: Basal metabolism, race and climate, a preliminary note, *Man, 251*:169-170, 1952a.

Roberts, D. F.: Basal metabolism, race and climate, *J. Roy. Anthropol. Inst., 59*:169-183, 1952b.

Suominen, Y. K.: Physical anthropology in Suomi, *J. Roy. Anthropol. Inst.*, *59*:207-230, 1929.

Turner, G. A.: *Some anthropological notes on the South African coloured mine laborer,* unpublished MSS. in the Department of Human Anatomy, Oxford.

Weiner, J. S. and Thambipillai, V.: Skeletal maturation of West African Negroes, *Am. J. Phys. Anthropol., N. S. 10*:407-418, 1952.

Wissler, C.: Growth of children in Hawaii, *Mem. Bernice P. Bishop Museum, Honolulu, 11*:109-257, 1930.

Nose Shape and Climate

Reprinted from *American Journal of Physical Anthropology*, N.S. Vol. 12, No. 4, pp. 1-4 (1954).

By J. S. WEINER

In 1923 Thomson and Buxton demonstrated a close association between the shape of the nose, expressed as the nasal index, and external climatic conditions. They reported, as did Davies ('32) on still larger samples, that the nasal index is more highly correlated with mean annual temperature than with the relative humidity of the air. For "predicting" the index they recommended the use of both air temperature and relative humidity in the regression formula, since temperature used alone was apt to produce considerable errors. The correlations led them to regard "temperature as a dominant factor" though "modified by various degrees of humidity." Davies also considered that "temperature exerts a stronger influence than humidity" in view of its higher correlation coefficient.

In their discussion of the functional significance of these relations, Thomson and Buxton made clear that both temperature and humidity were concerned. They suggested that the modifications of nose shape in different climates may reasonably be related to the need for moistening the inspired air; for this reason the humidity of the air is obviously of physiological significance. They indicated also that variation of nose shape might bear some relation to heat loss from the respiratory tract. They argued, for example, that "in the tropics the loss of lung water from the respiratory tract is undoubtedly of considerable physiological importance. In air containing the highest relative humidity the existence of a free passage of entry is of advantage, in order that sufficient air may be breathed in to absorb water from the respiratory tract."

That moistening of the air is a prime function of the nasal epithelium appears from the work of Proetz ('41) and Negus

('49). Negus gives physiological, pathological and clinical reasons for the importance of this moistening on the vitality and activity of the cilia, which are in fact more susceptible to changes in the consistency of the film in which they work (and therefore to drying out) than they are to quite large degrees of heating and cooling. According to Dawes and Prichard ('53), Perwitchscky's findings ('27) also suggest that warming is a less important function than moistening of the inspired air. Dawes and Prichard point out the means by which the inspired air is moistened and cleansed are closely related. In providing moisture additional to that contained in the inspired air so as to bring the moisture content to about 95% relative humidity at body temperature, the mucous membrane of the nose in dry climates may secrete even up to a liter of water per day (Proetz '41).

It follows from these considerations that if the shape of the nose bears some relation to the moistening of inspired air, the nasal index should be most closely associated with the physical factor primarily concerned in the exchange of water from nasal epithelium to inspired air. This factor is the absolute humidity and can be expressed either as the vapor pressure of the air or in terms of its moisture content (in grains per lb. of dry air). The loss of water from the respiratory tract induced by evaporative cooling which according to Thomson and Buxton might also influence the shape of the nose, is likewise governed by the vapor pressure of the inspired air. The amount of heat lost by this evaporative channel especially in hot climates, it may be mentioned, is a relatively small proportion of the total heat loss and the effectiveness of the respiratory tract in desert climates would be reduced by the heat gain from breathing air at temperatures above that of the body. In any case, evaporative heat loss from the respiratory tract and moisture addition to the inspired air would both be functions of the vapor pressure gradient between the external air and the virtually saturated surfaces of the tract. The vapor pressure of the latter may be assumed to remain relatively constant so that nose shape can be directly related to external vapor pressure.

The use of the two separate climatic variates, air temperature and relative humidity, though useful enough for indicating the type of climate associated with variation in nasal index, is thus not entirely adequate to express these postulated functions of water exchange by the nose. To combine them statistically does not furnish the correct physical specification of the outside air.

The data provided by Thomson and Buxton for some 150 living population samples have been re-examined in a preliminary way and the indications are that correlations with the external absolute humidity are likely to be as good as, and probably better than, those with air temperature and humidity. It has not yet been possible to assemble the rather formidable amount of meteorological data (and many of these are probably not available) necessary to obtain the true mean absolute humidity for these 150 locations, but as an approximation the absolute humidity has been derived from the mean annual temperature and mean annual relative humidity as given in Thomson and Buxton's paper. This approximation involves only a relatively small error for polar regions and is unimportant for hot regions (Sumner and Tunnel, '49). Table 1 shows that the original coefficients are appreciably lower than that with the wet bulb temperature or even more so than that with vapor pressure of the air. From the latter the relation between the nasal index and the amount of water to be secreted, say in 24 hours, to humidify the inspired air could be calculated, if desired.

TABLE 1

Nasal Index (116 Groups Living) Correlated with	Coefficient	Standard Error
*Dry bulb temp.	0.63	0.050
*Relative humidity	0.42	0.068
*Dry bulb temp. and rel. humidity	0.72	0.040
Wet bulb temp.	0.77	0.034
Vapor pressure of the air	0.82	0.027

*Thomson and Buxton ('23).

It would be worth extending the analysis on these lines to many more groups using more detailed meteorological data. The figures given should be regarded meanwhile as indicative of the functional basis underlying the nasal index-climate relationship, namely, the loss of water to the inspired air.

REFERENCES

Davies, A.:   A re-survey of the morphology of the nose in relation to climate, *J. Roy. Anthropol. Inst., 62*:337-359, 1932.

Dawes, J. D. K. and Prichard, M. M. L.:   Studies of vascular arrangements of the nose, *J. Anat., 87*:311-322, 1953.

Negus, V. E.:   The defense of the air passages with special reference to ciliary action, *Oxford Medical School Gazette, 4*:1952, 1949.

Perwitschscky, R.:   Die Temperatur und Feuchtigkeits-verhältnisse der Atemluft in den Luftwegen, *Arch. Ohr.-Nas.-und Kehlkheilk., 117*: 1-36, 1927.

Proetz, A. W.:   *Essays on Applied Physiology of the Nose,* St. Louis, Annals Publishing Co., 1941.

Sumner, E. J. and Tunnel, G. A.:   Determination of the true mean vapour pressure of the atmosphere from temperature and hygrometric data, *Meteorological Magazine, 79*:258-263, 295-301, 1949.

Thomson, A. and Buxton, D.:   Man's nasal index in relation to certain climatic conditions, *J. Roy. Anthropol. Inst., 53*:92-122, 1923.

The Biological Adaptation of Man to Hot Deserts

Reprint with deletion of one figure and the appendix from *The American Naturalist,* Vol. 92, No. 867, pp. 337-357 (1958).

By PAUL T. BAKER

CLIMATIC ADAPTATION

Modern man lives in almost all parts of the terrestrial globe. We attribute this wide distribution to his culture and believe that biological man is a semi-tropical animal who, without culture, could operate only in a very narrow temperature range. Technology has, undoubtedly, widened the temperature range within which man can live. Yet, with a very simple technology, man lived in such widely divergent climates as the Sahara desert and the wet-cold of Tierra del Fuego. While these groups had tools to help them in quest of food, their cultures provided very little protection from the climate. Even modern man should not be visualized as free of his climatological environment; rather, modern culture might be thought of as an insulation against the environment, mitigating but not destroying the climatological forces that act on human biology. This is particularly true of the desert where clothing does not greatly alter the effect of the climate on man.

In the desert, man may wear boots to protect his feet from the hot ground and clothing to reduce the radiation received on the body, but he remains basically dependent on his inherent heat dissipation mechanisms for survival. These mechanisms vary widely between men so that no two men are exactly alike in their ability to perform work in the heat. The obvious extremes are individuals born without sweat glands and those who can perform hard work when the desert temperature is even as high as 110° F. Those men without sweat glands never survive in hot environments, but what of the so-called "normal" man? In many cases within a group of healthy and apparently "normal" men working in the desert one will suddenly collapse and die of heat stroke (Schickele, '47), even though he was apparently performing the same work under the same external heat load as his fellow men who suffered no ill effects. Under standardized work conditions in the desert, individuals vary by as much as 100 per cent in their sweat loss, two degrees in rectal temperature, and 50 pulse beats per minute (Adolph, '47). These ranges often signify the difference between continued work and collapse. The large between-individual variation in response is not strongly affected by recent nutritional, work, or disease histories. Instead, the response is reproducible, that is, it can be measured in successive trials at approximately similar magnitudes even when several weeks' time have passed. Thus, it appears that the major amount of individual variation in resistance to heat is a product of inheritance plus life-long environmental adaptation. These factors cannot be modified in most cases, but by discovering them, it should be possible to classify a man's ability to withstand desert heat stress before he is actually placed in the stresful condition.

It appears that the final tolerance of men exposed to desert heat stress depends on biological tolerance. Psychological and cultural factors have a large influence on man's ability to prevent exposure to severe heat, but if exposure is inescapable for a group, man's biology limits his tolerance. For this reason a search for adaptation to heat must logically rest on a biological, not cultural, criterion. In actuality, no biological characteristic is free from cultural influences, and the physiological reactions of the man who finds himself in severe heat are modified by both his individual and cultural background. However, the use of biological measurements such as body temperatures are, without doubt, much more indicative of physical condition than the subjective judgements of either the subject or an observer.

In the present study rectal temperatures, pulse rates, and sweat losses, as well as heat stroke, have been used as indices of heat tolerance. Most of these variables are at best only indirect measurements of heat tolerance. With so many limitations already imposed on the criteria, it would be desirable to compare dircctly populations under desert heat stress conditions. As this is virtually impossible, this study attempts to construct a partial biological model for desert heat resistance. In this study the word model is used to connote ideal. That is, on the basis of the adaptive mechanisms utilized by the human body, what kind of man would be the most perfectly adapted to hot desert thermal conditions? Using the concept of a biological model, the major problem of how man adapts to a hot desert climate may be subdivided into three phases:

1.   Are there human morphological and racial variables which increase or decrease desert heat stress tolerance?

2.   If these variables exist, what arc the respective influences of the genetic and environmental forces on the adult phenotypic manifestation?

3.   How does the theoretical biological model compare with the actual world distribution of morphological and racial characteristics?

THE NATURE OF HEAT STRESS

'I'hc responses of the human organism to hot desert stress may be divided into two major categories: (a) *Responses referable to man's thermoregulatory mechanisms;* these may be termed systemic in that they affect the total body, and should be considered primary because the regulatory mechanisms must be adequate for the stress level or a serious performance decrement: sometimes death will result.   (b) *Responses of a non-thermoregulatory nature;* beside the primary strain of temperature regulation, the desert produces several secondary forms of strain in the sense that they affect only limited portions of the body and are not directly lethal, for example, eye strain, sunburn and extremity swelling.

In this study these many secondary strains have not been considered and attention was focussed on the primary problems of temperature regulation. The ability of a group of men to survive in the desert also depends on their being able to withstand secondary stress. However, for survival, adjustment to the severe systemic heat stress is of primary importance and is less subject to mitigation by technological aids.

The effects of desert heat on man are qualitatively as well as quantitatively different from the effects of hot wet climates. The external heat load on the individual in the desert is several times greater than it is in a hot jungle. In the jungle, dry bulb temperatures rarely exceed inner body temperature, while on the hot desert the reported temperature frequently is 10° to 20° F. higher than the body temperature. Even this comparison does not present the full difference between jungle and desert dry bulb temperatures. Conventional temperature readings are taken at four to five feet above the ground. In the wet tropics the ground temperature equals or is below the reading taken at four feet. In the desert, ground temperatures are much higher than four-foot temperatures. At Yuma, Arizona ground temperatures were found to run as high as 150° F. (Yuma Handbook, '54). At one foot and two feet above ground level dry bulb temperatures were still found to be two to three degrees higher than at the 48 inch level. These statistics indicated that in terms of man's micro-climate, the temperature contrast between the jungle and desert is even greater than is apparent from official temperature records.

There is, then, a decided quantitative difference between the heat loads of the tropics and the hot deserts. Yet the body heat storage and psycho-motor performance are not substantially different between these climates. Man's ability to function as well in the hot desert as in the tropics is related to the nature of his cooling mechanisms. As long as the ambient dry bulb temperature is lower than man's core temperature, some of the heat of metabolism is lost by radiation, convection, and conduction. The quantity of heat loss by these mechanisms depends primarily on the area of temperature contrast. Thus, if the skin temperature is 96° F. in a 90° environment, the heat loss from the body is greater than if skin temperature is 94°. In the heat it is, therefore, advantageous for man to have a high skin temperature and maintain a maximum rate of heat exchange between the deep body and the subcutaneous area. Several body mechanisms speed up this heat exchange when the individual is subject to heat stress. There is a general peripheral vasodilation allowing maximum surface blood flow, which brings the deep metabolically produced heat to the surface and carries back the cooled blood (Bass *et al.*, '55). However, the heat production of the body even under basal metabolic conditions exceeds the heat loss by radiation, conduction, and convection when the ambient temperature reaches about 85° F. A working man exceeds this potential at a much lower ambient temperature. When the body heat production exceeds loss through these mechanisms, then new avenues of loss must be utilized or the organisms will start to accumulate heat. A small heat accumulation can be tolerated by the body, but for the rare individual born without sweat glands adaptation ends here. Without the sweating mechanism man could not survive for long in environments over 85° F.

Although the ambient temperature reaches 120° F. in the desert, the dry bulb temperature just above the surface of a man's skin is below subcutaneous temperature due to sweat evaporation. Each gram of water absorbs 0.578 calories of heat when it evaporates on the skin. The total heat loss by sweating is thus determined by the amount of sweat produced and the ability of the environment to evaporate the sweat. While the sweat production of the body keeps close to cooling needs, the ability of the environment to vaporize water is dependent primarily on the wet bulb temperature and the size of the skin area over which the water is distributed. It is in the wet bulb temperatures or absolute humidity that we find another large difference between the tropical and the hot desert climate. While the dry bulb temperature of the desert is much higher than a tropical area, the wet bulb temperature is similar or even lower and thus in desert climates sweat evaporation is complete, while incomplete in tropical areas.

An analysis of the stress imposed on man by heat has indicated the necessity for distinguishing between the heat stress of the desert and the tropics. To summarize these differences we may say that the hot desert imposes a quantitatively greater heat load on man but because all sweat is evaporated in the desert, the body heat loss is limited only by the body's ability to produce sweat. In the tropics, however, where only limited quantities of sweat can be evaporated, heat loss is governed by the surface area of the individual. These statements are, of course, an oversimplification but do indicate some of the differences between the impingement of tropical and desert heat stress on human thermal regulation.

THE HUMAN BIOLOGICAL MODEL FOR
HOT DESERT TOLERANCE

There is considerable variation in human desert heat tolerance which occurs in healthy individuals and is probably species wide. How important this variation is for the survival of an individual or group is quite obviously a function of the culture. In present American society a man can survive and propagate in the hottest desert area even if he has a very low tolerance of heat. However, in an agricultural or hunting culture heat tolerance becomes more critical. Even within certain segments of our own society, such as the military, desert heat tolerance may be very important for individual survival.

The most definitive criteria of desert heat tolerance are death, or no death, from exposure to high heat stress. The only available published material of this nature was reported by Schickele ('47). She reported on 147 deaths from heat prostration. These deaths occurred during the training and maneuvering of soldiers in desert areas. From the medical records of these men she obtained height and weight data and compared these data to that found for 100,000 randomly selected soldiers. Her results indicated that the higher a man's relative body weight, the greater his susceptibility to fatal heat stroke. The maximum probability of fatal heat stroke was among men 55 or more pounds overweight. This was a trend over the whole scale of relative weight so that men 5 to 14 pounds above normal were four times more susceptible to fatal heat stroke than men of average weight. Even the men with an average relative weight were four times more susceptible than men 16 or more pounds under the average for their age and stature.

Weight deviations from a standard reflect both fat and muscle variation, but for individuals of the same racial and cultural background these deviations primarily reflect variation in adiposity. Thus Schickele's data indicates that the greater a man's adiposity, the lower his heat tolerance. It also suggests that a large muscle mass for a given stature reduces a man's desert heat tolerance.

Lacking survival data on which to base an adequate model, physiological data offer the next best criteria. Information on body temperature, sweat loss, and pulse rates indicates the level of strain which a man is experiencing. Presumably the strain level has a relationship to how closely a man is approaching collapse. It probably also has some significance on the man's performance potential. Studies using physiological criteria showed the same results as Schickele's data (Baker, '55). Using a direct measurement of fat, it was found that fatter men had higher strain levels. It was also found that men with compact bodies (low stature per unit weight) had lower tolerance of heat. Physiological data also indicate a skin color factor in heat tolerance. The dark skin when exposed to solar radiation, absorbs more energy and thereby raises the strain level (Baker, '58). On the other hand, a very light skin does not tan and therefore, leads to a much greater strain on the man when exposed to the sun for any extended time span. Thus, brunette skin which is capable of tanning, but has a minimum absorption of solar energy is the most adaptive skin color. In addition to skin color, there appear to be other racial factors involved in heat tolerance. These factors have not been isolated so that present evidence only indicates that Negroes have a greater physiological tolerance of hot wet conditions, but because of dark skin color do not have as great a tolerance of hot desert conditions (Baker, '58).

In addition to these morphological and racial criteria of heat tolerance, the physiological mechanism termed acclimatization must be included in a model. Bass *et al.* ('55), have demonstrated that men drastically improved their ability to perform work in the heat after working for two weeks under hot conditions. Acclimatization is presumably a universal phenomenon in man and, if so, it would appear to be a genetically inherited mechanism mediated by heat strain. However, to date, work on this mechanism has not indicated how much variation may exist between individuals and groups in their ability to acclimatize.

From the above characteristics a partial model may be constructed for desert heat tolerance. The application of this model does not predict all of the between-individual variation in heat resistance, but does indicate some of the important morphological and physiological features which characterize a man with high desert heat tolerance. The man should have low subcutaneous fat, large surface area per unit weight, brunette skin color, and be acclimatized to a high level.

THE GENETIC AND ENVIRONMENTAL BASIS OF THE BODY CHARACTERISTICS INVOLVED IN HEAT TOLERANCE

The basic characteristics by which man adapts to heat are genetically determined. The human infant shows most of these physiologic mechanisms at a very early age. He vasodilates and constricts, sweats, and increases blood flow with heat stress. In the very first days after birth these mechanisms are weak and sometimes completely fail. This may be a very important consideration for population size in the desert. Also, it seems quite probably that if adequate demographic data were available on hot desert populations, the per cent of the population born in the hot season and surviving to one year would prove to be much lower than comparable statistics for those born during the cool season. Despite the inadequacy of the newborn's temperature regulatory mechanisms, we have no evidence to suggest that prenatal environment has played an important role in modifying these mechanisms. Post-natal environmental effects on temperature regulatory mechanisms are equally unexplored. Therefore, investigation of the genetic and environmental influences on heat stress resistance is limited to an exploration of the characteristics which have been found related to the heat tolerance.

Skin Color

Skin color is primarily an inherited characteristic with a secondary environmental effect depending on ability to tan. It has been shown that variation in dermal melanin is the primary variable in solar energy absorption and also represents most of the racial variation which is observed in skin color (Edwards and Duntley, '39). Tanning is a secondary increase in dermal melanin in response to certain wave lengths of radiation and is found in people who are in the mid-range of skin colors. Individuals with very high skin melanin content do not increase their melanin enough to produce a significant change in solar radiation absorption, while individuals with very pale skin appear incapable of tanning, thereby rendering them incapable of prolonged exposure to the sun.

Tanning data collected at Yuma, Arizona, on soldiers (unpublished data) indicated that the average White, when tanned, absorbed 13 per cent more solar radiation than when untanned, while the American Negro skin only changed by 6 per cent. This suggests that within certain limits the higher the amount of inherited skin melanin, the less the solar radiation absorption will be affected by tanning.

Body Fat

The fatness of men is one of the characteristics which shows the greatest susceptibility to environment. However, there appears to be a genetic influence on the distribution of body fat even if the quantity is environmentally controlled. The most obvious evidence of inherited fat patterning is the Bushmen. The steatopygic pattern of fat deposition may be an adaptive feature in that stored energy in the form of fat is available, yet the fat is not deposited equally over the body in such a way that it would act as insulation. In recent family studies on White Americans, Garn ('55) found evidence for familial patterning of fat deposition. While no evidence can be cited, it is quite possible that the location of fat deposits even in non-steatopygic populations may be important in heat tolerance.

Stature

Inheritance is undoubtedly important in stature determination but environment can grossly modify the phenotypic development. It is usually accepted that genetic constitution sets a limit for the adult height of a specific individual while environment only controls how near one attains the genetic maximum. The recent generation increase in the stature of Europeans and Americans makes this concept tenuous because we would now have to assume that very few of us are attaining our true genetic potential (Trotter and Gleser, '51). A more complex genetic inheritance of stature should be proposed; a more realistic view might be that stature attainment is not directly inherited, but is a secondary attribute resulting from the patterning of inherited endocrine function. Within such a system environmental forces could easily act to decrease, increase, or even stop the inherited directed growth. The most obvious example of environmental effects is the anomalous growth that frequently results from damage to the pituitary gland.

Fat-free Weight

The adult fat-free weight as well as the stature of a man appears to be an indirectly inherited characteristic, that is, one determined by genetically directed growth potentials which act through the environment of the organism. However, fat-free weight is more subject to environmental modification probably because of the involvement of more genes, and more opportunity for environmental infringements. Climatic factors alone seem capable of exerting a strong influence on body weights even within racial groups. Newman and Munro ('55) found that, comparing the genetically similar State populations within the United States, there was almost a twenty-pound weight difference between the coldest and hottest States. Roberts ('53) similarly found a weight to climate relationship within the British Isles. In both cases the genetic compositions and cultural factors may vary somewhat with climate but the size of the weight difference suggests a rather direct biological influence of climate on weight.

From studies on men moving into hot areas for short periods, it appears that the effect of climate on the weight of a group is not a rapid short-term process (Baker, '55). Instead, the fact that the subjects studied by Newman and Munro ('55) were in their early twenties suggests that the climatic influences manifest themselves during growth. The studies of Mills ('42) on the growth of American children in Panama support this hypothesis. It is unfortunate that so little information on this subject can be drawn from the numerous growth studies in the literature. Steggerda's ('40) studies cover many climatic regions, but no two groups had similar genetic and cultural backgrounds. The numerous growth studies within the United States are confined to the north temperate areas and so cannot be used to determine the effects of climate on growth.

In summary, it appears that the characteristics which determine heat tolerance may be divided into several categories depending upon the genetic control. The major mechanisms by which man adapts to the heat are clearly and almost completely determined by genes. Among these mechanisms vasodilation, sweating and acclimatization are the most rigidly inherited. This is not to say that they are not subject to environmental forces because even the most entrenched characteristic is subject to environmental modification. Skin color as it affects heat tolerance is primarily inherited, although there is some environmental modification through tanning. Finally there are the numerous aspects of body composition and form which help determine the human adult's ability to remain in thermal equilibrium when exposed to heat. The fundamental development of these characteristics must be genetically directed, but it is known that a number of nutritional, climatic, traumatic, and infectious agents can drastically alter their phenotypic expression.

CONFORMANCE OF WORLD POPULATIONS TO THEORETICAL MODEL FOR DESERT HEAT TOLERANCE

Having developed a model for desert heat tolerance and investigated its genetic and environmental basis, we may now survey world populations to see how closely they conform. Theoretically, populations living in the desert should vary morphologically in the direction of the model. However, cultural factors might easily intervene to prevent adaptation to climate. For example, certain North African groups highly prize fat women and in this case the value system of the culture tends to inhibit the action of the climatic selection factors. There may also be other physical environmental factors which are more significant for survival than heat strain so that the morphological adaptation to climate is not found. As an example, fat can again be cited. In groups where the food supply is intermittent it may be more important to store energy in the form of subcutaneous fat than it is to have a slightly higher level of heat tolerance.

Considering all the potential modifying forces, one would not, in practice, expect all desert populations to conform perfectly to a model for heat tolerance, but if the model is valid, they should exhibit a general tendency in this direction.

Hot Deserts of the World

To compare the theoretical model with the actual populations living in hot deserts we must first establish where the hot desert areas are located in the world. The term "hot desert" is a somewhat arbitrary term which has been used in this study to designate world areas which are very arid and quite hot for part of the year. The physiologic responses that have been studied relate primarily to the dry and wet bulb temperatures; the type of terrain and vegetation are of secondary importance. However, in areas of high temperature and low humidity, desert terrain is usually encountered. The accepted desert areas may be used with the added limitation of high temperature . . . [The problem of mapping world deserts has been described.] by Francis Ramaley as part of a special report of the Research and Development Branch Office of the Quartermaster General ('52). As this report is not generally available, the following excerpt is included to describe the classification method.

"World deserts have been mapped by using various physical elements, such as landform types and systematic classifications of climate, soils and vegetation. In order to determine the geographical location and distribution of world deserts, several map sources based on each of these criteria were studied and compared. Seventeen such maps representing a typical cross section of criteria, are included in this report. The distribution of world deserts as shown by these maps varies according to the methods, type of criteria, and amount of environmental data used by each author. Differences between maps using similar criteria can be attributed to the amount and completeness of source data used in compiling each separate map. Unfortunately, most such maps are small scale and depend upon liberal interpolation because of gaps in the data used or available. Furthermore, the coincidence between specific climatic and terrain conditions often ascribed to the desert is frequently found only in the more extreme environments. Broad transitional areas representing modifications of these physical conditions present the major problem in delimitation."

Using the composite desert areas as the most valid delineation of true deserts, world maps showing mean July and January temperatures were used to sort out the hot deserts. While means are not necessarily the most valid temperature measurements for describing the heat stress level of a particular desert, in a gross world survey the averages conform adequately to other temperature measurements. The areas of highest monthly temperature are found in Southwestern United States, North Africa, Southwestern Asia and Northwest Australia. Jones' map of Desert Climates is the best available classification of deserts for the purpose of this study (Jones and Wittlesey, '28). His classification, "low latitude desert," conforms to what has been called "hot desert" in this study.

Many more areas have hot climates that periodically approximate desert humidities. For example, much of India has a spring climate that can be classified as hot and dry. However, the long summer period of tropical monsoon rains prevents the area from being classified as desert. Seasonal deserts cannot be utilized in this study because man is subjected to tropical heat stress in these areas as well as to desert heat stress. It cannot be concluded that these forces are similar, and, in fact, they might conceivably lead to quite different forms of adaptation.

Still other areas have not been classified as deserts by Jones because of atypical terrain. Certain of these places can be included in this study since it deals only with temperature and moisture factors. A recent analysis of the Middle East climate compared the temperatures and humidities (Analogs of Yuma Climate, '54) where most of the model information was developed. On the basis of this comparison, a much wider and important area may be included. This includes the Tigris-Euphrates Valley. Previous classification by Jones made the Indus River and Nile River areas desert. Thus, considering recent climatic conditions, three important loci of early "civilization" had hot desert climates even though atypical terrain.

Model Components

The relationship between the model characteristics and actual population measurements would ideally consist of a comparison of desert populations and those surrounding them. Unfortunately, not enough information about these populations is known for such a comparison and consequently a survey of all the known populations provides the maximum data which can be amassed on the subject.

Skin Color

The skin colors of desert populations have not been accurately measured, and we must rely on subjective judgements for estimates of melanin content. On this basis the desert groups appear to conform quite well to the model criteria of brunette skin. The darkest desert people are probably the Negroes who inhabit the southern fringes of the Sahara or perhaps some of the Australian groups; the lightest people are some of the North African Berber groups. Between these extremes are such groups as the Bushmen of the Kalahari, the Papago of the South Western United States desert, and the other Mediterraneans of the Sahara and Near East areas. Thus, as a generalization, we may say that hot desert populations are intermediate in skin melanin content.

Body Fat

Three methods have been used for assessing fat. The first of these is the direct measuring of skinfolds, body density, or x-rays. The second is the observational or somatoscopic technique, and the third is the relative weight criterion. Direct measurement methods are recent and only a few populations have been sampled to date. Fat data derived from specific gravity and x-ray methods are available only for North Europeans and North American populations. Skinfold measurements are simpler and, therefore, larger samples exist. The material published to date is summarized in Table 1. These skinfold measurements were made with differing caliper tensions rendering the measurements not completely compatible. However, it appears that the Northern and White populations are the fattest. This may be purely a matter of nutrition, but observation using the somatoscopic technique indicates that most hot climate populations have less fat than cold climate groups. Within the somatotyping system, which conforms quite well to direct fat measurement (Dupertuis *et al.*, '50), North American Whites are fatter than the Japanese (Kraus, '51), who are in turn still fatter

TABLE 1

SKINFOLD MEASUREMENTS FOR VARIOUS POPULATIONS

Group	Source	N	Age	Caliper pressure g/sq. mm	Skinfolds (mm) Arm	Back
U. S. White Soldiers (Newman '56)		2017	20.7	5	11.4	13.6
U. S. Negro Soldiers (Newman '56)		361	20.8	5	8.2	12.2
U. S. Students (Brozek & Keys '51)		133	20.3	35	10.9	14.3
U. S. Businessmen (Brozek & Keys '51)		122	49.0	35	14.4	19.9
Spanish Laborers (Keys *et al.* '54)		22	26.0	10	7.3	9.1
Spanish Professional (Keys *et al.* '54)		35	26.1	10	14.1	------
Chinese Soldiers (Crowley *et al.* '56)		1049	26.8	5	4.2	7.9

than Native East Africans (Danby, '53). It could still be argued that this is nutrition. However, Cullumbine ('53) has shown by direct fat measurement that the Ceylonese are quite low in fat despite an adequate diet. Henckel ('50) reports that the Indians of Southern Chile who had a simple hunting and gathering culture predominated in the "pyknic" body form. Thus, fat groups are found in cold climates even when the diet might be judged as poor. The extremely dubious method of inspecting available photographs also seems to support a cold climate distribution of fat peoples, while the hot desert populations such as the Mediterraneans, Bushmen, Hottentots, Nilotics, and Australians all appear very slender (Coon, Garn and Birdsell, '50). There are, of course, exceptions. Gabel ('49) observed that the Papago of the U. S. Southwestern desert were quite fat but considering all of the cultural and environmental forces which might modify a group in this direction, the few exceptions to the model are not at all surprising.

The third method of measuring fat by relative body weight was rejected for this study. Within a limited racial and cultural group this criterion has a relationship to body fat, but in comparing the linear Nilotic Negro with the short-legged Eskimo it is impossible to see how relative weight in any manner reflects body fat.

Body Mass and Surface Area

Recent anthropological interest in the relationship between climate and body form has concentrated on the body size and surface area in relationship to climatic indices (Roberts, '53; Schreider, '50 and '51; Schwidetzky, '52; and Newman, '55). The index of surface area over weight is presumably a double-edged sword because high mass per surface area helps heat conservation, while high surface area per unit mass helps the loss of heat. Scholander ('55) recently criticized the selective value of minor changes in this ratio for adaptation to cold. His criticism, while pertinent, is based on the gross adaptations exhibited by animals and as pointed out by Marshall T. Newman ('56) even slight variations in adaptations may be important to men living in critical climatic areas.

Certain very important limitations arise in any effort to study population differences in surface area. This characteristic is very difficult to measure directly and, consequently, almost all surface areas reported are estimated by means of the Du Bois ('36) formula using stature and weight:

$$\text{(Surface Area} = \text{Weight}^{0.425} \times \text{Height}^{0.725} \times 71.84).$$

These comparisons of weight to surface area are, therefore, merely some form of a height-weight ratio. For this reason in the present study we have dealt with the direct measurements. Although surface area over weight is physiologically a more rational index than height over weight, the lack of direct measurements of surface area makes height over weight a more valid ratio. Appendix A shows the height, weight and height/weight distributions for world populations. Beside the simple height/weight ratio, these body characteristics were combined in a calculated index called "theoretical sweat loss." Experimental studies (Baker, '55) indicated that sweat loss under specific hot desert conditions could be predicted with reasonable accuracy from height and weight. Therefore, the regression equation derived from these experiments was used to calculate a theoretical sweat loss (sweat loss in liters/hour) for world populations in order to indicate the potential significance of these measurements to desert heat tolerance. The use of a regression based on a small group of White soldiers for prediction of the sweat loss of many world populations is obviously a very speculative procedure. The prediction is made without regard to racial factors or local environmental conditions, but from the study of American Whites and Negroes it appears that racial differences in sweat loss are mostly referable to body composition differences (Baker, '58). Even if race does not strongly affect sweat loss, prediction for a very large sample from such a small sample means that the slope of the regression may be many degrees off the true slope. Only a few of the groups which have been considered will ever be exposed to conditions similar to those for which sweat loss has been predicted, and even in these groups the differing acclimatization and environmental backgrounds would probably cause their sweat loss to vary somewhat from that predicted. The prediction is, therefore, not to be considered a practical tool. Instead,

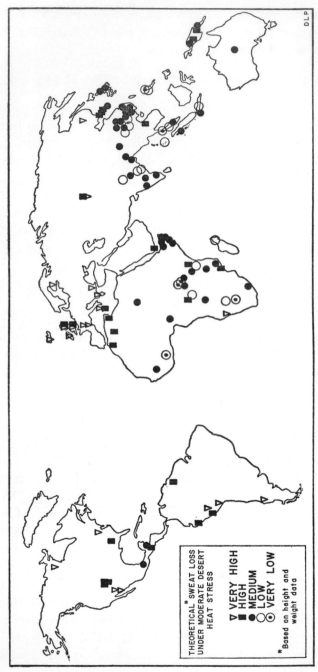

Fig. 1. Theoretical sweat loss—based on the relationship found between body weight, stature and sweat loss for a group of U. S. soldiers walking in a hot desert (redrawn from Baker '58, Fig. 2).

the theoretical sweat loss was calculated as a more rational expression of height and weight in relationship to the potential heat strain of various world groups.

In Figure 1 the world distribution of theoretical sweat losses has been plotted. There is a world regression in which, with some variation, the predicted sweat loss becomes lower as the climate becomes hotter. Within certain racial groups the relationship between theoretical sweat loss and climate is even more definite. The highest sweat loss among Whites is found in the North Temperate areas; in particular, high theoretical sweat loss is found among the Finns, Irish, Icelanders, U. S. soldiers, Parisians, and French soldiers. The intermediate sweat losses are found in Central and Southern European groups and the lowest values occur among the Mediterranean groups in Arabia and North Africa.

Eastern Hemisphere Mongoloid groups are distributed from very cold to very hot climates and these groups show a very close correspondence between theoretical sweat loss and climate. Even within the subgroups the relationship is very strong. Four Korean samples representing different provinces were found. Theoretical sweat loss was lower in the Southern provinces than in the Northern ones. In China where many samples were available there was a very decided regression of theoretical sweat loss on climate even though a few samples are out of line. Material on Western Hemisphere Mongoloids is sparse and shows little relationship. Within the New World population, settlement was quite recent and in many of the cases cited a movement of a few miles would drastically alter the climatic conditions encountered.

Theoretical sweat losses in African Negroes show a general relationship to temperature in that the highest sweat losses are associated with peoples dwelling in the temperate savannas and the lowest with the smaller groups of the tropical forests and deserts. In Africa the climatic differences encountered are primarily associated with altitude and it is, at this time, impossible to differentiate the biological responses which are associated with temperature from those associated with altitude.

The South Asian non-Mongoloids and Oceanic non-Mongo-

loids were merely geographic categories in which no genetic af-
filiation was intended.   There are several population aggregates
in which insufficient groups were available for within-population
analysis.   These population groups fit into the world relationship of theoretical sweat loss to climate but cannot be investigated for within-group variation.

Inspection of both the worldwide and within-group distribution of theoretical sweat losses shows that in cold climates
theoretical sweat losses are always high and in hot climates are
usually low.   However, in the intermediate or neutral climates
population groups may vary to the extremes in sweat loss.   This
strongly suggests that extreme climates act as selective forces.
Thus, biological characteristics show broad between-group variation in populations dwelling in non-selective neutral environments, but only populations which have the advantageous extreme
survive in the climatologically rigorous zones.

Desert populations do not have a mean theoretical sweat
loss significantly different from other populations living in hot
areas, but they do show more variation.   For example, Bushmen,
Australians, and Papagos encompass a range in body size equal
to any in the world.   The large range in body size and theoretical sweat losses is compatible with the experimental findings,
because for desert dwellers large size is not an important handi-
cap in thermal regulation provided adequate drinking water is
available.   However, from the experimental evidence it also appeared that individuals with low weight-per-unit stature showed
lower strain as indicated by sweat loss.   This seeming paradox
can be explained, if it is postulated that there is a species-wide
decrease in surface area per unit weight as weight increases and
that this relationship is not connected to desert heat tolerance.
However, individual or group departures from this species-wide
decrease do affect heat tolerance.   More simply stated, there is a
known high positive correlation between the weight-per-unit stature and weight.   By the nature of the human form large men
normally have a lower surface area or stature per unit of weight.
Thus, large men may be subject to strong negative selective
forces in hot wet areas where all sweat is not evaporated because

of high humidity, but this normal regression does not affect desert heat tolerance.   On the other hand, individuals who depart from the normal regression by having low or high surface areas for a given weight do show accompanying lower or higher desert heat tolerance.   If the preceding speculation is acceptable, then the findings based on the calculations of theoretical sweat loss would be reasonable, in that a selective force for small men is indicated for hot wet areas but not for dry ones.   The use of height and weight as indicators of biological desert heat stress resistance would require that we first approximate the normal parameter for the weight to weight-per-unit-stature regression, a calculation for which data on world populations is not at present adequate.

SUMMARY AND CONCLUSIONS

Man, who first evolved as a tropical animal, has spread over most of the climates of the world.   This has been made possible by his invention of cultural aids.   However, in many cases he has extended his habitat into alien climatic zones without important aids to modify the forces of the temperature regime. This has led several anthropologists to conclude that man has probably adapted to a climate as have other mammals.   The evidence for this conclusion has rested on the relationship between morphological characteristics and climate.   However, other environmental factors vary with climate so that it is difficult to be sure which environmental isolates are significant for adaptation. In this paper an experimentally derived model was developed for resistance to desert temperature stress.   By surveying the literature, a number of morphological characteristics were selected which have been demonstrated to affect man's ability to withstand the thermal stress which is unique to hot deserts.   Using these criteria, it was shown that a linear, acclimatized man with brunette skin and low body fat would be the best suited individual for work under hot desert conditions.   These morphological attributes were then reviewed to indicate the genetic and environmental forces which determine their adult phenotypic expression. It was found that a very significant fraction of the phenotypic appearance of these attributes is determined by genetic structure. Therefore, if the hot desert populations conform to the model, either selective migration or genetic adaptation must have occurred.

It must be recognized that, besides climate, other natural environmental forces and cultural forces act to form the phenotypic expression of these body characteristics. Many of these forces counteract climatic selection and thus an imperfect relationship between the theoretical model and the true desert populations is to be expected. However, a survey of the model characteristics in world populations indicated that, although we have scant data, the available material on desert populations conforms fairly well to the model. From this conformance, two conclusions may be drawn: first, that the model contains valid morphological characteristics for desert heat tolerance; and second, that man has to some extent genetically adapted to the climatic conditions found in a hot desert.

ACKNOWLEDGEMENTS

Parts of this paper were presented in a Ph.D. dissertation in anthropology for Harvard University. The author wishes to thank Drs. W. W. Howells, R. W. Newman and D. Bass for their very constructive criticism of this manuscript.

REFERENCES

Adolph, E. F. and associates: *Physiology of Man in the Desert,* New York, Interscience Publishers, 1947.

Anonymous: *Handbook of Yuma environment,* Env. Prot. Branch, Report No. 200, Research and Development Div., OQMG, 1953.

Anonymous: *Analogs of Yuma climate in the Middle East,* EPD ERB Research Study Report Yuma Analogs No. 1, QM R & D Center, 1954.

Baker, P. T.: *Relationship of desert heat stress to gross morphology,* Env. Prot. Div. Technical Report EP-7, QM R & D Center, 1955.

Baker, P. T.: Racial differences in heat tolerance, *Am. J. Phys. Anthropol. N. S.* 16:287-305, 1958.

Bass, D. E., Kleeman, C. R., Quinn, M., Henschel, A. and Hegnauer, A. H.: Mechanisms of acclimatization to heat in man, *Medicine,* 34:323-380, 1955.

Brozek, J. and Keys, A: The evaluation of leanness-fatness in man: norms and interrelationships, *Brit. J. Nutrition,* 5:194-206, 1951.

Cadbury, W. W.: Height, weight and chest measurements of Mongolian peoples, with especial reference to southern Chinese, *Philippine J. Science,* 25:733-742, 1924.

Coon, C. S., Garn, S. M. and Birdsell, J. B.: *Races: A Study of the Problems of Race Formation in Man,* Springfield, Thomas, 1950.

Crowley, L. V., Ryer, R. R. III, and Pollack, H.: Studies on nutrition in the Far East, *Metabolism,* 5:272-275, 1956.

Cullumbine, H.: The health of a tropical people. II: Environment, health and physique, *Lancet,* 264:1144-1147, 1953.

Danby, P. M.: A study of the physique of some native East Africans, *J. Roy. Anthropol. Inst.,* 83:194-210, 1953.

DuBois, E. F.: *Basal Metabolism in Health and Disease,* Philadelphia, Lea and Febiger, 1936.

Dupertuis, C. W., Pitts, G. C., Osserman, E. E., Welhan, W. C. and Behnke, A. R.: Relations of specific gravity to body build in a group of healthy men, *J. Appl. Physiol.,* 3:676-680, 1950.

Edwards, E. A. and Duntley, S. Q.: The pigments and color of living human skin, *Am. J. Anat.,* 65:1-32, 1939.

Gabel, N. E.: *A Comparative Racial Study of the Papago,* Albuquerque, University of New Mexico Publ. Anth., No. 4, 1949.

Garn, S. M.: Relative fat patterning: an individual characteristic, *Human Biol.,* 27:75-89, 1955.

Henckel, C.: The physical anthropology of the Indians of Chile, in *Handbook of S. A. Indians,* Vol. 6, Washington, U. S. Government Printing Office, 1950.

Jones, W. D. and Wittlesey, D. S.: *An Introduction to Economic Geography,* Vol. 1, Chicago, University of Chicago Press, 1928.

Keys, A., Vivance, F., Minon, J. L. R., Keys, M. H. and Mendoza, H. C.: Studies on the diet, body, fatness and serum cholesterol in Madrid, Spain, *Metabolism,* 3:195-212, 1954.

Kraus, B. S.: Male somatotypes among the Japanese of Northern Honshu, *Am. J. Phys. Anthropol., N. S.* 9:347-366, 1951.

Mills, C. A.: Climatic effects on growth and development with particular reference to the effects of tropical residence, *Am. Anthropol.,* *44*:1-13, 1942.

Newman, M.: Adaptation of man to cold climates, *Evolution, 10*:101-105, 1956.

Newman, R. W.: Skinfold measurements in young American males, *Human Biol., 28*:154-164, 1956.

Newman, R. W. and Munro, E. H.: The relation of climate and body size in U. S. males, *Am. J. Phys. Anthropol., N. S. 13*:1-17, 1955.

Newman, R. W. and White, R. M.: *Reference anthropometry of army men,* Env. Prot. Section Report No. 180, **OQMG** Research and Development Branch, 1951.

Ramaley, F.: *World deserts: limits and environmental characteristics,* Env. Prot. Br. Special Report No. 5, OQMG, Research Div., 1952.

Roberts, D. F.: Body weight, race and climate, *Am. J. Phys. Anthropol., N. S. 11*:533-558, 1953.

Schickele, E.: Environment and fatal heat stroke: an analysis of 157 cases occurring in the army in the U. S. during World War II, *The Military Surgeon, 100*:235-256, 1947.

Scholander, P. F.: Evolution of climatic adaptation in homeotherms, *Evolution, 9*:15-26, 1955.

Schreider, E.: Geographical distribution of the body-weight-body-surface ratio, *Nature, 165*:286, 1950.

Schreider, E.: Anatomical factors of body-heat regulation, *Nature, 167*:823-824, 1951.

Schwidetzky, I.: Selektionstheorie und Rassenbildung beim Menschen, Reprinted in *Yearbook of Physical Anthropology,* New York, Wenner-Gren Foundation, 1952.

Seltzer, C.: Physical characteristics of the Yaqui, *Texas Technical College Bulletin, 12*:91-113, 1936.

Steggerda, M.: Physical measurements on Negro, Navajo, and White girls of college age, *Am. J. Phys. Anthropol., 26*:417-431, 1940.

Trotter, M. and Gleser, G. C.: Trends in stature of American Whites and Negroes born between 1840 and 1924, *Am. J. Phys. Anthropol., N. S. 9*:427-440, 1951.

Wilson, E. A.: The basal metabolic rates of South American Indians, in *Handbook of S. A. Indians,* Vol. 6, Washington, U. S. Government Printing Office, 1950.

Physiological Regulations and the Origin of Human Types

Reprinted from *Human Biology,* Vol. 29, No. 4, pp. 329-336 (1957) .

By CHARLES G. WILBER

Anthropologists are hard put to explain the origin of human racial types in a scientifically acceptable manner. Of late they have called on ecology for help and are using certain ecological postulates as explanations for morphological variations among races.

For example, it is suggested that men who inhabit and thrive in the cold regions of the world necessarily have stocky bodies and relatively short extremities and that those in the tropics are necessarily lean and long-legged (Coon, '54, '55) . Such a view stems from an attempt to apply the generalizations of Bergmann and of Allen to *Homo sapiens.* Bergmann's "rule" or generalization asserts that homeotherms from colder climates tend to have a larger body mass and consequently less relative surface areas than do related forms from warmer climates. Allen's rule states that in homeotherms there is a marked tendency toward decrease in size of extremities and appendages in colder climates (Allee *et al.,* '49).

One does not question the need for consideration of human ecological problems within the framework of principles which have proven sound in the light of animal experience. One must be aware, however, that ecological extrapolation from animals to man is fraught with danger. Before such extrapolations are warranted the investigator must be certain of affirmative answers to the following questions:

a. Are the assumptions to be used based on sound ecological and physiological data for animals?

b. Are the conclusions derived in accord with the facts of human physiology?

107

c. Are the specified ecological forces which influence animals really affecting man in an identical manner?

The facts force me to say, "no," to each of the above questions when they refer to man and the postulates or so-called "rules" of Bergmann and Allen. A demonstration of the invalidity of these concepts in human ecology is the theme of this paper.

Do these rules apply to animals? Many examples are cited in the ecological literature to support the views of Bergmann and Allen. Rabbits are said to have leaner and longer ears as we progress southward from the polar regions; however, different species of rabbits are involved. The barren ground caribou is given as larger than the more southern forest species. The extensive migrations back and forth of these animals should not be ignored and the greater severity of cold in the subarctic forests is a pertinent factor. The penguins of the extreme south are said to be larger than those nearer the equator. But, large and small penguins are found together in some antarctic areas. In all these examples when one examines the basic data, the differences in size and weight are relatively trivial and do not in any clear manner give evidence of overwhelming cold survival value to the heavier forms (Scholander, '55).

Of basic importance to the acceptability of these "rules" is the assumption that in animals heat production is a function of mass and heat dissipation a simple function of surface area. The tenous nature of the latter assumption is clear from a careful examination of temperature regulating mechanisms in mammals.

I propose to refer to that school of thought which explains the origin of human racial types in terms of Allen's and Bergmann's postulates as "climatic determinists." It is my contention that their stand is based on inadequate data improperly interpreted. As I view human ecology, one constant factor repeats itself: Man, from his earliest origins, has not responded to his environment in a willy-nilly fashion but has rather done everything possible to control and shape that environment to conform to his ideas of comfort and convenience.

The climatic determinists ordinarily suggest that adipose tissue in animals serves as a dead, insulating blanket which inhibits effective heat exchange between the animal and its environment. Witness the so-called rule of Rensch which attempts to explain fat distribution in certain species on the basis of heat transfer "needs" of the animal. These generalizations show great inventiveness and may have a germ of truth but unfortunately are not completely in accord with physiological fact. Adipose tissue is not a dead, inactive thing, but is quite active metabolically (Schoenheimer, '46). For metabolic purposes the capillary bed of fat tissue is comparatively richer than that of muscle (Wertheimer and Shapiro, '48). The blood vessels are innervated by sympathetic nerve fibers. One wonders, then, what stimulus is adequate to induce the deposition of fat over all the body of cold-dwelling mammals and only in the tail or buttocks of certain dwellers in warm areas. From the physiological point of view climate does not impress one as adequate.

One is told that the seals of the Arctic Ocean have a layer of insulating blubber; but, the seals and sea lions from the warm waters of California are not particularly skinny; nor is the Florida manatee a striking example of spare build.

In the cold, homeotherms adjust for survival by increasing metabolic rate, by increasing insulation, by selecting a favorable microclimate, and by maintaining cold extremities to reduce heat loss from the core (Scholander, '55). For example, the Eskimo husky dog and the Arctic fox have a critical temperature of at least −40° C. The critical temperature, as you know, is the lowest air temperature at which an animal can maintain a resting or basal metabolic rate. This ability to remain in a resting metabolic state at very low temperatures is a result of increased insulating capacity of the fur which in these species is fluffed up in the cold. The typically Arctic lemming has a critical temperature around +10° C., but this species and others like it select suitable microclimates near freezing, and many build warm nests. In these cases behavior patterns and not morphological ones make for survival in cold. Caribou and sea gulls conserve body heat by maintaining cold extremities. The caribou on cold days keeps its thin legs at +10° C., or lower. Arctic gulls have been kept with their feet in ice water for several hours and the basal metabolic rate goes up only about 1.5% (Scholander *et al.,* '50). The gull preserves body heat by holding the tissue temperature of the legs near zero. Moreover, cellular adaptations occur which permit portions of nerve axons in these cold parts to conduct effectively at depressed temperatures (Chatfield *et al.,* '53).

Some arctic and subarctic dwellers meet the enormous heat losses by increasing metabolic rate for prolonged periods. The red squirrel of Central Alaska does just that, and it is not a particularly globular type of homeotherm but it seems well established in its northern neighborhood.

There is no clear-cut physiological evidence that homeotherms tend to a globular form with reduced extremities in the face of cold exposure. There is a wealth of evidence that adapted homeotherms in the cold decrease heat loss by increasing insulation and by maintaining cold extremities; some turn up the thermostat, as it were, and increase heat production. On the basis of our present knowledge the rules of Bergmann and Allen appear to be of historical or descriptive interest only and certainly are not valid generalizations for animals in the cold.

In the heat, the views of the climatic determinists are also open to question. For example, "Neither the ratio of surface area to body weight, nor the ratio of surface area to the two-thirds power of body weight, showed a significant difference between Jersey cattle and Sindhi-Jersey crosses, although the latter have appreciably greater heat resistance than do the former" (McDowell *et al.,* '53). In other words, heat tolerance could not be attributed to greater proportional surface, large dewlap or other morphological peculiarities.

Need one mention that the hippopotamus, rhinoceros, and elephant are built on the roly-poly, globular pattern, but are well entrenched in their tropical environments? The camel is adapted to its normal hot environment; not by reason of its morphology but because its tissues can withstand elevated temperatures for long periods. In order to conserve water, evaporative cooling is depressed to a minimum during water shortage in the camel; the rectal temperature may rise from 34.2 to 40.7° C. during the day with no harm to the beast (Kleiber, '56). It would seem that readjustment of cellular mechanisms and not alteration of body form is the key factor in animal adaptations to heat. Birds which live in the desert adapt in a similar fashion and many avian species respond to heat by reduced metabolic heat production (Gelineo, '55).

Mayr ('56) re-emphasizes the fact that the so-called rules of Bergmann and Allen are "purely empirical generalizations describing parallelisms between morphological variation and physiogeographic features." He admits that too many writers have elevated these purely descriptive comments to the status of laws. In reality these rules have "only statistical validity." It is good to know that competent zoologists appreciate this fact. However, the point at issue remains: Some anthropologists and sociologists are using these descriptive generalizations to explain human racial variations as if they were laws having causal value. Such usage is misleading and unjustified.

Do these rules apply to man? If the contentions of the climatic determinists are valid, one must visualize the historical Eskimo as a wretched creature with teeth and bones rattling from cold. Then in a good Lamarckian fashion he should have shortened his legs and arms and inflated his body to resemble "Mr. Five by Five." In this way he would produce much heat and lose little of it and thus be adapted to the severe Arctic. This globular form would be transmitted to his children and his children's children. Unfortunately for this view, the Eskimo never read about Bergmann's or Allen's rule; so they cheated. Instead of shivering they manufactured the warmest type of clothing known to man and devised homes which maintained rooms at tropical temperatures. On the trail their bodies, with exception to face and sometimes hands, were at temperatures of 80-90° F. At home they lived in sod or snow shelters with interior temperatures up to 100° F., so hot in fact that these people usually rested stripped to the waist (Stefansson, '21). Under such conditions the stimulus of climate is a tropical one which should have made them tall and skinny. In the face of a tropical microclimate (which is of course the real stimulus acting on the Eskimo) this race is held, by the climatic determinists, to develop morphological adaptations of positive survival value in the cold.

Jenness ('23) has pointed out that, with respect to all Eskimos, "The fur clothing in which they are habitually enveloped gives them an exaggerated appearance of corpulence, whereas in reality they incline towards slenderness, the body tapering a little below the broad shoulders."

The Eskimos living at Point Barrow during the last century showed no evidence of spherical build. The following data illustrate this fact:

	Males	*Females*
Average weight, lbs.	153.5	135.7
Average height	5'3"	4'11"

These results are from Ray's (1885) report of his expedition to Point Barrow between 1881 and 1883.

The only real cold people in the world were the aborigines of Tierra del Fuego and of Australia. The former were never studied from the metabolic point of view. However, Darwin and others have described them as thin, small people who lived, worked and rested stark naked even in severe snow storms. The Australian aborigines in their native state are able to rest naked at 0° C. while maintaining a basal heat production (Hicks *et al.*, '34). They are a small, skinny people whose build, according to climatic determinists, should have evolved in response to heat, whereas they show remarkable physiological adaption to cold. If any groups of men should show a globular form with relatively short extremities, it is the Australian aborigine and the Tierra del Fuegians. The fact that they show opposite of the expected response to the climatic determinist rules illustrates the danger of explaining human racial morphology in terms of Bergmann's and Allen's generalizations.

We are quite ignorant of the physiological adaptations to cold in the Fuegians. The Australian aborigine, on the other hand, has been studied metabolically. He shows physiological adaptations characteristic of Arctic animals: Extremely active control of cutaneous circulation which results in maintenance of cold skin and extremities in decreased environmental temperatures with consequent saving of heat (Wulsin, '49). These adaptations are functional and do not involve changes in exterior body form. They are the only clear-cut biological adaptations of man to cold that we know.

Bates ('53) contends that, "It is easy to assume that, since the races show a pattern of geographical distribution, they represent adaptation to different geographical environments; and, with a certain amount of ingenuity, all sorts of adaptive traits can be described." However, under careful study these schemes usually disintegrate. As a rule, diagnostic, structural peculiarities of human groups show no evidence of being adaptive; they may be correlated with differences in function or behavior and these latter are certainly adaptive. The solution of this problem lies in the experimental approach to racial matters and not in the use of descriptive generalizations as though they were causal agents in the formation of races.

Man a tropical mammal: Man in all his adaptations is ordinarily a tropical mammal. (The responses of the Australian native to cold are an exception.) He responds to cold by keeping his extremities warm (contrary to adaptation in true Arctic homeotherms which maintain cold extremities and thus conserve heat), a process wasteful of heat and characteristic of a tropical animal. He adapts to heat by measureable physiological adjustments: Increased volume of sweat, greater dilution of sweat, hemodilution, decrease in heart rate during activity. These adjustments make it possible for man to live and work effectively in hot climates without the aid of artifacts. There are few proven physiological adaptations of man to the cold. In the face of low ambient temperatures, man either adds clothing, heats his dwelling, or combines the two. Naked, he is usually helpless in the cold; naked, he adapts to the heat in an effective manner.

Newman ('56) has outlined the physiological adjustment that man makes to cold. It is true that the Eskimo is better able to live in the cold than is the Negro. But the Eskimo handles the problem by a typical tropical response: the maintenance of warm extremities. This in turn requires high caloric intake and expenditure, a fact which denies the Eskimo as an example of a heat conserving mechanism operating in the cold.

SUMMARY

This brief and rapid survey does not postulate that climate is without effect on man. At another time the ecological effect of this variable on man will be discussed. This presentation attempted to show in a sketchy fashion the following:

1. The rules of Bergmann and Allen find little support *as causal agents* in modern studies of temperature regulation in homeotherms.

2. The various formal examples often cited in favor of these ecological generalizations do not support the case of the climatic determinists. One is forced to conclude that the rules just do not apply causally to animals.

3. In man the ecological forces supposed to be acting are not doing so; Eskimos were not cold, the skinny aboriginal Australians were.

4. The rules of Bergmann and Allen have no causal role in the formation of racial differences in man. Such use of these rules on the part of some anthropologists is a source of misinformation and confusion.

5. Some human groups have met the demands of severe climate by technological and behavioral adjustments; the Eskimos are an example. Others have developed specific heat-conserving functional changes, with no gross morphological changes; the Australian aborigines are an example.

ACKNOWLEDGEMENTS

Sincere gratitude is expressed to Professor William L. Straus, Jr., and Professor George F. Carter, of the Johns Hopkins University, who read the manuscript critically and suggested important changes. It is emphasized, however, that all deficiencies in the final product are the author's.

REFERENCES

Allee, W. C., Emerson, A. E., Park, O., Park T. and Schmidt, K. P.: *Principles of Animal Ecology,* Philadelphia, Saunders, 1949.

Bates, M.: Human ecology, in *Anthropology Today*, A. L. Kroeber (ed.), Chicago, University of Chicago Press, 1953.

Chatfield, P. O., Lyman, C. P. and Irving, L.: Physiological adaptation to cold of peripheral nerve in the leg of the herring gull (Larus argentatus) *Am. J. Physiol.*, *172*:639-644, 1953.

Coon, C. S.: *The Story of Man, New York,* Knopf, 1954.

Coon, C. S.: Some problems of human variability and natural selection in climate and culture, *Am. Nat., 89*:257-280, 1955.

Gelineo, S.: Temperature d'adaptation et production de chaleur chez les oiseaux de petite taille, *Arch. Sc. Physiol., 9*:225-243, 1955.

Hicks, C. S., Moore, N. O. and Eldridge, E.: The respiratory exchange of the Australian aborigine, *Australian J. Exper. Biol & M. Sc., 12*: 79-89, 1934.

Jenness, D.: Characteristics of the Copper Eskimo, *Report of Canadian Arctic Expedition, 12*:1-89, Ottawa, 1923.

Kleiber ,M.: Energy metabolism, *Ann. Rev. Physiol., 18*:35-52, 1956.

Mayr, E.: Geographical character gradients and climatic adaptation, *Evolution, 10*:105-108, 1956.

McDowell, R. E., Lee, D. H. K. and Fohrman, M. F.: The relationship of surface area to heat tolerance in Jerseys and Sindhi-Jersey (F₁) cross-bred cows, *J. Animal Sc., 12*:747-756, 1953.

Newman, M. T.: Adaptation of man to cold climates, *Evolution, 10*: 101-105, 1956.

Ray, P. H.: *Report of the International Polar Expedition*, Washington, U. S. Government Printing Office, 1885.

Schoenheimer, R.: *The Dynamic State of Body Constituents*, Cambridge, Harvard University Press, 1946.

Scholander, P. F.: Evolution of climatic adaptation in homeotherms, *Evolution, 9*:15-26, 1955.

Scholander, P. F., Hock, R., Walters, V. and Irving, L.: Adaptation to cold in arctic and tropical mammals and birds in relation to body temperature, insulation, and basal metabolic rate, *Biol. Bull., 99*: 259-271, 1950.

Stefansson, V.: *The Friendly Arctic,* New York, Macmillan, 1921.

Wertheimer, E. and Shapiro, B.: The physiology of adipose tissue, *Physiol. Rev., 28*:451-464, 1948.

Wulsin, F. R.: Adaptations to climate among non-European peoples, in *Physiology of Heat Regulation*, L. H. Newburgh (ed), Philadelphia, Saunders, 1949.

VI. DISEASE-SELECTION AND RACE

No student of race in man can ignore the possible role of disease selection in bringing about racial differences. Human populations have always been plagued by diseases, and populations geographically and climatically separated have undoubtedly been screened by different infectious disorders at different intensities, and for different lengths of time.

The "childhood" diseases provide a tantalizing possibility. We know that American Indians and Eskimos were decimated by measles, mumps and whooping cough, diseases against which Europeans developed immunity in childhood. But how about the surviving natives? Were they possessed by superior immunochemical mechanisms which they passed on to their progeny? Is the far lower incidence of juvenile paralytic poliomyelitis in India or the Philippines due to ancient disease-selection, with consequent survival of those individuals most able to develop protective antibodies? One might ask similar questions about tuberculosis, typhoid and syphilis, or cholera, amoebic dysentery and elephantiasis.

With respect to one disease, however, our knowledge begins to become complete. Clearly, malaria has met its match in the sickle-cell hemoglobin, an abnormal and defective blood pigment which, nonetheless, affords protection against malaria. In malarial regions of the world the abnormal hemoglobin is far more common than above the frost line. Malaria has rapidly and unquestionably altered the genetic makeup of peoples living where this disease is pandemic.

The relationship between malaria and the sickle-cell trait, with the consequent discovery of the abnormal hemoglobins, was uncovered by a series of accidents and the whole complex picture of disease and genetic adaptation is yet to be worked out. Livingstone considers the sickle-cell trait in the following article. Further discoveries, however, should eventuate from more planned investigations. There are many diseases with distinct geographical and climatic limits against which some degree of genetically-determined immunity may have developed.

Disease selection, perhaps unlike climatic selection, operates invisibly and without the production of differences which can be measured with calipers, thermocouples or with a colorimeter. Nevertheless, if an exposed population comes to differ genetically from an unexposed population, the mechanisms of raciation and evolution are at work. Whereas some racial groups may owe their distinctive characters to climatic stress or nutritional inadequacy, microorganisms may be responsible for the unique genetic make-up of many other race-populations.

ADDITIONAL READINGS

Neel, J. V.: The study of natural selection in primitive and civilized human populations, *Human Biol.*, 30:43-72, 1958 (also published as Memoir Number 86 of the American Anthropological Association and as *Natural Selection in Man* (J. N. Spuhler, ed.), Detroit, Wayne State University Press, 1958).

Anthropological Implications of Sickle Cell Gene Distribution in West Africa

Reprinted, with the exception of one figure and references, from *American Anthropologist*, Vol. 60, No. 3, pp. 533-562 (1958).

By Frank B. Livingstone

During the past fifteen years, data on the frequency of the sickle cell gene have accumulated to such an extent that its world distribution can now be outlined in considerable detail. Frequencies of more than 20 per cent of the sickle cell trait have been found in populations across a broad belt of tropical Africa from Gambia to Mozambique. Similar high frequencies have been found in Greece, South Turkey, and India. At first it appeared that there were isolated "pockets" of high frequencies in India and Greece, but more recently the sickle cell gene has been found to be widely distributed in both countries (Choremis and Zannos, '56; Sukumaran, Sanghvi, and Vyas, '56). Moreover, between these countries where high frequencies are found, there are intermediate frequencies, in Sicily, Algeria, Tunisia, Yemen, Palestine, and Kuwait. Thus, the sickle cell gene is found in a large and rather continuous region of the Old World and in populations which have recently emigrated from this region, while it is almost completely absent from an even larger region of the Old World which stretches from Northern Europe to Australia.

When the broad outlines of the distribution of the sickle cell gene first began to emerge, several investigators attempted to explain various aspects of this distribution by migration and mixture. Lehmann and Raper ('49) attempted to show that the differences in the frequency of the sickle cell gene among the Bantu tribes of Uganda were due to varying degrees of Hamitic admixture; Brain ('53) and Lehmann ('54) postulated migrations from Asia to account for the distribution of the sickle cell gene in Africa; and Singer ('53), using an age-area type of argument, postulated that the sickle cell gene arose by mutation near Mt. Ruwenzori and diffused from there. However, it was recognized early in the development of the sickle cell problem that regardless of the extent to which migration and mixture explained the distribution pattern of the sickle cell gene, its high frequencies in various widely scattered areas raised some additional and striking problems in human population genetics.

Since persons who arc homozygous for the sickle cell gene very rarely reproduce, there is a constant loss of sickle cell genes in each generation. In order for the gene to attain frequencies of .1 to .2, which are equivalent to about 20 to 40 per cent of the sickle cell trait, there must be some mechanism which is compensating for this loss. In other words, there must be some factor which is tending to increase the number of sickle cell genes in the population. Neel ('51) first pointed out that there are two outstanding possibilities; either the sickle cell gene is arising frequently by mutation, or the heterozygote for the sickle cell gene possesses a selective advantage over the normal homozygote which offsets the selective disadvantage of the sickle cell homozygote (balanced polymorphism). Since the evidence (Vandepitte *et al.*, '55) indicated that the mutation rate was not sufficient to maintain the high frequencies, selection in favor of individuals with the sickle cell trait seemed to be implicated as the factor which was maintaining them.

When Allison ('54a, '54b, '54c) advanced the hypothesis that the heterozygote for the sickle cell gene possessed a relative immunity to falciparum malaria, he marshalled the first clear evidence for the mechanism by which selection maintained the observed high frequencies. In addition to experiments on sicklers and nonsicklers which seemed to show that the sicklers could cope more easily with a malarial infection, Allison ('54b) also showed that the tribal frequencies of the sickle cell gene in Uganda and other parts of East Africa could be explained as well by his malaria hypothesis as by varying degrees of Hamitic admixture. Thus, Allison's work showed that selection must be taken into consideration in any attempt to explain the distribution of the sickle cell gene.

Although selection has undoubtedly played a major role in determining the frequencies of the sickle cell gene in the populations of the world, in many areas other factors in addition to selection may well be involved. Allison ('54b) has shown that most of the tribes of East Africa seem to have frequencies of the sickle cell trait which are in approximate equilibrium with the amount of malaria present, but there appear to be many populations in West Africa and elsewhere for which this is not so. It will be the purpose of this paper to show how the distribution of the sickle cell gene in West Africa is the result of the interaction of two factors, selection and gene flow. Gene flow will be used here to include both migration and mixture; the term migration is used where the gene flow involves the movement of breeding populations or large segments of them, and mixture where the breeding populations remain rather stationary and the gene flow involves the exchange of individuals between them. Of course, any actual situation is usually a combination of these two "polar" concepts.

According to modern genetic theory as developed by Wright and others, there are five factors which can contribute to gene frequency change: selection, mutation, gene drift, gene flow, and selective mating. Strictly speaking, an attempt to explain the distribution of any gene must take into consideration all five. However, three of these factors—mutation, gene drift, and selective mating—are thought to have had relatively little effect on the features of the distribution of the sickle cell gene in West Africa which this paper will attempt to explain, and thus will not be discussed at any length in this paper.

The general plan of the paper will be as follows. First, the distribution of the sickle cell gene in West Africa will be plotted; then an attempt will be made to correlate this distribution with that of falciparum malaria in West Africa. It will be assumed that the high frequencies of the sickle cell gene are in equilibrium with the particular endemicity of malaria in which they are found. Thus, by comparing these two distributions we can determine where the frequencies of the sickle cell gene appear to be explained by selection (i.e. are in equilibrium), and we can also determine where the frequencies appear to be very far from equilibrium and hence where other factors in addition to selection appear to be involved. The rest of the paper will then be concerned with the populations which do not appear to be in equilibrium. In order to explain why the frequencies of the sickle cell gene in these populations are not in equilibrium with the present-day endemicity of malaria, it is necessary to have some idea of the ethnic and culture history of West Africa. The literature on the culture history of West Africa is rather sparse, so the major part of this paper will be an attempt to infer its broad outlines from the distribution of language and of certain domesticated plants in West Africa.

THE DISTRIBUTION OF THE SICKLE CELL GENE IN WEST AFRICA

In the following compilation of data on the distribution of the sickle cell gene in West Africa, several early publications of surveys have been omitted. In all of these reports, the tribe of the persons tested is not given, and the reports could thus contain subjects from several breeding populations with very different frequencies of the sickle cell gene. Data by tribe are available for the areas covered by these surveys, except for part of Evans' ('44) survey. His sample from the Cameroons has been included since there are no other data from this area.

Where the same tribe has been tested by different investigators, differences in the frequency of the sickle cell trait have been tested by a chi-square test. If the differences were not significant, the results have been combined. However, for several large tribes which extend over considerable distances and into several different countries, the samples have been kept separate when they were obtain in different countries.

For the surveys in which paper electrophoresis or other biochemical tests were done on the bloods, all individuals who would have been positive for the sickle cell test were counted as positive without regard to whether they appeared to be homozygous or heterozygous for the sickle cell gene. Thus, the frequency of the sickle cell trait, as used in this paper, includes both hetero-zygotes and any living homozygotes for the sickle cell gene. How-ever, recent studies (Lehmann and Raper, '56) indicate that homo-zygotes for the sickle cell gene rarely survive the first years of life, so that most likely very few homozygotes are included in the tribal samples. Throughout the discussion, sickle cell trait fre-quencies will be used instead of gene frequencies, since the trait frequencies are used by most investigators and hence their sig-nificance is more easily comprehended. Since very few homo-zygotes are included in the samples, the gene frequency would be close to one-half the trait frequency in all cases.

Except for the Ivory Coast, Dahomey, and the Cameroons, the compilation is by tribe. The Dahomey and Cameroons samples have been included in an effort to fill up large gaps in the distribution in areas where tribal investigations are nonexist-ent. These samples have combined several tribes and thus have probably combined data from isolates which differ significantly from one another in the frequency of the sickle cell trait. Since they are also quite small samples, this paper will not consider them in detail.

Due to the lack of investigations, and also to the multiplicity of small tribes which inhabit the Ivory Coast, the tribal samples from there are all rather small. Since the frequency of the sickle cell trait is 0 percent in Liberia to the west of the Ivory Coast and greater than 20 percent in Ghana to the east, the Ivory Coast is an area of crucial concern to this study. For this reason, the tribal samples have been combined into larger linguistic units to increase the sample sizes and thus give them more reliability. The tribes which have been combined are very closely related, since in most cases they speak the same language with only dia-lectic differences between them. Although the individual tribal samples are small, there is no indication that this procedure has combined tribes which have very different frequencies of the sickle cell trait.

Table 1 shows the frequency of the sickle cell trait for West Africa by tribe and also by country. For the purposes of further discussion, the spelling of all tribal names has been standardized.

TABLE 1

THE FREQUENCIES OF THE SICKLE CELL TRAIT IN THE TRIBES OF WEST AFRICA*

Country Tribe	Sickle Cell Trait (%)	Country Tribe	Sickle Cell Trait (%)	Country Tribe	Sickle Cell Trait (%)
Senegal		*Sierra Leone*		*Upper Volta*	
Wolof (Ouolof)	6.63	Creole	23.81	Samogo	6.67
Lebu (Lebou)	5.94	Timne	28.95	Bobofing	24.57
Serer	3.30	Mende	29.36	Lobi	20.00
Soce	15.71			Mossi	11.59
Fulani (Peul)	9.03	*Liberia*		Gurma	8.82
Tukulor		Kissi	19.46	Gurunsi	7.14
(Toucouleur)	9.46	Mende	16.88		
Dyola	5.13	Gbandi	15.34	*Ghana*	
Mandiago	0.99	Vai	13.98	Mossi (Moshie)	4.13
		Kpelle	13.03	Dagarti	11.34
Gambia		Loma	12.72	Dagomba	4.23
Mandingo-		Gola	12.02	Ewe	23.28
Western Division	10.78	Belle	10.34	Fanti	23.53
Mandingo-Keneba	6.25	Bassa	7.15	Ga	18.26
Mandingo-Jali	6.09	Dei	3.77	Twi	21.62
Mandingo-Manduar	16.95	Mano	2.12	Ashanti	22.55
Mandingo-		Gio	2.10	Frafra	9.71
Tankular	24.24	Grebo	1.45		
Fulani (Fula)	18.90	Krahn	0.65	*French Togoland*	
Dyola (Jola)	16.99	Kru	0.68	Kabre	9.87
Wolof (Jolloff)	17.31	Webbo	0.00		
Saracole (Serahuli)	8.33			*Dahomey*	
Bainunka	16.67	*French Sudan*		Dahomeans	9.09
		Moor (Maure)	5.71		
Portugese Guinea		Saracole	9.18	*Niger*	
Papel	3.00	Bambara	10.31	Djerma (Zabrama)	21.74
Mandlago		Mandingo		Tuareg	5.38
(Mandjaca)	3.20	(Malinke)	16.00		
Balante (Balanta)	5.00	Fulani (Peul)	14.47	*Nigeria*	
Feloop (Felupe)	1.72	Songhoi	11.00	Yoruba	24.53
Baiote	1.27			Igalla	18.06
Nalu	2.79	*Ivory Coast*		Ibo	21.57
Saracole	8.39	Senufo	24.24	Cameroons	15.22
Mandingo		Agni-Baule	13.21	Kerikeri	10.69
(Mandinga)	15.00	Dan-Gnouro	0.00	Fulani	16.85
Biafada (Beafada)	15.25	Lagoon	4.17	Hausa	17.51
Pajadinca	18.44	Bete	0.89		
Fulani (Fula-Foro)	23.00	Bakwe	1.59	*Lake Chad*	
Fulani				Mohur (Mobeur)	17.95
(Fula-Preto)	25.12			Kanembu	
				(Kanembou)	22.37
French Guinea				Mangawa	20.69
Fulani (Foula)	15.98			Sugurti	
Susu	31.25			(Sougourti)	16.22
Kissi	22.22				
Loma Kpelle					
(Toma-Guerze)	20.00				

*Abridged from the original.

On Table 1 the names used by the original investigators are shown in parentheses after the standardized name.

The distribution of the frequency of the sickle cell trait in West Africa is shown on Figure 1. In order to make the general configuration of the distribution more easily visualized, the frequencies have been grouped into five categories: 0-2, 2-8, 8-15, 15-22, and greater than 22 percent. The frequency of the sickle cell trait can be seen to exhibit extreme variability, sometimes over very short distances. In many cases there are significant differences in the frequency of the trait even within the same tribe. For example, the Fulani have frequencies ranging from 8 to 25 percent, and the Mandingo in the Gambia vary from 6 to 28 percent. Although this great variability impedes generalizing about the distribution, some significant generalizations can nevertheless be made.

Generally, the higher frequencies tend to be toward the south, and, despite many exceptions, there is some indication of a north-

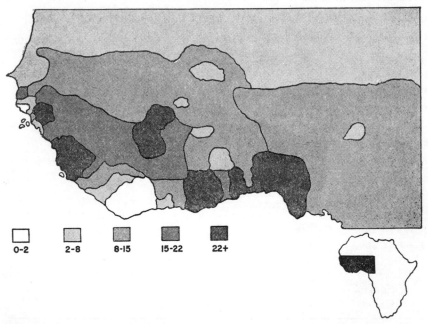

Fig. 1. The distribution of the frequency of the sickle cell trait in West Africa.

south gradient in the frequency of the sickle cell trait. The distribution of falciparum malaria follows a similar gradient, and, in addition, all the populations which have sickle cell trait frequencies greater than 15 percent inhabit areas where malaria is either hyperendemic or holoendemic.

In an environment in which malaria is hyperendemic or holoendemic, the disease is transmitted throughout most of the year, so that the individuals are continually being reinfected. The average number of infective bites per person per year is always greater than about 5, and in some areas ranges up to 100 or more. Thus, infants are infected with malaria shortly after birth, and for about the first five years of life every child is engaged in a mortal struggle with the parasite. During these years the parasite rate (i.e., the percentage of individuals harboring malaria parasites) is close to 100 percent, and there is a considerable mortality from the disease. Those individuals who survive this struggle have a solid immunity to malaria. In later years they are being continually reinfected with malaria but are able to keep their infection at a subclinical level. The parasite rate then decreases among older children and is lowest in adults. In holoendemic malaria the adult parasite rate will be about 20 percent and the adults will almost never have any clinical symptoms of malaria, while in hyperendemic malaria the adult parasite rate will be somewhat higher and the adults will sometimes have clinical symptoms, usually chills and fever. However, in both these conditions there is seldom any adult mortality from malaria.

It is in an environment in which malaria is either hyperendemic or holoendemic that the heterozygote for the sickle cell gene has been postulated to have a selective advantage over the normal homozygote. Allison ('54a) and Raper ('55) have shown that, although sicklers are infected with falciparum malaria almost as readily as nonsicklers, in the younger age groups the very high densities of parasites are not found as often among sicklers. In addition, Raper ('56) has shown that the sicklers do not suffer from cerebral malaria and blackwater fever as much as nonsicklers. Since these are the complications of falciparum malaria which result in death, the sicklers had a lower mortality rate from falciparum malaria. In addition, I have postulated ('57a) that if the sickling females did not have as heavy falciparum infections of the placenta as did normal females, they would have a higher net reproduction rate and hence this could be another mechanism by which malaria was maintaining the high frequencies of the sickle cell gene. Although the evidence is not conclusive, it seems for the most part favorable to this hypothesis. When the evidence for both these mechanisms is considered as a whole, it seems to be conclusive that malaria is the major cause of the high frequencies of the sickle cell gene. One would therefore expect to find high frequencies of the sickle cell trait in areas in which malaria is either hyperendemic or holoendemic.

From about the latitude of the Gambia south, West Africa is almost entirely characterized by hyperendemic or holoendemic malaria; hence, high frequencies of the sickle cell trait would be expected. However, there are many populations in this region with very low frequencies of the trait. The majority of them are found in three areas: (1) Coastal Portuguese Guinea, (2) Eastern Liberia and the Western Ivory Coast, (3) Northern Ghana. The low frequency populations which are found in Northern Ghana differ from those in the other two areas by having high frequencies of the gene which is responsible for Hemoglobin C. This gene is an allele of the sickle cell gene (Ranney, '54), so that in Northern Ghana the sickle cell locus is a tri-allelic system. Since the selective values associated with the various phenotypes of this system are not known at present, the equilibrium frequencies for these populations cannot be ascertained (see Allison, '57 for further discussion of this problem). Thus, one cannot say whether or not these populations are in equilibrium for this locus. The rest of this paper will therefore be concerned with the two areas, Coastal Portuguese Guinea and Eastern Liberia-Western Ivory Coast, where the Hemoglobin C gene is almost completely absent (Neel *et al.*, '56).

Cambournac ('50) in Coastal Portuguese Guinea and Young and Johnson ('49) in Eastern Liberia found malaria to be either hyperendemic or holoendemic in these areas where low frequencies of the sickle cell trait are found. Thus, these frequencies appear to be very far from equilibrium, and hence do not seem to be explained by the factor of selection alone. An attempt will now be made to show how the explanation involves the two factors, selection and gene flow. More specifically, two hypotheses will be advanced to explain these low frequencies:

(1)   The sickle cell gene has been present in some parts of West Africa for a considerable time, but, due to the comparative isolation of the low frequency populations in Portuguese Guinea and Eastern Liberia, is only now being introduced to them.

(2)   The environmental conditions responsible for the high frequencies of the sickle cell gene have been present for a relatively short time among these populations, so that the spread of the sickle cell gene is only now following the spread of the selective advantage of the gene.

In order to demonstrate these propositions, two general types of evidence will now be considered; first, the distribution of language in West Africa, from which an attempt will be made to ascertain the general outlines of the migrations which have occurred there; then, the archeological evidence and the distributions of certain domesticated plants in West Africa, from which an attempt will be made to determine the broad outlines of the culture history of the area. From a consideration of the culture history of West Africa and the relationship between culture patterns and the endemicity of malaria, the spread of the selective advantage of the sickle cell gene will be inferred.

THE DISTRIBUTION OF LANGUAGE IN WEST AFRICA

In the following discussion Greenberg's ('55) classification of African languages will be used, since it is the most recent and also the most widely accepted. In addition, Greenberg is attempting to make a "genetic" classification of African languages. Languages are said to be genetically related when their similarities are due to their development from a common ancestral language. It is this type of linguistic relationship which is most likely to have biological significance, since the ancestors of the speakers of genetically related languages were probably once members of the same breeding population and thus biologically related. Greenberg's classification is concerned with the larger linguistic families of Africa and the larger subgroupings within these families. Since it will be necessary at times to separate the languages into smaller subgroups, other sources will be used, but only when these agree with Greenberg's overall classification.

Except for the Songhai, Hausa, Kerikeri, Tuareg, Moor, and the tribes around Lake Chad, all the tribes listed on Table 1 speak languages belonging to the Niger-Congo family. The exceptions noted above speak either Songhai, Central Saharan, or Afro-Asiatic languages. These tribes are in the northern and eastern parts of West Africa and a considerable distance from the two low frequency areas of the sickle cell trait with which we are concerned. Therefore, this discussion will be concerned only with the Niger-Congo languages.

The Niger-Congo family contains seven subfamilies: (1) West Atlantic, (2) Mande, (3) Gur, (4) Kwa, (5) Central Group, (6) Ijo, (7) Adamawa-Eastern. All of these subfamilies have some member languages in West Africa, but, with the exception of the Adamawa-Eastern speakers in northern Central Africa, the Niger-Congo languages in Central, East, and South Africa all belong to a single subfamily (Central Group) and even to a single subgroup (Bantu) within that subfamily.

Because of the great linguistic diversity in West Africa, this area appears to have been inhabited for a relatively long time by speakers of Niger-Congo. On the other hand, because of the similarity of language in the area inhabited by the Bantu peoples, this area has undoubtedly been peopled by a relatively recent spread of those peoples. As Greenberg ('55:40) states:

"If the view of the position of the Bantu languages presented here is accepted, there are certain historical conclusions of considerable significance which follow. When Sapir demonstrated that the Algonkian languages were related to the Wiyot and Yurok languages of California, it was clear that, if this demonstration was accepted, it constituted a powerful argument for the movement of the Algonkian-speaking peoples from the west to the east. Here we have not two languages, but twenty-three separate stocks all in the same general area of Nigeria and the Cameroons. The evidence thus becomes strong for the movement of the Bantu-speaking peoples from this area southeastwards. The usual assumption has been a movement directly south from the great lake region of East Africa. It will also follow that this is a relatively recent movement, a conclusion which has generally been accepted on the basis of the wide extension of the Bantu languages and the relatively small differentiation among them." In discussing the archeological and ethnological evidence, an attempt will be made to give reasons for the relatively recent spread of the Bantu from Nigeria, as well as to show that this other evidence seems to support the linguistic evidence.

In West Africa west of Nigeria, there are four subfamilies of Niger-Congo: West Atlantic, Mande, Gur, and Kwa. With the exception of the rather recent movement of the Fulani pastoralists across the entire length of West Africa, the West Atlantic languages are all located along the coastal fringe of West Africa. The Kwa languages are distributed along the Guinea Coast from Liberia to Central Nigeria, with the great majority of them located in the tropical rain forest. In the central part of West Africa, in two large blocks, are the Mande languages on the west and the Gur languages on the east. These languages are for the most part located in the sudan, although several Mande groups have penetrated the tropical rain forest in Sierra Leone, Liberia, and the Ivory Coast.

The tribes with low frequencies of the sickle cell trait in Portuguese Guinea speak West Atlantic languages, but some Mandingo groups in the Gambia, who speak a Mande language, also have relatively low frequencies. In Eastern Liberia and the Western Ivory Coast, the tribes with low sickling frequencies include speakers of Kwa and Mande languages. Thus, with the exception of Gur, all these subfamilies include some languages whose speakers are far from equilibrium with respect to the sickle cell gene. Since these subfamilies also include some languages whose speakers have high frequencies of the sickle cell trait and seem to be close to equilibrium, the frequency of the trait is not correlated with language. This seems to indicate that the gene has been introduced into this part of West Africa since these sub-families of Niger-Congo began to separate. However, since there is considerable linguistic diversity within the subfamilies, their separation occurred long ago.

Although there is no correlation of the frequency of the sickle cell trait with the linguistic subfamilies in this part of West Africa, the tribes with low frequencies in both Portuguese Guinea and Eastern Liberia seem to be the indigenous inhabitants of West Africa who have been forced back into these areas by later migrants from the east. The distribution of the West Atlantic languages along the coast with some isolated pockets in the interior indicates that the speakers of these languages were once more widespread and have been forced back to the coast by more recent invaders (Forde, '53). This retreat of the West Atlantic speakers is documented to some extent, and there is general agreement that the general trend of migration has been toward the west. Of course, the West Atlantic peoples probably occupied the coastal regions at an early time also, but their present concentration there results from their displacement from a wider area by invaders from the east.

Several authorities state that the Baga, who now inhabit the coastal regions of French Guinea, originally inhabited the Futa Djallon, which is the highland area of Central French Guinea. The Baga were forced out of there by the Susu, who were in turn forced out by the Fulani (Houis, '50; Demougeot, '44; Joire, '52). This forcing back of the West Atlantic speakers was also noted by Beranger-Ferand (1879:285) in the Casamance River area of the French Senegal. He divides the populations of this region into three groups:

A. Peuplades primitives (Feloupes, Bagnouns).

B. Peuplades envahissantes (Balantes, Mandingues, Peuls).

C. Peuplades adventives (Ouolofs, Saracoles, Toucouleur, Mandiagos, Machouins, Taumas, Vachelons). He then states that A are the indigenous inhabitants; B are the fighters who conquered; and C are the traders or farmers who infiltrated in small groups. In Gambia the same migrations have been noted by Southorn ('52) and Reeve ('12). Reeve ('12:17) states:

"The only relics that are to be found today of the primitive negro race which originally occupied the forest belt between the Senegal and the Rio Grande are the Serreres on the coast, north of the Saloum River, who are pagans and were cannibals; the Feloops, Floops, or Flups, as called by early voyagers, but now, in the valley of the Gambia, known as the Jolahs, occupying the territory between the seacoast and the headwaters of the Vintang Creek, about one hundred miles inland, the Patcharis or Pakaris in the Middle Valley, and the Bassaris including the Kunyadis, in the Upper Valley. These will be again referred to, and it is evident, from the chronicles of the different writers on the subject of slavery in this part of West Africa, that it was these Arcadians and forest dwellers, with their simple manners and customs of sustaining life from the products of the forest, field, and streams, who supplied the bulk of the trade, under the pretext that they worshipped idols, and therefore were considered to be outside the pale of humanity by the races that had adopted the Koran." Thus, it can be seen that these writers agree that the Feloops, who have one of the lowest frequencies of the sickle cell trait, are one of the indigenous tribes. In addition, Reeve states that the Serer, who also have a low frequency of the trait, are the indigenous inhabitants in the north and in the past were hunters and gatherers and not agriculturalists. It should also be noted that Leite and Ré ('55), who tested the tribes of the Portuguese Guinea for sickling, give a similar explanation for the differences in the frequency of the sickle cell trait which they found.

The tribes with low sickling frequencies in Eastern Liberia and the Western Ivory Coast include speakers of Mande languages and of Kwa languages. All of the speakers of Kru and Lagoon languages, which belong to the Kwa subfamily, have very low frequencies of the sickle cell trait, and the positives for the trait who do occur among these peoples are in the eastern tribes where they are in contact with the Agni, Baoule, and other Akan speakers. On the other hand, the Kwa speakers who are to the east of the Kru and Lagoon peoples all have relatively high frequencies of the sickle cell trait. Viard ('34) states that the Guere, who speak a Kru language, came from the east, and Yenou ('54) makes a similar statement for the Alladians, who speak a Lagoon language. Since the linguistic relationships point to the east, these statements are probably true. Much has been written about the migrations of the Akan, Ewe, Ga, and other Kwa speakers who are to the east of the Kru and Lagoon speakers, and most authorities agree that the general direction of migration of these tribes has been to the southwest. Since the Lagoon languages are quite similar to the Togo Remnant languages (Bertho, '50), it seems that the speakers of these languages were forced back into peripheral areas by the Akan peoples (i.e., Ashanti, Fanti, Agni, Baoule), when they migrated to Southern Ghana. The movement of the Agni and Baoule into the Ivory Coast is quite recent—17th century according to most authorities. Thus, it seems that some Kwa speakers were more widespread through the tropical rain forest when the later Kwa migrants entered it and were then forced back by these later migrants. Since the later migrants have high frequencies of the sickle cell trait, it appears that they introduced the sickle cell gene into this part of West Africa.

In addition to the Kru and Lagoon-speaking peoples, there are several tribes with low sickling frequencies who speak Mande languages in Eastern Liberia and the western Ivory Coast. These are the Mano, Gio, Dan, Gouro, and other smaller groups. At the border between the Mano and the Kpelle, the frequency of the sickle cell trait increases sharply. Although these peoples both speak Mande languages, they belong to different subgroups of the Mande subfamily (Prost, '53). Kpelle is related to Mende and Susu to the northwest in Sierra Leone, and this tribe has undoubtedly come into Liberia from that direction. However, Mano and the other Mande languages whose speakers have low frequencies of the sickle cell trait are related to several Mande languages in the Upper Volta Province of French West Africa and also to a Mande language in Nigeria. Vendeix ('24) states that the Dan, and Tauxier ('24) that the Gouro, came into their present habitats from the northeast. Donner ('39) states that the Dan came from the north into the forest and forced the Kru peoples ahead of them. It would thus appear that these Mande tribes with low sickling frequencies came into their present location by a different route than that of their Mande neighbors to the northwest in Liberia and Sierra Leone. The Bobofing, who speak a language related to these Mande languages whose speakers have low sickling frequencies, have 25 percent of the sickle cell trait and are some distance to the northeast of the Dan and Gouro; so that it seems that the sickle cell gene was introduced after the separation of these languages. The Mandingo are to the north of the Mano, Dan, and Gouro, and between them and the Bobofing. From the 12th to 15th centuries A.D. when the Mali Empire, which was ruled by the Mandingos, was at its height, these people are known to have expanded out from their original homeland. It would appear that this expansion of the Mandingo forced the Mano, Dan, and Gouro into the forest and separated them from their relatives to the northeast.

The two areas of low frequencies of the sickle cell trait thus seem to be inhabited by peoples who have been forced back into these peripheral areas by later migrants from the east and northeast. However, this does not mean to imply that all the later migrants had the sickle cell gene. It is possible that the Kwa migrants to Southern Ghana introduced the gene into this part of West Africa by migration; but along the West Atlantic coastal fringe, the sickle cell gene seems to have spread in the past by mixture, and is still spreading in this manner today.

In the Central Ivory Coast on the border of the Kru and Lagoon peoples on the west and the Akan peoples on the east, there is a sharp increase in the frequency of the sickle cell trait. Since all the Kwa peoples from the Akan east to the Ibo in Nigeria have very high frequencies of the trait, it seems that these peoples possessed the sickle cell gene when they migrated into these regions from the east and northeast. However, along the Atlantic Coast of West Africa from the Senegal to Central Liberia, the gene does not seem to have been introduced by large-scale migration. The highest frequencies of the sickle cell trait in this region are found in the Gambia and in Sierra Leone, which are also the two places where Mande peoples have penetrated to the seacoast in large numbers. Since the Mande peoples were the migrants from the east, it would appear that they introduced the sickle cell gene into this part of Africa. However, the smooth gradient in the frequency of the trait in Sierra Leone and Liberia seems to indicate that the gene was introduced after the original Mande migrations. Starting with the Susu in northwest Sierra Leone who have a sickling frequency of 31 percent and proceeding southeastward, there is a smooth gradient in frequency which is not correlated with language. The speakers of Southwest Mande-fu languages, the Mende in Sierra Leone, the Mende in Liberia, the Gbandi, Loma, and Kpelle, have 29, 17, 15, 13, and 13 percent, respectively, while the West Atlantic speakers, the Timne, Kissi, and Gola, have 29, 19, and 12 percent respectively. The Vai, who speak a Mande-tan language and are the latest immigrants from the interior (McCulloch, '50), have a frequency of 14 percent, which is also in agreement with this gradient. In Portuguese Guinea, where the Mande peoples have not penetrated in great numbers, there is also a smooth gradient in the frequency of the sickle cell trait. Starting on a small section of the seacoast between the Casamance River and the Rio Cacheu where the Feloop and Baiote have 1 to 2 percent, the frequency increases going inland to 5 percent among the Mandjak, and then to 15 percent among the Biafada and Mandingo. It thus seems that along the West Atlantic coastal fringe of West Africa the sickle cell gene has spread and is still spreading by mixture and not by large scale migration, while the gene appears to have spread through the tropical rain forest along the Guinea Coast by the migration of the Akan and other Kwa-speaking migrants from the east. The archeology and culture history of West Africa will now be examined in an attempt to provide some explanation for the manner by which the sickle cell gene has spread there.

THE ARCHEOLOGY OF WEST AFRICA AND ORIGIN OF THE WEST AFRICAN NEGRO

Although there has been less archeological excavation in West Africa than elsewhere in Africa, it is now beginning to appear that West Africa was inhabited during most of man's cul-

tural development, as was most of the continent. Lower Paleolithic hand axes and Middle Paleolithic Levallois flakes have
been found in scattered places throughout West Africa (Alimen,
'55). However, no rich sites comparable to those in East and
South Africa have been excavated for these stages. Nevertheless, the scattered finds indicate the presence of man in West
Africa during these periods, which lasted up to the end of the
Pleistocene. Following these periods in time, microlithic sites
are documented for Ghana (Shaw, '51), French Guinea (Joire,
'52), Nigeria (Fagg, '51), and other places in West Africa. Some
of these microlithic cultures seem fairly recent and perhaps attributable to the ancestors of the present Negro inhabitants.
However, little skeletal material has been found.

The earliest skeletal material which is found close to West
Africa is a skull from Singa in the Sudan. This find has been
dated by Arkell ('52) as Upper Pleistocene and is associated with
a Levallois culture. The skull is stated to be archaic Bushman
and related to the Boskop skull from South Africa. From this find
it appears that the Bushman was once much more widespread
than today and in Upper Pleistocene times Bushman-like peoples
were in the Sudan. This statement is supported by the presence
of Bushman-like rock paintings and archeological cultures similar
to that of the present day Bushman over most of the southern
half of the African continent. The presence today in Tanganyika of the Hatsa, who speak a Khoisan language and still have a
predominantly Stone Age culture (Fosbrooke, '56), also supports
it.

The first appearance of skeletal material which has Negroid
affinities is in this same area of the Sudan, but apparently much
later. At Esh Shaheinab, which is on the Nile near Khartoum,
several skeletons with Negroid affinities have been found in association with a microlithic hunting and gathering culture, which
also had pottery. Around the fringes of the Sahara there are other
finds of Negroid skeletal material, all of which seem to belong
to this general period. The famous Asselar skull from north of
Timbuktu, which is considered to be Negro, is from this general
period, and Alimen ('55) also indicates that some of the skeletal

material associated with the Capsian culture in Tunisia has Negroid affinities. In addition to this skeletal material, many of the early rock paintings in the Sahara seem to depict Negroid peoples.

The Esh Shaheinab site has been dated by radiocarbon as 5200 years ago, or shortly after the beginnings of agriculture in Egypt. The radiocarbon dates on the Capsian culture are about 7500 years ago. Alimen ('55) indicates that the Neolithic of Capsian tradition is found in French Guinea, but this is probably much later than the Capsian sites which have been dated by radiocarbon. It should also be noted that in this context Neolithic does not mean food-producing, but only that the culture had polished stone artifacts.

The first archeological evidence of the Bantu in South and Central Africa is much later than the evidence from northern West Africa, and appears to be after the beginning of the Christian era. Alimen ('55:304) states: "Iron entered the Congo very late, by means of the Bantu invasion, which later spread to the Rhodesias in only 900 A.D." Further, Alimen states ('55:370) that ironworking came to the upper valley of the Orange River in the 13th century A.D. and here too is associated with the arrival of the Bantu. Previous to the expansion of the Bantu, East and South Africa were inhabited by Bushman-like peoples.

The archeological evidence thus seems to indicate that at about the time of the introduction of agriculture into Africa, Negro peoples with a microlithic culture were living around the fringes and even in the middle of the Sahara, while most of South and East Africa was inhabited by Bushman-like peoples. Since the Pygmies would seem to be indigenous to Central Africa, they were perhaps responsible for the microlithic cultures found there. For West Africa there are numerous legends of Pygmies (summary in Schnell, '48), so it is possible that at this time Pygmies also inhabited West Africa. However, Joire ('52) thinks there is no evidence for Pygmies in West Africa and assigns the microlithic sites in French Guinea to the Baga tribe. The diffusion of agriculture through Africa, and its effect on the preceding distribution of peoples will now be considered.

THE INTRODUCTION OF AGRICULTURE AND IRON WORKING INTO AFRICA

The first evidence of a farming economy in Africa occurs in Egypt at Fayum, which dates about 4000 B.C. Because of the domesticated plants and animals associated with this culture, it is thought to be derived from Asia Minor (Alimen, '55). Seligmann ('39:52) shows instances of Egyptian contact with Negroes in the late predynastic period, which he dates at about 3000 B.C., and Negroes are also known to have been living in the Sudan at Esh Shaheinab at about the same time. The inhabitants of Jebel Moya in the Sudan are also stated to be Negroes, who were forced westward by the Arabs around 700 B.C. (Mukherjee, Rao, and Trevor, '55). Thus, agriculture seems to have spread from Egypt to the Negro peoples who have since been forced south and west by the Arabs and by Berber peoples such as the Tuareg.

Iron working was also introduced into Africa from Asia Minor via Egypt (Forde, '34; Arkell, '55). There was a considerable iron industry flourishing at Meroe in the Sudan in 600 B.C., about which Arkell ('55:147) states: "Indeed there is little doubt that it was through Meroe that knowledge of iron working spread south and west throughout Negro Africa." The next evidence for the spread of iron southwest of the Sudan is in Northern Nigeria where Fagg ('56) has discovered the Nok culture, which is dated in the second half of the first millennium B.C. by geological methods. Assuming that iron working spread here from Meroe, this is about the date which would be expected. This culture contains both iron and stone axes; but since the iron axes have the same shape as the stone ones, this appears to be a transitional culture which had only recently adopted iron working. Since Mukherjee, Rao, and Trevor ('55) found the inhabitants of Jebel Moya to be most similar in physical type to the West African Negro, the westward migration of these people in the first millennium B.C. could very likely have been the method by which iron working was introduced to West Africa. In any case, this appears to be one route by which iron working was introduced into West Africa.

In the western part of West Africa, iron working seems to be somewhat later, and the evidence seems to indicate that it was not introduced via Meroe. Corbeil, Mauny, and Charbonnier ('48) think that iron working was introduced into the Cape Verde region around Dakar by Berbers who arrived there from the north about 300 B.C. Later, Mauny ('52) states that iron working was introduced into this region by the Phoenicians in the first century A.D., since the words for iron in many of the languages of this region seem to be derived from Phoenician. Although it is possible that some peoples along the coast obtained iron from the Phoenicians, it would seem more likely that iron working was brought across the Sahara, since contact with the Phoenician ships would not seem to have been close enough for the transference of all the techniques which iron working requires. Cline ('37) states: "Within the bend of the Niger lies the only large area where iron remains have been found associated with stone-using cultures." However, Nok culture in Northern Nigeria had not been discovered at the time Cline was writing, so that there appear to be two areas with these transitional cultures. In the same area Cline ('37) describes another type of iron working site which has copper and a much richer assemblage altogether. These sites he associates with the Ghana Empire. This empire was founded about 300-400 A.D. (Fage, '55), at about the time the camel was introduced into the western Sahara, and its rise to eminence is associated with increasing trade with Mediterranean civilizations. It thus appears that iron working was introduced into the western part of West Africa shortly before this empire was founded and probably was introduced from the north across the desert.

The preceding evidence indicates that both agriculture and iron working were introduced into West Africa from Asia Minor via Egypt, although both were no doubt diffused along several different routes. Agriculture was present in Egypt centuries before iron working and probably began to spread through Africa before iron working was introduced from Asia Minor. However, this early spread of agriculture seems to have been mostly by stimulus diffusion, since the basic crops of Egypt, wheat and barley, did not spread to the Sudan. Even today, millet and sorghum are the basic crops throughout the Sudan. Both millet and sorghum, or at least some species of them, are considered to have been domesticated in Africa (Miege, '51; Viguier, '45) and to have been cultivated there "since antiquity" (Miege, '51). Viguier ('45:165) states: "Aug. Chevalier considers the western sudan and its saharan border as one of the centers of the origin of domesticated sorghum." Since the agricultural methods used for them are similar to those for wheat and barley, and in addition the crops are all grains, it would seem reasonable to postulate that an early spread of agriculture from Egypt involved these crops. The techniques involved in the cultivation of these grains did not entail any considerable technological change from that of a microlithic hunting and gathering culture. The tool assemblage at Fayum in Egypt is not very different from that of the Natufian in Palestine or that of the Capsian. As this early agricultural economy spread, it either drove the hunting cultures before it or perhaps was adopted by these peoples. However, one of the hypotheses of this paper is that this economy could not spread throughout tropical Africa.

Although a Neolithic millet and sorghum economy could spread through the sudan, it was not until the introduction of iron working and/or better yielding tropical crops that the Negro agriculturalists could exploit the tropical rain forest. Thus, the forest remained the home of primitive hunters until quite recently. In West Africa these hunters appear to have been Negroes whose descendants can be seen today in the low sickling frequency areas of Portuguese Guinea and Eastern Liberia; and in Central Africa they were Pygmies, whose descendants are the low sickling frequency "true" Pygmies, the Babinga of French Equatorial Africa (Hiernaux, '55).

A combination of three factors prevented the spread of this agricultural economy through the tropical rain forest: (1) the poor quality of the soils, which wear out after a few crops; (2) the difficulty of clearing the forest with stone tools; and (3) the low yields of millet and sorghum.

In Northern Ghana and Northern Nigeria, where millet and sorghum are still the basic crops today, in many places the same fields are cultivated year after year (Manoukian, '52; Gourou, '50). On the other hand, in Sierra Leone a new field is cleared every year (McCulloch, '50), and in the forest regions of Nigeria, Gourou ('50) states that it takes 30 years for the soil to recover after one crop, while Forde ('51) indicates that the fields are cultivated for three or four years before being left fallow. Some comparison of the relative yields of the various crops can be obtained from Gourou's ('50:39) figures of yields in the French Sudan, although this is not tropical rain forest. Millet yields 5 cwt. per acre; yams, 15 cwt. per acre; and cassava, 32 cwt. per acre. However, from a nutritional standpoint the important yield is the number of calories per unit of land. Combining data from several African countries, Brock and Autret ('52) give the following figures for the yields of various crops in thousands of calories per hectare: millet yields 1,530; sorghum, 1,854; yams, 3,554; and cassava, 7,090. Thus, when these three factors are considered together, it would seem to be difficult for a Neolithic millet and sorghum economy to exist in a tropical rain forest environment. It should be emphasized, however, that this hypothesis does not mean to imply that there were no agriculturalists in the tropical rain forest prior to the introduction of iron working and tropical root crops. There was undoubtedly some agriculture and "whittling away" at the tropical rain forest in the areas which border on the sudan. However, these innovations were a necessary prerequisite for the great explosion of the Bantu peoples out of Nigeria, which filled up half a continent in a relatively short time.

Together with iron working, the domestication of two indigenous crops opened the tropical rain forest as a habitat exploitable by the Negro agriculturalists. Chevalier ('52:16) states that the yam, *Dioscorea latifolia,* was domesticated in West Africa. Today the most widespread species of yam in Africa is *D. cayenensis,* which is derived from *D. latifolia* (Chevalier, '46). From its distribution it would seem most probable that these yams were domesticated in Nigeria. With the yam and iron working, the Bantu peoples then spread throughout the Central African tropical rain forest from their original homeland, which

Greenberg ('55:116) places in the central Benue River valley in Nigeria. In many places today the Bantu do not have the yam as a staple crop, but this theory only attempts to explain the original rapid spread of the Bantu. This theory is supported by linguistic evidence, by the fact that transitional iron working cultures are known in Northern Nigeria, and also by the fact that the spread of iron working in Central and South Africa is associated with the spread of the Bantu. In addition, in several areas where yams are no longer the Bantu staple there is still ritual associated with this crop, which seems to indicate that it was previously more important. For example, among the Kpe in the Cameroons, where cocoyams are now the staple crop, Ardener ('56:46) states: "Although subsidiary in Kpe agriculture, this crop (i.e. yam) is remarkable for the fact that it is the only one to which some degree of ritual is attached . . . The ritual elements in the cultivation of the yam, the present economic importance of which is quite small, suggests that this crop . . . may have been a staple food in the past history of the Kpe."

Also from Nigeria, some of the Kwa peoples spread in similar fashion through the West African tropical rain forest to the Ivory Coast and forced other Kwa peoples, the Kru and Lagoon speakers, westward into the Ivory Coast and Liberia. The Kru and Lagoon peoples were probably in the tropical rain forest as hunters and gatherers prior to this spread of agriculture. Agriculture has since been introduced to most of the Kru and Lagoon peoples, but it usually has rice as the basic crop, which comes from a different center of dispersal, or manioc, which was introduced into West Africa from the New World. Even today in the Ivory Coast, as several botanists (Miege, '53; Chevalier, '52) have remarked, there is a sharp boundary of yam cultivation on the Bandama River, which is also the border between the Baoule and Kru peoples. In addition, the yam cultivators, such as the Agni, have an elaborate ritual associated with the yam harvest (Rahm, '53; Miege, '53), which indicates great reliance on this crop. Although the Kru peoples have for the most part adopted agriculture, there is still more reliance on hunting in the Kru area (Kerharo and Bouquet, '49), and there are some groups

who are still mainly hunters. In Eastern Liberia, Schwab
(’47:79) states: ". . . there is one clan or small tribe . . .
living to the north of the Tchien near the Nipwe River who
have a reputation as elephant hunters, like the pigmies of the
southeastern Cameroun.''

The cline in the frequency of the sickle cell trait coincides
with this spread of yam cultivation. The Kru and Lagoon peoples have almost 0 percent of the sickle cell trait, except where
they come in contact with the yam cultivators, while the yam
cultivators in the Eastern Ivory Coast, Southern Ghana, and Nigeria, all have high frequencies of the trait. Thus, it seems
that the sickle cell gene was brought into this part of Africa by
the migrations of the yam cultivators westward from Nigeria,
and at present both agriculture and the sickle cell gene are spreading to the hunting populations, which were in the forest prior
to the spread of yam cultivation.

Perhaps a little later than this spread of yam cultivation,
there was another spread of agriculture through the West African tropical rain forest. Porteres (’49) has shown that some-
where around the Middle Niger River Valley, a wild African
species of rice, *Oryza glaberrima,* was domesticated. He dates
this domestication at about 1500 B.C. (*ibid.*:560), but the spread
of this crop through the tropical forest seems to be much later
than the postulated date, and even later than the introduction of
iron. There is evidence (Little, ’51:26) that the first Mande
peoples to enter the tropical rain forest were hunters. Little
dates this migration at least 400 years ago. However, the most
plausible date seems to be about 1300 A.D., when the Susu appear to have migrated to French Guinea from the Middle Niger
region (Joire, ’52). Thus, it would seem that the Mande and
West Atlantic peoples in the tropical forest were still hunters
about 600 years ago, and that rice agriculture has since been introduced to them. Joire (’52) assigns the microlithic archeological
sites which are known in French Guinea to the Baga people, who
speak a West Atlantic language. These people thus were in the
tropical forest prior to the immigration of the Mande peoples
and to the later spread of rice agriculture.

The spread of iron working and rice cultivation through this part of the West African tropical rain forest, after the original Mande migration, does not seem to be associated with any large scale migration; it probably occurred by diffusion, since the Mande peoples who have now adopted rice cultivation were in the same location as hunters.   Thus, according to the evidence, the spread of rice agriculture by diffusion seems to coincide with the spread of the sickle cell gene by mixture.   In addition, the spread of rice cultivation appears to be later than the original Mande migration, as does the spread of the sickle cell gene.   Rice cultivation also diffused to the West Atlantic-speaking peoples, as did the sickle cell gene.   Thus, the type of gene flow—in one case migration and in the other mixture—which was responsible for the spread of the gene in West Africa seems to be related to the manner of the spread of agriculture.   However, agriculture seems to have spread farther than the gene.   The Kru peoples in Eastern Liberia, and the West Atlantic peoples in coastal Portuguese Guinea, are today rice cultivators.   The reason for this lag in the spread of the sickle cell gene is due first of all to the fact that it takes several generations for the gene to build up to appreciable frequencies, but it also seems to be due to the relationship of the selective advantage of the sickle cell gene to slash and burn agriculture.   This relationship is due in turn to the complex epidemiology of malaria in West Africa, which we will now consider.

MAN, MALARIA AND MOSQUITO IN WEST AFRICA

In West Africa the relationship between man, malaria, and mosquito is very highly evolved, due largely to the habits of the major vector of malaria, *Anopheles gambiae*. This mosquito is attracted to human habitations and usually rests in the thatched roofs of an African village. It bites man regularly, and breeds in a variety of places. Wilson ('49) has estimated that 75 percent of the malaria in Africa is due to *A. gambiae*. Its breeding places are so diverse that, when attempting to delimit them, entomologists usually state where it cannot breed. *A. gambiae* cannot breed in (1) very shaded water, (2) water with a strong current, (3) brackish water, (4) very alkaline or polluted water (Holstein, '53).

If we now consider the types of water which would be found in the tropical rain forest, it can be seen that there would be few places for *A. gambiae* to breed in unbroken tropical rain forest. The high emergent shade trees and the trees of the middle "story" of the forest so effectively shade the ground that there would be few, if any, areas that were unshaded. In addition, the layer of humus on the forest floor is very absorbent, so there would be few stagnant pools. It is only when man cuts down the forest that breeding places for *A. gambiae* become almost infinite (De Meillon, '49). First, with continued cutting of the forest, the soil loses all of its humus and becomes laterized. At this stage it is practically impervious to water; puddles are constantly renewed by the frequent tropical rains and so persist indefinitely. Second, man's refuse and his villages provide more abundant breeding places for the mosquito. Third, the swamps become open and hence possible breeding places.

In a hunting population, which does not destroy the forest, malaria would thus not develop this complex relation with man. Malaria could still be present, but not the holoendemic malaria which characterizes most of Africa today. Hunters do not build the type of permanent habitation in which *A. gambiae* lives, and since a hunting population moves frequently the mosquito could not keep up with the human population, so to speak. Also, in the epidemiology of any disease there is a critical size for the population below which the disease cannot persist. Since hunting populations are small, they would be closer to this critical size and perhaps even below it.

The Pygmies provide an example of such a hunting population, but unfortunately no malaria surveys of hunting Pygmies are available. Schwetz, Baumann, Peel, and Droeshant ('33) did examine three groups of Pygmies for malaria and found that they had less than the surrounding Negroes, but these Pygmies were building houses and farming, and so cannot be considered a hunting population. Putnam ('48), who lived with the hunting

Pygmies for 20 years, states that they do not suffer from malaria. His account also shows that the Pygmies do not cut down the forest and do not build their rude huts in a clearing but in the middle of the forest. These customs would appear to be the reasons for the absence of malaria among them.

If this complex relationship between parasite, host, and vector which is characteristic of holoendemic malaria could not have developed in hunting populations, then the selective advantage of the sickle cell gene would not be present in these populations. If, as has been postulated, the Feloop and other peoples in Portuguese Guinea and the Kru peoples of Eastern Liberia and the Western Ivory Coast were the last remnants of hunting populations which once were spread through the tropical forest, then the absence of the selective advantage of the sickle cell gene in these populations would have prevented it from becoming established, even if there had been some gene flow from neighboring Sudanic peoples. Although considerable areas of tropical rain forest are shown on any vegetation map of West Africa, these are greatly broken up by agricultural settlements and fields. Nevertheless, the last northern remnants of the forest are located in Portuguese Guinea near one area of low sickling frequencies, and the other area in Eastern Liberia is in the center of the largest remaining block of tropical rain forest.

The frequencies of the sickle cell trait among the Pygmies also support this theory, although the comments of several authorities might seem to contradict it. Regarding the Pygmies and Pygmoids, Hiernaux ('55:463) states; "They generally show a lower frequency of sicklemia than the surrounding populations . . . In all cases but one, the frequency is lower in the Pygmoids. The most striking difference is between the Bondjo and Babinga, who are true Pygmies." Since most Pygmy groups have formed symbiotic relationships with their Negro neighbors, the frequencies among them can easily be explained by mixture, which is known to be occurring (Putnam, '48).

There is other evidence that *A. gambiae* has spread rather recently through the West African tropical rain forest. In the area around the Firestone plantation in Liberia, shortly after the forest had been cut down, Barber, Rice, and Brown ('32) found that *A. gambiae* accounted for 46 percent of the mosquito population found in the native huts, while *A. funestus* accounted for 51 percent, and *A. nili* for 3 percent. However, at the present time in this same area, *A. gambiae* accounts for almost 100 percent of the mosquito population (Max J. Miller, personal communication). Barber, Rice, and Brown ('32) found holoendemic malaria, which is not present today; however, this change is due to malaria control and not to changes in the mosquito population. These figures thus indicate a significant increase in *A. gambiae* when the forest is cut down. Even more significant are Barber, Rice, and Brown's comments on the effects of reforestation on the mosquito population. They state ('33:629): "We felt that it would be interesting to know what would be the condition of things when the rubber trees had grown and the unplanted ravines and swamps had become "rejunglized." We surveyed Mt. Barclay Plantation where the stream borders have grown up with brush or long grass. After a long search in the streams we found only two or three larvae, *A. mauritianius* and *A. obscurus*. In a pool near a village *A. costalis* was plentiful." It can thus be seen that *A. gambiae* (the authors call the species *A. costalis*) was not present in natural water but only near a village. The authors also discuss "rejunglization" as a means of malaria control, but state that it would not be feasible due to the breeding places which would persist around the villages. In the absence of these villages, which are not built by hunting populations, and in the presence of unbroken tropical forest, the intensity of malaria would be much less. This seems to have been the situation in West Africa prior to the spread of slash and burn agriculture. Therefore, the spread of this agriculture is responsible for the spread of the selective advantage of the sickle cell gene, and hence for the spread of the gene itself.

SICKLE CELLS, DISEASE, AND HUMAN EVOLUTION

The preceding explanation of the distribution of the sickle cell gene and its relation to the culture history of West Africa has broad implications for the role of disease in human evolution. In considering the epidemiology of the sickle cell gene, Neel ('57:167) suggested that either the mutation which resulted in the sickle cell gene was very rare or else the spread of the gene was at present favored by special circumstances of relatively recent origin. The detailed arguments of this paper would seem to show that there are indeed special circumstances of recent origin, while at the same time not excluding the possibility that the mutation is quite rare. The special circumstances are considered to be the conditions necessary to maintain holoendemic malaria due to *Plasmodium falciparum*. This parasite is in fact regarded as evolutionarily the most recent species of malaria to parasitize man (Boyd, '49). If, as has been proposed, a mobile hunting population in the tropical rain forest could not develop holoendemic malaria, then this high endemicity would perhaps be even later than the adaptation of the parasite to man as its host. Since the agricultural revolution occurred only about 7000 years ago and spread much later to Africa, it appears that the development of the environmental conditions which are responsible for the spread of the sickle cell gene are relatively recent, as Neel postulated they should be.

The agricultural revolution has always been considered an important event in man's cultural evolution, but it also seems to have been an important event in man's biological evolution. Prior to this revolution, the size of the human population was controlled to a large extent by the size of its food supply, and man's ecological niche was comparable to that of the large carnivores, or more closely perhaps to that of a large omnivore such as the bear. With the advent of the agricultural revolution, the food supply was no longer the major factor controlling the size of human populations. Man broke out of his ecological confinement and there was a tremendous increase in the size of the human population, an increase which was limited only by the available land. Haldane ('49, '56) has stated that disease became the major factor controlling the size of human populations at this time, and his statement seems to be supported in one case by the spread of holoendemic malaria.

Two results of the agricultural revolution seem to account for this change in the role of disease in human evolution: (1) the great changes in the environment, and (2) the huge increase in the human population. Both of these seem to be involved in the development of holoendemic malaria. First, when man disrupts the vegetation of any area, he severely disrupts the fauna and often causes the extinction of many mammals, particularly the larger ones. When this happens, there are many known instances of the parasites of these animals adapting to man as the new host (Heisch, '56). It is thus possible that the parasitization of man by *P. falciparum* is due to man's blundering on the scene and causing the extinction of the original host. Second, concomitant with the huge increase in the human population, this population became more sedentary and man also became the most widespread large animal. Thus, he became the most available blood meal for mosquitoes and the most available host for parasites. This change resulted in the adaptation of several species of the Anopheline mosquito to human habitations and the adaptation of many parasites to man as their host. Under these conditions, holoendemic malaria and probably many other diseases developed and became important factors determining human evolution. It should be noted, however, that through domestication man has created large populations of other animals and these have influenced the epidemiology of several human diseases including malaria (for malaria examples, see Hackett, '49; Draper and Smith, '57). The sickle cell gene thus seems to be an evolutionary response to this changed disease environment. Hence, this gene is the first known genetic response to a very important event in man's evolution when disease became a major factor determining the direction of that evolution.

Note

During the course of this study the author has been the recipient of a Public Health Service Predoctoral Fellowship from the National Heart Institute. The findings were submitted in partial fulfillment of the requirements of the degree of Doctor of Philosophy at the University of Michigan. The author is indebted

to James V. Neel and James N. Spuhler for their advice and assistance both during the course of the study and the writing of the
manuscript.

VII. GENETIC DRIFT AND RACE

In 1931 Sewall Wright called attention to the small-sample effect, which has since been termed "genetic drift" or the Sewall Wright phenomenon. Wright pointed out that purely random variations in gene frequency operating in numerically small populations could (in the absence of selection pressure) result in temporary genetic differentiation.

The possible role of drift, in bringing about racial differences, has had special appeal to many students of man. During the Pleistocene, the widely scattered human populations must have been small, ideal for random fluctuations in gene frequency. Even today populations with a stone-age economy tend to include fewer than 100 individuals of breeding age, with the consequent possibility of large generation-to-generation differences due to sampling error alone. One can postulate a situation in which a small and isolated population changed radically due entirely to drift, with their altered gene frequencies then becoming "fixed" after a period of explosive population growth.

Drift, furthermore, provides a possible explanation for the small, almost random differences that one encounters in a system of contiguous local races or microraces. Though natural selection can never be ruled out, invoking drift provides a simple alternative explanation for what would otherwise be an inexplicable set of data. It is possible, at least, that some racial differences are due to the mechanism of genetic drift, operating when the original populations were small and isolated.

Investigating drift, rather than just talking about it, poses a number of problems. While the ideal experimental design would be to select a number of small contiguous isolates, and then to wait and watch, such a procedure could not yield results in this century. The most practical alternative is to select one or more isolates of relatively recent origin and to compare their gene frequencies with that of the parental population. If natural selection can be ruled out, any differences could then be attributable to drift. This is the procedure adopted by Glass and his associates in their studies in the Old Order Dunkers in the United States.

Their procedure, however, has its limitations. As with any isolate formed under political or religious pressure, it is questionable whether the "Dunker" population was genetically representative of the West German population from which it stemmed. Further, accepting the differences that do appear in the Dunker population, it is manifestly impossible to rule out natural selection as a possible cause.

Nevertheless, this study is methodologically and conceptually important. One cannot forget the fact that many Polynesian, Melanesian and Micronesian Islands were settled by single boatloads of travelers. The distinctive flavor of many European mountain and fjordside populations is undoubtedly due to the peculiar genetic makeup of the original migrants as much as it is due to random losses and gains of particular genes. That genetic drift is probably responsible for some part of racial differentiation seems likely. How much, is a matter for us to determine.

ADDITIONAL READINGS

Glass, B.: Genetic changes in human populations, especially those due to gene flow and genetic drift, *Advances in Genetics, 6*:95-139, New York, Academy Press, 1954.

Birdsell, J. B.: Some implications of the genetical concept of race in terms of spatial analysis, *Cold Spring Harbor Symposia on Quantitative Biology, 15*:259-314, Cold Spring Harbor, the Biological Laboratory, 1950.

Lasker, G. W.: Mixture and genetic drift in ongoing human evolution, *Am. Anthropol., 54*:433-436, 1952.

Wright, S.: Classification of the factors of evolution, *Cold Spring Harbor Symposia on Quantitative Biology, 20*:16-24, Cold Spring Harbor, The Biological Laboratory, 1955.

Human Evolution in Contemporary Communities

Reprinted from *Southwestern Journal of Anthropology*, Vol. 10, No. 4, pp. 353-365 (1954).

By Gabriel Ward Lasker

Wright and others have developed a theory which permits the construction of a genetic model for the study of on-going human evolution (Wright, '32). This theory describes evolution as a change in the frequency of genes in a breeding population. Four factors, which can alter gene frequencies, are visualized as interacting with each other. The resultant gene frequency change is the rate of evolution. These four factors—mutation, natural selection, accidental variation (random genetic drift), and admixture—act in different ways.

Models based on this theory have so far been little used in connection with empirical data on man. Here I can only outline one or two first steps in the application of such models. I have begun the collection of suitable data, but their mathematical analysis is an undertaking for the future.

The four factors influencing evolution do so by varying the frequency of genes in a population of interbreeding individuals. For mankind, interbreeding involves mating between members of each segment with those of contiguous segments, and hence the whole human species is involved. Nevertheless, the structure of this total population is so complex and the probability is so much greater of mating with individuals close at hand and of the same social group, that it is easier to use as a base for our model the "breeding population," the largest unit within which relatively random mating occurs. In primitive or folk cultures this frequently is more or less synonymous with the community. However small this breeding population may be, and however its boundaries are defined, there still will be patterns of mate selection within it. Although departures from random mating are usually unimportant in their effects, in special cases the effects of incest tabus or, more especially, inbreeding may be significant enough to be considered as a fifth evolutionary factor.

With the "breeding population" defined as limited to the community within which most mates are found, it becomes necessary to further qualify the term. Only persons who become parents have significance for evolution. Furthermore, the variability in number of offspring still further reduces the size of the "effective breeding population," which is, thus, only a fraction of the size of the community. For the purposes of our model we may calculate the size of this effective breeding population and represent it with black and white marbles in the ratio of some gene frequency—such as the ratio of genes for M and N blood groups (and these frequencies can be hypothetical or observed ratios).

Now we come to the question of a unit of time. The most available one is the generation, and this will have to suffice, but it is well to bear in mind that in man there is considerable overlap in generations—one can recall cases where uncles or aunts are younger than their nieces and nephews. This factor, however, is ordinarily not of sufficient moment to prevent our ignoring it in a preliminary model.

Shall we assume that our population is demographically stable: deaths and emigration equaling births and immigration? What shall we add to, or subtract from, our stock of black and white marbles that represent the ratio of a gene and its allele in the population?

First there is mutation. Mutation rates have been estimated for some human genes. However, I know of no satisfactory estimate in man for a mutation rate for two alleles at the same locus. The best we can do, then, is to assume that the mutation rate for the various alleles is equal. Mutation, therefore, would tend to maintain both alleles in the population and, in the absence of other factors, would tend to give a 50-50 gene ratio. In small breeding populations mutation rates of the order of one per 1,000,000 or one per 100,000 would be of little consequence in any case.

Second, consider natural selection. Here actual evidence for human subgroups is still wanting. Most hypotheses concerning adaptive advantages of one or another racial type are *ex post facto* explanations of observed distributions. Natural selection must be at a maximum when very different species are considered; it must be at a minimum between closely related groups, for they differ in only a few and adaptively unimportant traits. Selective survival may be important in respect to genes associated with pathologies and maladaptations, but it is so far unrecognized in empirical studies of human race formation. At some time we may achieve useful estimates of natural selection of individuals in respect to genes now thought to be adaptively neutral. But for man "natural" selection is largely overshadowed by the importance to survival of cultural factors. For the present purpose, no estimate of the effects of natural selection in man will be attempted. Instead we ask: "In the absence of adaptive advantage or disadvantage, what is the likelihood of a changed frequency of an inherited trait in the population?"

This brings us to the third and fourth factors: genetic drift and admixture, influences for which I shall now attempt quantification for some human groups.

In a previous preliminary note I made an estimate of the possible effects of genetic drift and admixture in a Mexican town, Paracho (Lasker, '52). Subsequently, in the summer of 1952, my wife, Bernice Kaplan, and I made a complete census of the town, and more accurate estimates are therefore now possible. Through the cooperation of Charles Leslie, an anthropologist resident in another Mexican town—Mitla, Oaxaca—we have also collected some data there. Some comparable information for other communities is available in published sources. It is well to bear in mind, however, that the reported figures are not all of equal reliability even when the appropriate demographic data are presented or can be derived. Our own experience in collecting additional material in a town we had previously surveyed shows that estimates may be in considerable error.

The revised estimate of the total breeding population of Paracho is approximately 1,555. It is larger than I had thought. This represents the total number of parents living with their offspring in Paracho in 1952. One might increase this estimate because of the omission of parents whose children have left home and of those parents who have separated. On the other hand, the estimate of the number of parents might be reduced because in its present form it includes persons of all ages and it spans more than a generation. Any lack of randomness in choice of mates also would have the same effect as reducing the effective size of the breeding population. We may calculate the breeding population in another way more comparable with that which we have previously used. It yields a similar result. Estimating, as previously, 39% of the total population to be married and 90% of those married to be parents, one would have 35.7% of 4,593 persons as parents, that is, 1,640.

To get an estimate of the *effective* size of the breeding population one also needs to know the variance in number of gametes contributed to the next generation. Previously, we have attempted to estimate this on the basis of the total number of children born to a sample of parents interviewed in 1948. It seems to me, however, that (as children who die and those who leave the community do not enter into the breeding population of the town) such an estimate would set an upper limit, while the number of children living with the nuclear families in our census of 1952 gives a more reasonable estimate. This figure for mean family size is 3.4 with a standard deviation of ± 2.10.

Following the same formula as that previously used, $N = (4N' - 2) / (\sigma_k^2 + 2)$ in which N' represents the number of parents and σ_k^2 represents the variance in number of gametes contributed to the next generation, one gets the effective breeding population equal to 967. The effective breeding population is thus roughly only 1/5 of the total population.

Applying to the Paracho data the formula for random genetic drift, $\sigma \Delta q = \sqrt{q\,(1 - q)\,/2N}$, one would get ± 1.1 for genes with frequencies most subject to this factor (i.e., for genes with a frequency, q, of 0.5).

As in my previous estimate of admixture into Paracho, the method of estimation followed is to take the place of birth of both parents of individuals now living in the town. This means that the parents get recounted for every surviving child, a fact tending to eliminate any inequalities there may be in parental fertility or infant mortality between the new families and those previously established in the community. For all individuals *living* in Paracho in 1952, 34.9% of the parental element was from outside Paracho and 4.8% were in question. However, of 3,390 individuals *born* in Paracho, both parents were born elsewhere in 315 cases, and one parent was born elsewhere in 741 cases. Thus the parental element is from outside Paracho in 20.2% ($\frac{741}{2}$ + 315 of 3,390 individuals). Another 2.4% of the parental element was in question (place of birth not given by the census respondent).

Mitla is a town similar in size to Paracho but contrasting with Paracho in that it is essentially self-sufficient in food production and seems to have greater population stability. Leslie says that a census of Mitla made in late 1953 lists 2,951 people and that one taken in 1949 listed a population of 2,690. Records of marriages for 1918, 1924, and all years since 1927 (except 1951) were examined in the town hall. Not all marriages in Mitla have been registered. Nevertheless, the registered marriages seem to represent a cross-section of the established unions with, perhaps, some over-representation of wealthier individuals and of longstanding unions (registration often takes place years after the establishment of a union). There is, however, no reason to expect bias in respect to recorded place of birth. Of 1,064 persons whose marriages are recorded in the registry in Mitla, 202 (19.0%) were born in places other than Mitla (and the place of birth of 45, 4.2%, is not given). This 19% includes, however, couples living in nearby places where no marriage registry exists and who are not, properly speaking, members of the Mitla population. A more useful estimate of the immigration into Mitla is obtained from the data given on place of birth of parents of those married. Of those stated to be born in Mitla for whom the birthplace of the parents is also given, only 41 (3.5%) of 1,173 were born elsewhere. This is possibly an underestimate as this datum was not always registered, and selective factors may have been involved; birthplace of mother was not recorded in 182 cases and that of the father was not recorded in 273 cases. Not infrequently the identity, let alone the place of birth, of the father was recorded as unknown. In any case, the rate of admixture is less than that for Paracho.

A rate of immigration intermediate between that occurring in Paracho and that estimated for Mitla has been reported for several other Middle American communities. Tzintzuntzan, a town of 1,231 persons has, according to Foster, 145 (11.78%) residents born elsewhere. Foster ('48) says, "A high degree of inbreeding appears to characterize Tzintzuntzan, which must be reflected in homogeneous physical type; adequate measurements to verify or disprove this hypothesis are lacking."

Brand gives immigration data for the *municipio* (county) of Quiroga. In 1945, 713 (22.56%) of the 3,161 inhabitants of the *cabecera* (county seat) came from other parts of the *municipio* or from elsewhere (Brand, 51). Unfortunately data are not given separately for each of the small populated, outlying *ranchos* of the *municipio,* but together they had 998 individuals of whom 82 (8.22%) were reported as born elsewhere. As there were also 21 individuals living in a different *rancho* from that in which they were born, the average *rancho* would have $\frac{998}{6}$ = 166 individuals of whom $\frac{82+21}{6}$ = 17.17 (10.34%) are immigrants—a very low rate for such small communities.

Kelly and Palerm ('52) give some data for two Totonac communities. There were 1,102 persons in the 186 families which—by reason of place where communal service is given—pertained to Tajín in 1948. Of 354 heads of families and their wives, 104 (29.4%) were born elsewhere. Of the 777 persons in Aguacate, on the highway to Tuxpan, 498 speak Totonac and of the latter 114 (22.9%) were born elsewhere.

The rate of admixture in a Guatemalan Indian community can be adduced from Tax's ('53) data. Like Mitla, Panajachel is dependent on agriculture and trading. Tax reports that of about 780 Indians in the town, 688 might be called Panajacheleños "having at least some Panajachel blood or family connections." Of these, 7 men and 25 women were from elsewhere but were married to Panajacheleños, and 1 man and 3 women from elsewhere were related in other ways. Thus the immigration rate would be 36 per 688 = 5.23%. In addition 92 other foreign Indians were living within the confines of the community and if these were included in the estimate (as they should be if their children become full members of Panajachel) one would have 92 + 36 per 780 = 16.41% immigration.

Tax reports that there are also approximately 400 *Ladinos* living in the same town. They may be presumed to have a much higher rate of admixture: the very term *Ladino* implies mixture of Indians with descendants of the Spanish. To the extent that some of the local Indians may have local *Ladino* fathers, therefore, the estimates of the admixture rate given above for Panajachel Indians should be revised upward.

In the other cases, we have assumed that all persons living in each of the places are members of a single breeding community. However, any "structure" of the breeding population within the community (with more or less endogamy of smaller social units) has the effect of further restricting the size of the effective breeding population. Paracho lacks sharp racial distinctions and caste-like endogamy is not involved in the breeding pattern (Kaplan, '53; Lasker, '53). The same is probably true of Mitla —but we did exclude data on two Protestant missionaries whose marriage was recorded in the Mitla town hall.

In the cases cited, except for Panajachel, the breeding community is not smaller than the town, but is it larger? Apparently not. The contrast between *cabecera* and *ranchos* in Quiroga and the rarity of intermarriage is paralleled in our own experience of the relationships between the *cabecera* of Paracho and its dependent villages. In contemporary Middle America it appears to be usual that the populated place, whether *rancho, pueblo,* or *cabecera,* is coextensive with the breeding community.

For simple communities in other parts of the world a few data on admixture are available.

Spier ('28) collected demographic data on a well-nigh aboriginal American Indian group, in 1918-1921. He states that marriages were not often contracted with foreigners. "The situation today," he wrote, "represents the condition fairly well: there are six Walapai women and one Yavapai married to Havasupai, while a few natives are wives of Walapai . . . I was told that Hopi women were never married, but Cushing saw one there in 1881. Occasionally Paiute and Navaho women were married." Spier lists 43 females over the age of 18 in his Havasupai census of 1919. If we assume that the seven non-native women were among these, and that the Havasupai women married to Walapai were not counted, then 16.3% of matings were with outside women and the admixture rate was 8.1%. Spier also tabulates 67 marriages past and present. Of these 8 were with Walapai, two with Yavapai, 1 with a Paiute. These yield a rate of 14.9% of marriages with outsiders and 7.5% intermixture.*

Spuhler and Kluckhohn ('53) state that for 317 fertile matings of Ramah Navaho between 1820 and 1948, 35 (11.1%) involve a mate from outside the Ramah population; this is an admixture rate of 5.6%.

In another contemporary American Indian town, by contrast, Jones ('53) found a very high rate. Chuichu, Arizona, is a Papago community of 223 people, 52 of whom had migrated there within ten years; of 12 recent marriages 11 brought in an individual from outside.

Oberg ('53) says of some of the most isolated groups in Brazil: "It must be mentioned at the outset that a certain amount of intermixture has taken place among the Upper Xingú tribes for a long time. Among the 110 Camayurá were 5 Suyá women captured in raids, two or three Waurá women and one Mehinácu woman . . . obtained in marriage, three or 4 Waurá men who had married Camayurá women, and two Juruna men . . . who were brothers, had been captured when boys from the Suyá who in turn had taken them from the Juruna."

Tindale ('53) concludes, from a study of various Australian aboriginal tribes, that 7% to 21% of marriages contracted prior to appreciable White influence are intertribal; this gives an

---

*In a private communication Spier suggests that such estimates may be somewhat low for one can never know the number of illicit unions with visitors. He says that in the case of the Havasupai other Indians came very infrequently and Whites practically never. He thinks that if we just double the number of outside marriages we would take care of this situation.

TABLE 1

DEMOGRAPHIC DATA AND EVOLUTIONARY FACTORS

	Community Size	Effective Size of Breeding Population	Rate of Random Genetic Drift per Generation for a Gene with Frequency of 0.5 %	Percentage of Individuals Born Elsewhere %	Rate of Admixture %
Paracho, Michoacán (*cabecera*)	4593	967	±1.1	34.9	20.2
Quiroga, Michoacán (*cabecera*)	3161	665?	1.4	22.6	22.6?
Mitla, Oaxaca	2951	621?	1.4	19.0?	3.5?
Tzintzuntzan, Michoacán	1231	259?	2.2	11.8	11.8?
Tajín	1102	232?	2.3	29.4	29.4?
Aguacate	777	163?	2.8	22.9	22.9?
Panajachel, Guatemala	688-780	145-164?	2.8-2.9	16.4	5.2?
Ramah, Navaho	614-634	129-133?	3.1	4.9	5.6
Havasupai	177	39	5.7	——	7.5-16.2
Australian aborigines	100-1500	20.7-316?	2.0-7.8	——	3.5-10.5
Ranchos of Quiroga	133 avg.	28?	6.7	10.3	10.3?
Camayurá, Brazil	110	23?	7.4	11.8-13.6	11.8-13.6?

The figures which are questioned represent rough estimates. See text for description of methods and assumptions involved.

average admixture rate of 7.5% for the widely scattered tribes which he studied.

It is interesting to speculate whether admixture rates for communities of small or moderate size are sufficiently low for a random genetic drift free enough from the offsetting factor of admixture to be important in race formation. In island communities such as Pitcairn and Tristan da Cunha the admixture rate may be low enough and the breeding population small enough for random genetic drift to be important, at least for a limited number of generations. However, the opportunities for a subsequent rapid expansion of population and establishment of a racial type as a result of the previous genetic drift would seem minimal on small islands. Whether small dependent communities like Quiroga's *ranchos* could provide for such drift and expansion would seem worthy of further investigation.

Table 1 summarizes the estimates for rates of genetic drift and admixture. As only the data for Paracho was collected for this purpose, the other estimates are not of equal value. Calculation of the effective size of the breeding population in the other communities (and hence the estimate of rates of random genetic drift) is based on the assumption that the variability in average number of offspring is the same as that adduced for Paracho. This assumption is only justified for crude estimations. The excess in family size above that for a stable population (3.4 rather than 2) is at least in part ascribable to the fact that Paracho is growing. For the rest, the excess is due to the form of the census—the size of the nuclear family having been lenos "having at least some Panajachel blood or family connec-determined rather than the number of adult offspring achieving marriage. With stable or decreasing populations the family size would be smaller, smaller families would be less variable, hence the size of the "effective breeding population" would be larger. The values given for random genetic drift in Table 1 therefore may be somewhat overestimated. The findings shown in Table 1 give no reason to suppose any simple relationship between size of the breeding population and rate of admixture. Birdsell ('51), speaking of the aboriginal tribes of Australia, says that tribal boundaries are primary barriers to intermixture, but that the remnants of decimated tribes are sometimes absorbed by others. Oberg mentions that one of the tribes of the Upper Xingú in Brazil, the Iwalapeti, number 28 persons but have no village and live scattered among other tribes; they plan, however, to rebuild their village. This mechanism making for a minimum limit to the possible size of a group may be less—rather than more—apparent among sedentary agriculturists, for the tiny *ranchos* of Quiroga are reported to maintain moderately low admixture rates.

From our limited sample of communities there is no clear correlation between rates of admixture and cultural level. The nomadic Australian, the semi-agricultural Havasupai, the pastoral Navaho, the *rancheros* of Quiroga, the truck farmers of Panajachel, the farmer-fisherman of Tzintzuntzan, and the farmer-merchants of Mitla have low rates of admixture. Apparently in some towns with specialized small industries and highly developed trade (Paracho and Quiroga) and even in agricultural towns, if their structure is less cohesive (Tajín and Aguacate), a higher admixture rate may prevail. One would like to learn more about the population size and exogamy rate of additional communities of various types.

One other assumption, concerning the connection between the racial evolutionary genetic model and the empirical data available, is that admixture does not greatly alter the genetic composition in the area from which subsequent admixture will come. This simply means that those marrying into a town are assumed to come from varied and widely distributed communities and not just from a few small dependent villages.

In the cases cited this assumption seems well founded. Migrants to Paracho have come from over 175 places, half of them over 50 km away. The 41 immigrant parents of persons born in Mitla have come from 16 places, half of them over 20 km from Mitla. Of the 145 immigrant residents of Tzintzuntzan, Foster ('48) reports that 91 were born within a radius of 15 km, 46 others were born in the state, and 8 were born in other states of Mexico. Similarly, for the county seat of Quiroga, 135 of the persons came from the *ranchos*, 4 from other villages of the *municipio,* 389 from various adjacent *municipios,* 134 from other places in the state of Michoacán and 56 from elsewhere. For the *ranchos* of Quiroga, 18 were from the town, 21 from another *rancho,* 59 from adjacent *municipios,* and 5 from elsewhere (Brand, '51). In the case of Tajín the migrants came from at least 27 different places, and although these were all Totonac places, some of the parents and grandparents had come from non-Totonac communities. In the case of Aguacate, Kelly and Palerm ('52) list 23 other places of birth and state: "Here again we have the impression that the local population is in a considerable state of flux, but that the essential elements are all Totonac, from the lowlands about Papantla." Although most of the admixture of Havasupai was due to matings with Walapai, four other tribes are also mentioned by Spier ('28) as occasionally involved. According to Kluckhohn and Griffith ('51), 90 persons born in Ramah had one parent from elsewhere. The parents were Navaho from various other groups in 70 cases, and in the remaining cases they came from 6 other tribes. The 13 to 15 persons of other tribes living among the Camayurá came from 4 tribes, only one of which is one of the friendly neighboring groups, while approximately half the outsiders are captives of war (Oberg, '53). For the Australian aborigines, too, each group for whom any quantity of data is available, usually has instances of intermarriage with more than one group, and there is frequent mixture between non-contiguous groups (Tindale, '53).

In conclusion, I should like to urge the collection, from a variety of human populations at different cultural levels, of data on size of the breeding population and rates of admixture. In conjunction with estimates of mutation rates and hypotheses concerning rates of natural selection, the genetic model now available should permit the elaboration of a theory of rates of human evolution. Such a theory would be independent of estimates based on the fossil record or on counts of changing frequencies of characteristics in contemporary or recent peoples; it provides a new method of approach to the problem.

SUMMARY

In various Middle American communities residents born elsewhere range from about 5% to at least 35% of the population. Rates of admixture may range from 3.5% to 21%. Population size for the communities studied ranges from 110 to 4,593 and the size of the effective breeding populations is probably only one-fifth of this. Random genetic drift in populations of this size may vary around 1% to 8%. There is no inverse relation between community size and rate of admixture, and even small communities may be largely endogamous. Immigrants usually come from enough different and sufficiently distant places so that, for present purposes, the immigrants reasonably can be assumed to be drawn from a population approaching infinity in size. Under the assumption of negligible natural selection and mutation, the effect of such demographic facts on human evolution (through random genetic drift and admixture) is determinable. Calculation of theoretical rates of evolution over many generations on the foregoing basis would afford an estimate independent of those based on the fossil record or on changing frequencies of characters in contemporary and recent peoples.

REFERENCES

Birdsell, J. B.: Some implications of the genetical concept of race in terms of spatial analysis, *Cold Spring Harbor Symposia on Quantitative Biology, 15*:259-314, Cold Spring Harbor, The Biological Laboratory, 1951.

Brand, D. D.: *Quiroga, A Mexican Municipio,* Washington, Smithsonian Institution, 1951.

Foster, G. M.: *Empire's Children, the People of Tzintzuntzan,* Washington, Smithsonian Institution, 1948.

Jones, C. F.: Demographic patterns in the Papago Indian Village of Chuichu, Arizona, *Human Biol., 25*:191-202, 1953.

Kaplan, B.: Ethnic identification in an Indian Mestizo community. I. Socio-cultural factors, *Phylon, 14*:179-186, 1953.

Kelly, I. and Palerm, A.: *The Tajin Totonac. I. History, Subsistence, Shelter and Technology,* Washington, Smithsonian Institution, 1952.

Kluckhohn, C. and Griffith, C.: Population genetics and social anthropology, *Cold Spring Harbor Symposia on Quantitative Biology, 15*: 401-408, Cold Spring Harbor, The Biological Laboratory, 1951.

Lasker, G. W.: Mixture and genetic drift in ongoing human evolution, *Am. Anthropol., 54*:433-436, 1952.

Lasker, G. W.: Ethnic identification in an Indian Mestizo community. II. Racial characteristics, *Phylon, 14*:187-190, 1953.

Oberg, K.: *Indian Tribes of Northern Mato Grosso, Brazil,* Washington, Smithsonian Institution, 1953.

Parsons, E. C.: *Mitla, Town of the Souls,* Chicago, University of Chicago Press, 1936.

Spier, L.: Havasupai ethnography, *Anthropol. Papers Am. Museum Nat. Hist., 29*:1928.

Spuhler, J. N. and Kluckhohn, C.: Inbreeding coefficients of the Ramah Navaho population, *Human Biol., 25*:301, 1953.

Tax, S.: *Penny Capitalism, a Guatemalan Indian Economy,* Washington, Smithsonian Institution, 1953.

Tindale, N. B.: Tribal and intertribal marriage among the Australian aborigines, *Human Biol., 25*:169-190, 1953.

Wright, S.: The role of mutation, inbreeding, crossbreeding and selection in evolution, *Proc. 6th Intl. Congr. of Genetics 1*:356-366, 1932.

Genetic Drift in a Religious Isolate; An Analysis of the Causes of Variation in Blood Group and Other Gene Frequencies in a Small Population

Reprinted, with the exception of one figure, from *The American Naturalist*, Vol. 86, No. 828, pp. 145-159 (1952).

By Bentley Glass, Milton S. Sacks, Elsa F. Jahn, *and* Charles Hess

By general recognition race is now increasingly defined in terms of differing gene frequencies, and the origin of such differences has become of very great interest. Sewall Wright, in a notable series of papers ('31, '32, '40, '43, '48) has developed the theoretical aspects of the interaction of the four factors which can upset existing gene frequency equilibria and establish new gene frequencies, namely, mutation, selection, migration, and genetic drift. In particular, he has pointed out the limitation upon the effectiveness of mutation, migration, and selection pressure in those populations wherein $4Nv$, $4Nm$, or $4Ns$, respectively, are less than 1 (N = effective size of the population; v = mutation rate; m = net migration rate; s = coefficient of selection pressure). Whenever v, m, and s are less than $1/2N$, genetic drift sets in. That is to say, gene frequencies oscillate about their equilibria, the oscillations become larger in magnitude as the population size becomes smaller, and the cumulative effect over a number of generations may lead to the elimination of some alleles and the fixation of others, as well as to any intermediate frequencies. Wright ('48) has calculated that this can happen even in populations of an effective size up to 250,000 when the mutation rate is of the order of 10^{-6} and when selection and migration are also extremely low. By observation, we know that mutation and migration may quite often be so low as that. It is far more difficult to show that competing alleles are sufficiently neutral to satisfy this condition.

166

Fisher and Ford ('47, '50) have studied the fluctuations in frequency of a gene in an isolated population of the moth *Panaxia dominula* L. over a period of eight years, and this study has been extended by Sheppard ('51) to cover four additional years, through 1950. Considerable fluctuations in the gene frequency of the medionigra gene were observed in a population calculated to be too large for such shifts to be attributable to genetic drift. This may be so. Still, to prove that the fluctuations in the frequencies of the alleles at one locus are due to selection rather than genetic drift has no direct bearing on the question whether the fluctuations at some other locus are attributable to the one or the other. If the critical size of the population is $\frac{1}{2s}$, then a population (say of 10^4 individuals) which is "enormous" with respect to a gene having a selection value of 0.2 will be "small" with respect to a gene at some other locus for which $s = 0.0001$. The real difficulty, as Sheppard has pointed out, is to be sure that characters of neutral survival value actually are such, especially since survival value undoubtedly, in many cases such as that of the medionigra gene, itself varies from year to year and place to place.

In the application of these concepts to human evolution and the origin of human racial differences, it must be kept in mind that "throughout the greater part of his history the . . . breeding populations of man appear to have been very small. Peoples at the lower hunter stage of cultural development at the present day rarely if ever attain a breeding population size of 1,000" (Montagu, '50:329). It is also important to remember that the genetically effective size of a population is characteristically smaller, often very much smaller, than the number of individuals it contains. In a fluctuating population which undergoes periodic reductions in size, N is the harmonic mean of the maximum and minimum sizes of N and is therefore very much closer to the minimum. According to Wright, if n_0 and $10^6 N_0$ are the respective minima and maxima in a 7-generation cycle, then N = $6.3 N_0$. Probably many existing human populations are the derivates of once very small genetic isolates which have undergone an explosive increase in size, either at the dawn of agriculture or later. In that case gene frequencies in different races might well reflect the fortuitous results of genetic drift in the original isolates, since in a population with an effective size of 200 an allele would require a selective advantage of 0.01 to avoid the action of drift, and consequently many genes might be effectively neutral.

Numerous examples of divergent gene frequencies in small and relatively isolated human populations are to be found. One of the most extensive studies of this sort of situation is the contribution by Birdsell to the 1950 Cold Spring Harbor Symposium. Birdsell found "inter-isolate fluctuations suggestive of genetic drift" in the native tribes of Australia, which average about 500 persons in size (N, ca. 200) and correspond approximately to genetic isolates. The very plausible attribution of such differences by Birdsell and others (Birdsell and Boyd, '40; Boyd, '50; Laughlin, '50; Montagu, '50; Dobzhansky, '50) to genetic drift has, however, been challenged by those who hold that all such differences are more probably attributable to differential selection. The interesting discussion on this point between Cain, Birdsell, and Dobzhansky (Birdsell, '50) has served to emphasize that genetic drift and selection are not alternative explanations but are factors which may often act in conjunction, as Sewall Wright has constantly maintained. Nevertheless, the conclusion that genetic drift is at all responsible for the observed differences in gene frequencies in the Australian tribes is rendered uncertain by the possibility that selection might operate in these circumstances and be the chief or sole cause of the genetic differences.

What appears to be needed for a clearer solution of this problem is the analysis of a genetic isolate of known size, age, and origin and which in particular shares an environment indistinguishable from that of the major population with which it is to be compared. The situation ideal for study would be that of a genetic isolate interspersed within a larger population, so intermingled that the individuals of the isolate do not differ from those of the general population in any aspect of life except their assortative breeding restrictions. The requirement is to find a type of isolate neither geographic nor economic, since such isolation factors might indeed be correlated with selective factors. Nor is an ethnic isolate very suitable, since in such a case one would presumably have to deal with initial differences in gene frequency as well as with possible differences in environment that might have a selective effect. The very type of isolate desired exists, however, in the communities of certain endogamous religious sects.

RELIGIOUS ISOLATES

A significant study of this type has been made by Sanghvi and Khanolkar ('49), who have reported that in six endogamous groups (castes or subdivisions of castes) in India the frequencies of blood group genes (ABO, A_1A_2, MN, P, and Rh) and of the genes for P. T. C. taste capacity and color vision differ significantly in many intergroup comparisons. Two closely related groups were identical. Of the remainder, "the endogamous groups V. N. B. and C. K. P. differ from all the three other groups and from each other in more than two characters, with a high degree of significance. The group K. B. differs significantly from the groups D. B. and M. K. in only one character, viz. OAB blood groups. Groups D. B. and M. K. do not show significant differences between them for any character." The gene frequency analysis of the Indian population is clearly not properly carried out unless due attention is given to the existence of these endogamous groups. As to the causes of the differences, however, nothing certain can be said. Although the groups studied were all Hindu, the size of only one of them is given, and it is large (3,650,504 persons in the Bombay Presidency). Others are presumably much smaller, but may still number 10,000 persons or more. No historical record is available regarding the origin of these endogamous groups. As to their similarity of environment (nutrition, medical care, etc.), it is by no means clear that extensive differences do not exist. Consequently it seems impossible to conclude that the differences are entirely due to a single variable, and rather likely that both selection and "migration" have played their part. Only genetic drift would appear to be ruled out, except in so far as the isolates were once of small effective size or the genes concerned essentially neutral as to selection.

In the United States similar, but smaller endogamous religious groups exist. In some of these, such as the Amish, the religious community is in fact a microgeographic isolate. In others, the individuals are dispersed in the general community. Their children go to the public schools, and their homes, clothing, food, medical care, and hygiene exhibit no distinctions of magnitude in contrast to the generality of the population. A comparison of the gene frequencies in such an isolate with those of the surrounding population should indicate more decisively than previous studies the extent to which genetic drift can cause gene frequencies to vary.

This paper is a preliminary report of the study of one such religious isolate, a study conducted by Mr. Charles Hess of the religious community, and by Dr. Milton Sacks, Miss Elsa Jahn, and myself, of the Baltimore Rh Typing Laboratory. Much of the detailed analysis remains to be completed, but enough is apparent at this point to throw some light, I believe, on the effectiveness of genetic drift in altering gene frequencies in human populations.

THE DUNKER ISOLATE

The religious isolate studied is an Old Order "Dunker" (Old German Baptist Brethren) community in Franklin County, Pa. It includes 298 adults and minor children (over 3 years of age and under 21), and a total of about 350 persons when adults are included who, although not members of the religious group themselves, are the children of members and still live in the locality. The effective size of the population may be estimated directly. Among white Americans at the present time, according to Dublin ('51), the average age of mothers at the birth of their children is 26 years. The average age of all fathers is 30 years. Thus 28 years may be taken as the current length of generation. In the Dunker isolate the age distribution of individuals is in good agreement with that of the general population, so that 28 years may be taken as the length of generation in the isolate too. By actual enumeration, persons within the isolate aged 1 to 28 years had 90 parents also belonging to the isolate. This seems to be the best estimate of N. Among living members of the community, both for the generation 1895-1923 and for 1904-1931, there were 84 persons who were parents. Thus a confirmatory value for N of slightly under 100 is obtained. In a population of such size and in the absence of mutation, selection, or immigration, according to Wright, $\frac{1}{2N}$, i.e., in the present case 1/180 or 0.555 percent of the loci will become fixed or eliminated in each generation. If the number of gene loci in the human species is roughly 20,000, and if no more than 10 percent of these are variable in the population, then 11 loci would become fixed per generation under the stipulated conditions. The number of loci that would show detectable drift would of course be far greater. Actually, since at least immigration is considerable in the present case, the tendency toward equilibrium will offset the effect of genetic drift to a considerable extent. Instead of fixation one would expect only wide fluctuations around the expected gene frequencies.

It was hoped that we could study 100 percent of the individuals making up the group, but the time and effort required to get in touch with the last few persons has proved prohibitive. At the present time genetic information has been obtained on 265 persons, of whom 231 are among the 298 persons coming within the more strict definition of the isolate. The general sampling of the isolate is therefore 77.5 percent complete, although for individual characteristics the sampling is somewhat less adequate because of the omission or failure of certain tests or items of information. It seems very unlikely, even so, that complete sampling would change the results to any significant degree.

The history of the isolate is briefly as follows. The sect of the German Baptist Brethren was established in 1708 in the Rhineland, Krefeld being a chief center. In 1719 there was a migration of 28 persons from Schwartzenau and the vicinity to Germantown, Pennsylvania. These German Baptists were later joined by others, the number being uncertain but probably several hundred, the majority coming mainly from the same German region, although at least one man was a scion of the nobility of Saxony.   In 1881 the sect split into three groups, the largest being the Church of the Brethren, and the next largest the Progressive Church, while a small minority, the most orthodox in retaining the original practices of the German Baptist Brethren, formed the third group.   It is this sect, the Old German Baptist Brethren, which provided the community studies as an isolate in the present project.   There are at the present time about 3,500 members in approximately 55 communities belonging to the sect, located as follows:

Pennsylvania	3	Illinois	2
Maryland	1	Missouri	2
Ohio	16	Michigan	3
West Virginia	2	Wisconsin	1
Virginia	4	North Carolina	1
Indiana	10	Florida	1
Kansas	5	California	3
		Canada	1

Individuals of the sect dress distinctively, but not to the degree practiced by the Amish.   The sect does not maintain separate parochial schools, nor does the general way of life of its members differ perceptibly from that of other Americans of the same localities.

It follows that the isolate may be regarded as having been in existence as a religious community in America for over two centuries, with a drastic restriction in the size of the mating group having occurred 70 years ago.   The religious community in Franklin County, Pennsylvania, now comprises some 20 extended families, each composed of one to more than a dozen families.   A tabulation indicates that over a period of 3 generations approximately one-fourth of the persons reaching adulthood have left the religious group in each generation.   These losses are compensated in the most part by the large sizes of the families, so that the size of the group has remained quite stable. There are relatively few childless marriages.   In the generation 1895-1923, 85 percent of persons now living are parents, and only 2 percent were married but childless. In the generation 1904-1931, only 73.6 percent of those now living are parents, but of course this lower proportion is to be expected because more persons in the group are young and either unmarried or very recently married. The sizes of the families in one extended family were 5.4, 5.25, 3.78, and 3.2 children per family in succeeding generations. In spite of the decline, this is even now well above the replacement level of 2.83 (Dublin, '51).

A tally of all known marriages of members born since 1850 yields the following information about gene flow into the isolate. About 64 percent of the members of the isolate marry other members of the group (48% of all marriages, A). The frequency of endogamous marriage has remained surprisingly constant over the past three generations. About 9 percent (13% of all marriages, B) marry individuals of other communities of the sect, mainly from the adjacent community in Frederick County, Maryland. Nearly 27 percent of the members have married non-members, 10 percent with those who remained non-members (15% of all marriages, C) and 16.5 percent with persons who entered the community as converts (24% of all marriages, D). With very few exceptions, the marriages with non-members who remain such represent losses to the isolate rather than gains. Hence the maximum gene flow into the isolate is $B + D/2 (A + B + D)$, or 22.0 percent. In actuality this is diminished by the degree to which the contributing communities of the sect or locality resemble the isolate in composition by corresponding deviations from the general average of the population of the United States. This reduction might well be as much as 8 percent. Dr. Sewall Wright (by letter) has kindly provided a rough estimate of m, the gene flow into the isolate, by another method. This is based on the calculation of the inbreeding coefficient

$$\left\{ F = \frac{\sigma_q^2}{q_r (1 - q_r)} = \frac{1}{4Nm + 1} \right\}$$

from the gene frequencies in the Dunker isolate (q) and in the U. S. population (q_r) for the six genes I^A, I^B, I^O, M, r and dht. The estimate of F is .0254, from which it follows that $Nm = 9.3$

and m is about .10. This appears to be of about the order of magnitude expected from the previous considerations. The gene flow into the isolate will therefore be regarded as amounting to 10 or 15 percent per generation.

The genes lost to the isolate by emigration might be considered to represent a random sample were it not for the effect of the emigration of family units in addition to single individuals. About 8 percent of the married couples moved away from the geographic area covered by the isolate. Most of these emigrants were young, their families still in the future at the time of leaving. Thus for these cases too the loss to the isolate was random. The non-random losses must be few. To illustrate: within the isolate at the present time there are 25 persons with distal hyperextensibility of the thumb. Of these, no less than 10 belong to one extended family, comprising one couple of grandparents and the families of their five children. Had this entire family moved out of the isolate, the frequency of the doublejointed trait mentioned would be shifted from 16.8 percent to 12.6 percent, and the difference from the general population in this respect would be even more striking than it is (see Table 5).

Inasmuch as the isolate has remained small and rather stable in size since 1881 in spite of high fecundity, it is obvious that the loss of individuals through their removal to other regions or through their failure to remain in the sect has been considerable. The maintenance of the group as a genetic isolate has thus depended not so much on the failure of marriages with outsiders to occur, as rather upon the characteristic exclusion from the group of those who do marry outside. The equilibrium is maintained by high fecundity. Thus in each generation the influx of approximately 10 or 15 percent of genes from the general population, an influx which tends to make gene frequencies in the isolate more like those of the general population, is opposed in part by the effect of genetic drift resulting from the chance exclusion of approximately 10 percent of the genes within the isolate. The genetic drift resulting from accidents of sampling because of the small effective size of the population (N) appears therefore in this community to be compounded of three elements: (a) the accidental composition of the original community in Franklin County; (b) the effects in each generation of the random sampling of gametes in a very small population; and (c) the chance exclusion of genes borne by those who leave the community.

THE GENETIC CHARACTERS ANALYZED

The primary criteria for characters suitable for the analysis of gene frequencies in a human population may be stated, to paraphrase Boyd ('50), as follows:

A useful anthropological character must be inherited according to a known mechanism, preferably simple. It must be accurately, and preferably easily, classifiable. It should be relatively stable and non-adaptive. It must be relatively common, not rare. It must vary in frequency in different populations. If it is morphological rather than physiological, and if it is a feature of parts that endure after the death of the individual, i.e., if it is skeletal, so much the better.

The number of such traits known at the present time is decidedly limited, and when one is further limited by lack of reliable data as to frequency in one or both of the general populations (West German and United States) to be compared with the isolate in question, the restriction is indeed severe. In the present study the traits used were the following: ABO blood groups; MN blood groups; Rh blood groups; Middigital hair; Distal hyperextensibility of the thumb; Ear lobes; Handedness. It was intended also to include taste capacity for phenylthiocarbamide (PTC), but owing to an unfortunate technical error a test solution was used that is below the sensory threshold for even the majority of genetic tasters, and for the present this very useful trait must be omitted. The others will be discussed in order.

The ABO Blood Groups: Samples of blood cells were collected from the individuals, diluted in physiological saline solution, and transported to the Baltimore Rh Testing Laboratory for ABO, MN, and Rh typing. Because of unavoidable delays, some samples became hemolyzed en route, and since it was not always

TABLE 1

FREQUENCIES OF ABO BLOOD GROUPS

	No.	A	B	AB	O		
(1) W. Germany* (Duisberg)	5,036	2,245 44.6%	504 10.0%	237 4.7%	2,050 40.7%	} $\chi^2 = 25.47$	
(2) Dunker Isolate	228	135 59.3%	7 3.1%	5 2.2%	81 35.5%		
(3) U.S.A.† (New York City and N. Car.)	30,000	11,840 39.5%	3,350 11.2%	1,250 4.2%	13,560 45.2%	$\chi^2 = 42.14$ D. F. = 3 $P \ll .001$	
(1) and (2)		P = nearly .001	P = nearly .001	P = .10-.05	P = .30-.20		
(2) and (3)		$P \ll .001$	$P < .001$	P = .20-.10	P = .05-.02		

GENE FREQUENCIES

	W. Germany	Dunker Isolate	U.S.A.
I^A	.2862	.3778	.2583
I^B	.0743	.0253	.0409
I^O	.6395	.5969	.7008

*Data of Rinkel (from Boyd, 1939).
†Combined data of Tiber and Snyder (from Boyd, 1939).

possible to replace these samples, the total number of tested individuals is below the total number of individuals from the isolate who supplied genetic information for the survey. Table 1 presents the frequencies of the four major ABO blood groups in the isolate in comparison with the frequencies in West Germany and in the United States, taken from Boyd ('39). It is at once apparent that whereas the frequencies in West Germany and in the United States are very similar, those found in the isolate are very different from either. As the χ^2 values show, the deviation is highly significant, and the partition of χ^2 shows that this is due to a marked increase in the frequency of type A and a decrease in that of type B (and AB). The frequency of type O is probably also significantly lower in the isolate than in the U. S. population. The lower portion of the table gives the calculation of the gene frequencies for the three alleles I^A, I^B, and I^O, according to Fisher's new formulae (see Race and Sanger, '50, p. 21). No combination of values of the frequency of I^A as high as that in the Dunker isolate, nor of I^B as low, have ever previously been reported for a group of Western European origin. One must search among American Indians, Polynesians, or Eskimos to find the like.

The individual origin of the 7 individuals of type B and the 5 of type AB throws added light on the low frequency of the I^B allele in the isolate. Two of type B and one of type AB are children of others in the group of 12. Three of type B and one of type AB are members from another community who entered the isolate by marriage. Two of type B and two of type AB entered the group from the local community by marriage. Of them all, therefore, only one person, of type AB, is of parents both of whom were born in the isolate. The father of this person, presumably of type B or AB since his wife was found to belong to group A, was among those from whom samples of blood were not obtained. It thus appears that the gene I^B had virtually disappeared from the isolate prior to the recent reintroductions from outside.

Subtyping for A_1 and A_2 was also carried out, although not shown in the table. Of 140 type A or AB individuals, 128 were found to be A_1 or A_1B; 12 were A_2 or A_2B. The ratio of A_2/A_1 is given by Boyd ('39) as 0.20 to 0.23 in W. Germany. Values for the United States are quite variant, Wiener and Rothberg (Wiener, '35) finding 0.48 in 440 individuals typed in New York City, whereas Landsteiner and Levine ('30) obtained a ratio of 0.136 in 194 individuals in the same city. At any rate, the ratio in the United States is probably not very different from that in Western Europe, which is in general above 0.20. The ratio for the Dunker isolate of A_2/A_1 is 0.09. This is significantly different from the combined values for W. Germany obtained in Heidelberg and Köln ($\chi^2 = 7.43$; D.F. $= 1$; P less than .01).

The data presented for the ABO blood types show that whereas in the general population of the United States, in comparison with W. Germany, type O has increased somewhat, no such increase has occurred in the isolate. Instead, type A shows a

TABLE 2

FREQUENCIES OF MN BLOOD GROUPS

	No.	M	MN	N	
(1) W. Germany* (Bonn, Frankfurt am Main, and Köln)	6,800	2,028 29.85%	3,396 49.9%	1,376 20.2%	$\chi^2 = 23.68$
(2) Dunker Isolate	229	102 44.5%	96 41.9%	31 13.5%	
(3) U. S. A.† (Brooklyn, New York City, and Columbus, Ohio)	6,129	1,787 29.16%	3,039 49.58%	1,303 21.26%	

D.F. $= 2$

P $\ll$ .001   P $= .10 - .05$ P $= .05 - .02$ P $\ll$ .001

GENE FREQUENCIES

	W. Germany	Dunker Isolate	U. S. A.
M	.548	.655	.540
N	.452	.345	.460

*Combined data of Crome, Laubenheimer, and Laves (from Boyd, 1939).
† Combined data of Landsteiner and Levine, Wiener, Herman and Derby, and Hyman (from Wiener, 1935).

significant increase, particularly in subtype A_1; and type B has reached the vanishing point. It is worth noting in particular that in the isolate the most extreme departure from the expected gene frequencies (a reduction by two-thirds) applies to the allele which has the lowest frequency in Western Europe and America, namely, I^B, and the least departure from expectancy applies to the allele which is most common, namely, I^O. This would seem to be expected from the combination of genetic drift and the lower reliability of estimates of small frequencies. On the other hand, there is no reasonable ground for supposing that within the isolate selection can be acting strongly in favor of I^A while in the general United States population the frequency of I^A has been reduced below that which prevails in West Germany.

The MN Blood Groups: In Table 2 are given the frequencies of the M, MN, and N groups and the calculated gene frequencies of M and N. Again it is apparent that the frequencies are significantly different, M being increased and N decreased by approximately 10 percent. One must look among the Finns, Russians, and Caucasians, or in the Near East for frequencies comparable to these in the isolate. These M and N alleles seem particularly suitable for the purpose of the present study, for their almost equal commonness in nearly all human populations implies either that they are selectively neutral, or that the heterozygote is superior to either homozygote, or that a condition of balanced polymorphism prevails, with now M and now N superior to the other. The considerable decline in the frequency of heterozygotes in the isolate, compared with the frequencies in either of the base populations, rules out the possibility of the superiority of the heterozygote; and the identity of general environment of the isolate and the U. S. general population at least greatly weakens the likelihood of balanced polymorphism. Genetic drift is the remaining explanation.

The Rh Blood Groups: The frequencies of the Rh types are given in Table 3. No testing for the alleles C^w, C^u, c^v, or D^u was carried out. Not only were testing sera unavailable, but in any case no data for the frequencies of these alleles in the base popu-

TABLE 3
FREQUENCIES OF RH BLOOD TYPES

	No.	rh	rh'	rh"	rh'"	Rh_0	Rh_1	Rh_2	$Rh_{1.2}$	
(1) England*	2,000	307	16	19	—	42	1,062	279	275	Actual
		15.10%	0.77%	0.94%	0.02%	2.06%	53.40%	14.08%	13.63%	Theor.
(2) Dunker Isolate	206	23	—	—	—	2	119	32	30	
		11.15%				0.97%	57.9%	15.5%	14.5%	
(3) U.S.A.† (N.Y.C.)	8,317	1,204	89	47	1	187	4,456	1,225	1,108	
		14.48%	1.07%	0.56%	0.01%	2.25%	53.58%	14.73%	13.32%	

$\chi^2 = 2.0 \ (1,2)$
$P = .20 - .10$

$\chi^2 = 4.32 - 4.51$
$P = .05 - .02$

$\chi^2 = 7.01$
D.F. $= 4$
$P = .20 - .10$

*Combined data of (a) Fisher and Race, and (b) Race, Mourant, Lawler, and Sanger (from Race, Mourant, Lawler, and Sanger, 1948).

†Combined data of (a) Unger, Weinberg, and Lefkon, and (b) Wiener (from Race and Sanger, 1950).

lations are available.

In contrast to the ABO and MN groups, the Rh frequencies in the isolate present a pattern that conforms closely to the standard for England and the United States. (No frequencies for the subtypes in any German population could be located.) The only deviation of possible significance is found by grouping the rarer types rh', rh", and Rh_o. There seems to be a reduction in these rare types within the isolate. There is a small decrease of type rh, but the data are not extensive enough to indicate whether this has significance or not. The commoner types may have increased slightly within the isolate.

The most significant aspect of these data is perhaps the indication that even in an isolate of size sufficiently small to allow genetic drift to operate, still only some of the genes drift in frequency. This is again in accord with theory.

TABLE 4

FREQUENCIES OF MID-DIGITAL HAIR TYPES

	No.	Md_0	Md_1	Md_2	Md_3	Md_4	Others	
(1) Dunker Isolate	234	123	44	23	28	5	11	
		52.5%	19.7%	9.8%	11.9%	2.1%	4.9%	$\chi^2 = 72.8$
(2) Baltimore more	541	146	65	91	146	55	38	
White (56% ♂♂)		26.99%	12.01%	16.82%	26.99%	10.17%	7.02%	
								D.F. = 5
χ^2		30.8	5.3	5.4	16.4	13.5	1.4	P<<.001
P		<<.001	.05 — .02	.05 — .02	<.001	<.001	.30 — .20	

Middigital Hair Types: In Table 4 are presented the frequencies for the five main types of middigital hair pattern, supposed to be inherited through a series of multiple alleles, with dominance in ascending order from Md_0 to Md_4. Regrettably, no data on middigital hair patterns from any German population seem to have been compiled. Our own control series represents frequencies from Whites of Baltimore, Maryland, from a study by

Mr. Henry Plaine, to whom thanks are due for making these data available. The frequency of expression of middigital hair is higher in males than in females. In the Baltimore series, data were taken mainly from high school students, of whom a majority (56 percent) were males. In the Dunker isolate, because of the greater difficulty of getting in touch with adult males than with adult females or children, there was a preponderance of females (55.4 percent). Even with correction for the sex difference, the two distributions yield a χ^2 of 65, which for D.F. = 5 gives a P value $<<.001$. The partition of χ^2 indicates a highly significant increase in the frequency of fingers without hair on the middigital segment, counterbalanced by a significant decrease in frequency of individuals with hair in this segment on three or four fingers.

TABLE 5

FREQUENCY OF DISTAL HYPEREXTENSIBILITY OF THE THUMB

	No.	*Dht*	*dht/dht*	
(1) Dunker Isolate	149	124 83.2%	25 16.8%	
				$\chi^2 = 4.36$
(2) Baltimore Whites	895	674 75.3%	221 24.7%	
				D.F. = 1
		P = .05 — .02		

Distal Hyperextensibility of the Thumb: This trait has recently been studied by Glass and Kistler (unpub.) and has been demonstrated to be due to a Mendelian recessive with a gene frequency of .496 and a penetrance of 96.5 percent. Inclusion of examination for this trait was begun in the study of the Dunker isolate only well along in the work, so that the number of individuals scored is much below the total examined for other traits. In Table 5 the results are given. The frequency of this type of double-jointedness is significantly lower in the isolate than in the Baltimore white population studied (P = .05 — .02). The most striking finding is not indicated in the table, namely, that of the

25 individuals with the recessive trait, no less than ten belong to a single family (three generations) in which both parents, and consequently all children, were affected. It follows that the frequency of the gene *dht* in the remainder of the families making up the isolate must be even lower than the frequency .41 which is the square root of the frequency of the trait.

TABLE 6

EAR LOBES

	Attached	*Unattached*	*Total*
Dunker Isolate	61 25.3%	180 74.7%	241
Baltimore Whites	154 40.5%	226 59.5%	380
$\chi^2 = 15.2$	D.F. = 1		P<.001

Ear Lobes: The control series from Baltimore is not as representative of the surrounding U. S. population in Southern Pennsylvania as perhaps might be wished, but it is all that is available at present. The data indicate a considerable and significant difference between the two populations in this minor anatomical trait, which is regarded as a single gene difference with free lobes dominant over attached lobes.

Handedness: The frequency of lefthanded plus ambidexterous individuals in the Dunker isolate is 17/243, or 7.8 percent. This does not appear to be significantly different from the frequency of lefthandedness in the general population. Rife ('45) gives a summary of pooled data for the U. S. population: 93 percent righthanded; 3 percent ambidexterous; 4 percent completely lefthanded. The total of 7 percent agrees very closely with the frequency in the Dunker isolate, so that in this characteristic, which may well be subject to selection, no deviation is apparent.

DISCUSSION

It is sufficiently apparent from this study that in isolates of about 250 to 350 individuals, and in which N is under 100, considerable deviations in gene frequency occur, both in comparison with the frequencies in the population of origin of the isolate and also with those in the surrounding population. These genetic differences can develop and be maintained, in spite of a gene inflow of 10 or 15 percent per generation, when promoted by chance sampling of the population in the accidental composition of the original individuals, by the random sampling of gametes in a small population, and by the chance exclusion of genes borne by those who elect to leave the isolate. The study has included analyses of 7 loci, at 3 of which there occur series of multiple alleles that to some extent can vary independently. At 5 of these loci variations in gene frequencies have occurred that are most reasonably attributable to genetic drift. Considering the degrees of freedom among the multiple allelic series, there are in all 15 degrees of genetic freedom between alleles at the 7 loci in the analysis. Eleven of these manifest deviations from the base populations significant at the 5 percent level. Considering the fact that the traits studied are in all cases common and considering also the homogeneity of environment of the individuals comprising the isolate and those in the surrounding American population, it seems unnecessary to attribute these divergences to some hypothetical influence of selection. In fact, the very loci where selection most demonstrably operates, namely, the Rh and handedness loci, are those where no appreciable drift appears to have occurred.

The conclusion to be derived from the study, that genetic drift can in fact determine gene frequencies to a considerable extent in small human isolates, is still a tentative one. The present analysis should serve chiefly to call attention to a method of attacking the problem and to the existence near at hand of genetic isolates particularly suitable for its investigation.

REFERENCES

Birdsell, J. B.:   Some implications of the genetical concept in race in terms of spatial analysis, *Cold Spring Harbor Symposia on Quantitative Biology*, *15*:259-314, Cold Spring Harbor, The Biological Laboratory, 1950.

Birdsell, J. B. and Boyd, W. C.:   Blood groups in the Australian aborigines, *Am. J. Phys. Anthropol.*, *27*:69-90, 1940.

Boyd, W. C.:   Blood groups, *Tab. Biol.*, *17*:113-240, 1939.

Boyd, W. C.:   *Genetics and the Races of Man*, Boston, Little, Brown, 1950.

Dobzhansky, Th.:   Human diversity and adaptation, *Cold Spring Harbor Symposia on Quantitative Biology*, *15*:385-400, Cold Spring Harbor, The Biological Laboratory, 1950.

Dublin, L. I.:   *The Facts of Life*, New York, Macmillan, 1951.

Fisher, R. A. and Ford, E. B.:   The spread of a gene in natural conditions in a colony of the moth *Panaxia dominula* L., *Heredity*, *1*: 143-174, 1947.

Fisher, R. A. and Ford, E. B.:   The "Sewall Wright effect," *Heredity*, *4*:117-119, 1950.

Landsteiner, K. and Levine, P.:   On the inheritance and racial distribution of agglutinable properties of human blood, *J. Immunol.*, *18*: 87-94, 1930.

Laughlin, W. S.:   Genetic analysis of racial traits. II. Blood groups, morphology and population size of the Eskimos, *Cold Spring Harbor Symposia on Quantitative Biology*, *15*:165-173, Cold Spring Harbor, The Biological Laboratory, 1950.

Montagu, M. F. A.:   A consideration of the concept of race, *Cold Spring Harbor Symposia on Quantitative Biology*, *15*:315-336, Cold Spring Harbor, The Biological Laboratory, 1950.

Race, R. R., Mourant, A. E., Lawler, S. D. and Sanger, R.:   The Rh chromosome frequencies in England, *Blood*, *3*:689-695, 1948.

Race, R. R. and Sanger, R.:   *Blood Groups in Man*, Springfield, Thomas, 1950.

Rife, D. C.:   *The Dice of Destiny*, Columbus, Ohio, Long's College Book Company, 1945.

Sanghvi, L. D. and Khanolkar, V. R.:   Data relating to seven genetical characters in six endogamous groups in Bombay, *Ann. Eugen.*, *15*:52-76, 1949.

Sheppard, P. M.:   A quantitative study of two populations of the moth

Panaxia dominula (L.), *Heredity*, 5:349-378, 1951.

Wiener, A. S.:   *Blood Groups and Blood Transfusion*, Springfield, Thomas, 1935.

Wright, S.:   Evolution in Mendelian populations, *Genetics, 16*:97-159, 1931.

Wright, S.:   The roles of mutation, inbreeding, crossbreeding and selection in evolution, *Proc. 6th International Congr. Genet., 1*:356-366, 1932.

Wright, S.:   The statistical consequences of mendelian heredity in relation to speciation, in *The New Systematics*, J. S. Huxley (ed.), Oxford, Clarendon Press, 1940.

Wright, S.:   Isolation by distance, *Genetics, 28*:114-138, 1943.

Wright, S.:   On the roles of directed and random changes in gene frequency in the genetics of populations, *Evolution, 2*:279-294, 1948.

VIII. NATURAL SELECTION AND HUMAN POLYMORPHISM

*H*omo sapiens exhibits considerable polymorphism, both as a species, and in each of his geographical and local races. Even in an isolated Australian horde, or a tiny Bushman band there is notable diversity in form and feature. Though the older claim that man is the most variable primate has proven incorrect, it is clear that an important human trend has been in the direction of heterozygosity and away from homozygosity.

Why polymorphism? Darwin's explanation for the continuation of polymorphism in man was that the diverse traits involved were adaptively neutral and that they persisted simply because they were neither selected for, nor against. Later, even in the twentieth century, anthropologists saw in polymorphism evidence of admixture, seeming proof that even the simplest population was the product of ancient miscegenation. From the variety of forms and types that could be identified in a given population, they tried to deduce the number and even the proportion of the racial elements involved.

There is now growing evidence that polymorphism, (or its genetic counterpart, heterozygosis) is important in its own right. Clearly, the population with greater genetic diversity has better long-term chances of survival. While a narrow range of genotypes may be temporarily advantageous, potential evolutionary safety lies in the broadest possible pool of genes. Lerner has shown that the chief effect of domestication of animals with its intensive artificial selection and diminution of heterosis, has been to reduce overall fitness for survival in a "natural" environment, whereas in nature a much wider range of genotypes obtains, and in general, serves to maintain the fitness of the population as a whole.

A hypothetical example of adaptive polymorphism might involve the genes X and x, in which the genotype Xx is favored over either XX or xx. This would insure the continuation of both the X gene and its x counterpart, so that the population would always contain some XX individuals, some Xx individuals and some xx individuals. Even if only a few genotypes were so involved, a rather large degree of polymorphism would thus be insured even if both homozygotes were lethal. In all probability the continuation of light and dark eyes, curly and straight hair, and late and early maturers in various European populations represents both adaptive and balanced polymorphism at work.

Recent studies have confirmed the existence of adaptive polymorphism in man. The most dramatic example, of course, comes from studies of the sickle cell trait where both the normal and the sickling gene are preserved in some populations because of the greatly increased fitness of the heterozygotes. Polymorphism with respect to the ABO genes similarly appears to exist, possibly because the heterozygotes AB, OB, AO are favored over the corresponding homozygotes, points which Allison considers in the following article.

If polymorphism is adaptive, why is the apparent degree of polymorphism so much greater in some races than in others? Why, for example, are such populations as the Australian aborigines or the American Indians nearly homozygous for N and M respectively whereas in Europeans the majority of individuals are of the heterozygotic MN genotype? The likely suggestion is that in Europeans, the MN genotype is more strongly favored over NM or NN. If so, there should be descriptive and experimental evidence, possibly through investigation of the differential survival of individuals possessing the several MN genotypes. Clearly, polymorphism in man constitutes a problem to be investigated as well as a state to be described.

ADDITIONAL READINGS

Levine, P.: The influence of the ABO system on Rh hemolytic disease, *Human Biol., 30*:14-28, 1958.
Lerner, I. M.: *Genetic Homeostasis,* New York, John Wiley, 1954.

Matsunaga, E.: Selection in ABO polymorphism in Japanese populations, *Am. J. Human Genet.*, *11*(2):405-413, 1959.
Buckwalter, J. A.: Selective factors in ABO polymorphism, *Am. J. Human Genet.*, *11*(2):419-420, 1959.

Aspects of Polymorphism in Man

Reprinted, with deletion of one figure and the appendix, from *Cold Spring Harbor Symposia on Quantitative Biology*, Vol. 20, pp. 239-255, Cold Spring Harbor, The Biological Laboratory (1955).

By A. C. ALLISON

INTRODUCTION

When considering the factors which affect the frequency of a gene in a natural population, particular attention must be paid to the conditions favoring a constant gene frequency or equilibrium. Most common contrasting alleles are in or near equilibrium with one another; otherwise, with certain exceptions which will be described, they would not have survived to be observed. Three main types of genetic equilibrium can be distinguished: neutral, stable and unstable . . . In a *neutral equilibrium,* the genes segregate and assort themselves at random according to the Hardy-Weinberg principle. The essential condition for equilibrium is that no genotype shall have any selective advantage, expressed either in terms of fecundity or vitality, over any other genotype. Gene frequency changes which take place by chance (random drift) —usually in small populations—remain permanent. In *stable equilibrium,* the gene ratio tends to be restored to the equilibrium value whenever it is disturbed from this value in either direction. This type of equilibrium depends on opposed forces and can be produced in three main ways: (a) recurrent mutation and elimination of an unfavorable gene; (b) when a heterozygote has a selective advantage over both homozygotes; and (c) when two or more groups of alleles interact in such a way as to alter one another's selective values, for example, with alleles P, p and Q, q controlling contrasting characters, when P is at an advantage to p in the presence of Q but disadvantageous in combination with q while Q is advantageous with p but not with P (Fisher, '30).

190

Provided that the sequence of fitnesses of the several genotypes is not disturbed, a change in the magnitude of the selective
forces will not make such an equilibrium unstable: it will merely
alter the gene frequency at which stability is achieved. There
is no such restitution to the previous state when deviation from
an *unstable equilibrium* takes place: on the contrary, the further
the gene frequency departs from the stable value, the greater the
instability. In other words, an equilibrium of this kind is easily
destroyed, the commoner gene becoming universal at the expense
of its allele. An unstable equilibrium is produced when a heterozygote is at a disadvantage to both homozygotes, by some chrom-
osomal abnormalities and in the presence of certain types of social
selection. These generalizations can now be applied to human
populations.

Man is one of the most variable of animal species. This is
partly geographical variation: any species can assume distinct
forms in different regions. But even in the same region, man
shows a great deal of variability, which has both genetic and environmental components. The genetic component can be divided
for analysis into four classes (Ford, '40): (1) disadvantageous
varieties maintained at a low level by recurrent mutation of the
genes controlling them; (2) variation due to the effects of genes
neutral as regards survival value; (3) variation dependent on
genes maintained by a balance of selective forces; and (4) advantageous varieties controlled by genes spreading through the population and displacing their allelomorphs.

The first class includes the numerous hereditary abnormalities, affecting every bodily organ, listed in the textbooks of medical genetics. Since the spread of genes giving rise to even small
disadvantages tends to be checked at an early stage (Fisher, '30),
each of the genes in this class is maintained at a low stable
equilibrium through recurrent mutation. Nevertheless, because
of the enormous number of loci involved, the total variability
produced in this way is considerable. The selection against the
gene will, of course, be greater and the equilibrium frequency
will be correspondingly lower for 'dominant' characters (i. e.
those controlled by genes with observable effects in the hetero-

zygous phase) than for fully recessive genes producing effects of comparable severity. Important though these conditions are from the point of view of medical practice and eugenics, they are of only limited interest in population genetics.

It is not known how much the second class contributes to the variability of man. However, Fisher ('30) has shown that for a gene to be effectively neutral, that is, for a neutral equilibrium to be maintained, the balance of advantage between the gene and its allelomorph must be very exact. Moreover, the chances of random survival of such mutant genes are small. Human genes have usually been placed in this class through ignorance of their selective effects. Thus, the human blood group genes were supposed for 40 years to be neutral as regards selective value, but more recent evidence indicates that this interpretation is incorrect.

Since mutation rates are low, of the order of 10^{-5} per gene per generation in man (Haldane, '49), mutation alone cannot greatly accelerate the spread of neutral genes through a population. Hence, when any form is found to occupy as much as a few percent of a fairly numerous population it can generally be assumed that its increase has been facilitated by selection. In this way the third and fourth classes mentioned above, which constitute polymorphism, are produced. Polymorphism can be defined as the occurrence together in the same habitat of two or more discontinuous forms of a species in such frequencies that the rarest of them cannot be maintained by recurrent mutation (Ford, '40). The term polymorphism covers two conditions which are produced by quite different genetic mechanisms although they are often difficult to distinguish from one another in practice. The fourth class, transient polymorphism, continues until the gene determining the advantageous variety has so far displaced its allelomorph that the latter is preserved only by recurrent mutation. An instance of transient polymorphism in man is the presence of the sickle cell gene in the colored population of the United States. Another example may be the polymorphism of Rh-positive and Rh-negative individuals in Western Europe, where the former are gradually replacing the latter according to

Haldane ('42) and Wiener ('42). These examples will be discussed more fully below.

In a balanced polymorphism two or more forms of a species coexist in a population in stable proportions through the effects of opposing selective agencies. When a single pair of alleles is involved, one allele has a selective advantage until a certain gene ratio is established, above which the advantage is converted into a disadvantage. The simplest stable equilibrium of this kind occurs when a heterozygote has a selective advantage over either homozygote: this may be due to linkage of the gene to a lethal recessive, or to a difference in the effects of a gene when in single and double dose. Striking examples of linkage to lethal recessives are quite numerous in insects (Ford, '45) but are so far unknown in man. However, one of the most fully investigated examples of the latter situation is that of the sickle cell gene in Africans.

SICKLE CELL POLYMORPHISM

It was demonstrated by Neel ('49) that persons who are heterozygous for the sickle cell gene have the sickle cell trait, which does not produce a significant morbidity, while those who are homozygous for the gene suffer from a hemolytic disease, sickle cell anemia. In the same year, Pauling, Itano, Singer and Wells ('49) discovered that the sickling phenomenon was produced by an abnormal hemoglobin, which they named sickle cell hemoglobin, in the erythrocytes of affected individuals. The genetic and biochemical evidence was united by their demonstration that in persons with sickle cell anemia the hemoglobin is all of the sickle cell type whereas in carriers of the sickle cell trait there is a mixture of normal and sickle cell hemoglobins in approximately equal proportions. The dilution of sickle cell hemoglobin in the cells of heterozygotes prevents the sickling phenomenon—with attendant hemolysis—from taking place in the circulating blood.* This rule of inheritance is now universally

---

*Sickling would be expected to occur *in vivo* when the proportion of abnormal hemoglobin is about 65 per cent or higher.

accepted, but requires qualification. Diseases very similar to sickle cell anemia occur in individuals who are heterozygous for both the sickle cell gene and another gene controlling hemoglobin synthesis, notably the thalassemia gene and the hemoglobin C gene. These conditions will be considered more fully below.

Analyses of the proportion of sickle cell hemoglobin in homozygotes and heterozygotes has yielded further information on the quantitative expression of the sickle cell gene. From the pattern obtained by electrophoresis of a hemoglobin specimen the genotype and also the quantitative expression of the genes concerned can usually be read directly: this must be one of the most favourable known cases for precise analysis of the effects of a mutant gene and its normal allele. The main results of such tests are summarized in Figure 1.

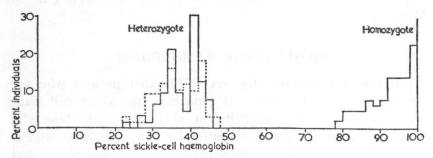

Fig. 1. Frequency distribution curves of the proportion of sickle cell hemoglobin in sickle cell homozygotes and heterozygotes. The continuous line represents heterozygotes in the United States (data of Wells and Itano, 1951); the interrupted line represents heterozygotes of the Luo tribe from Kenya (Allison, unpub.).

Wells and Itano ('51) found that some cases of sickle cell anemia have, in addition to a large component of sickle cell hemoglobin, a small hemoglobin component of apparently normal electrophoretic mobility. This component does not appear to be normal adult hemoglobin, and it has all the properties of fetal hemoglobin (Singer, Chernoff and Singer, '51; Itano, '53). Indeed, synthesis of normal adult hemoglobin would not be expected in the absence of the normal allele of the sickle cell gene, whereas the synthesis of fetal hemoglobin appears to be under independent genetic control (Allison, '54c). Thus biochemical variability in the sickle cell homozygote depends upon the proportion of fetal hemoglobin synthesized, which rarely exceeds 20 percent of the total hemoglobin. This appears to be true in all the populations so far investigated—in the United States, Africa and Greece. It is remarkable that higher proportions of fetal hemoglobin do not occur, since sickle cell homozygotes producing more fetal hemoglobin (of the order of 40% of the total) might be protected to a considerable extent from hemolysis; and they might therefore be expected to have a greater fitness than homozygotes producing little or no fetal hemoglobin. Why the proportion of fetal hemoglobin should always be so restricted in sickle cell anemia is unknown; in thalassemia major the total quantity of fetal hemoglobin synthesized is much larger, so that in some cases it comprises all the circulating hemoglobin (Rich, '52). Nevertheless, the consequence of this fact—that the biochemical variability of the sickle cell homozygote is quite strictly limited and that all homozygotes are liable to develop hemolytic disease, though not all do so to the same extent—is important in reducing the fitness of the genotype.

Some years ago many investigators in Africa thought that sickle cell anemia was an uncommon and rather mild disease in that country. Comparing the relatively few cases of sickle cell anemia then described with the very high trait frequencies known to be present, Raper ('50) was led to suppose that "the appearance of sickle cell anemia depends not only upon the extent to which the trait is present in the community, but also on the extent to which admixture with other genetic strains has occurred." Since 1950 many hundreds of cases of sickle cell anemia have been reported from Africa, and the number of affected children identified in different populations is close to the number of sickle cell homozygotes expected from the known heterozygote frequency (Lambotte-Legrand and Lambotte-Legrand, '51; Vandepitte, '54; Welbourn and Raper, '54). Moreover, Neel ('53) was unable to find any correlation between the severity of sickle cell anemia and the estimated degree of non-Negro admixture in homozygotes in the United States. From published reports it appears that the mortality from sickle cell anemia in African children is at least as great as it is in the United States. A few sickle cell homozygotes can be recognized in the young adult population of East Africa (Allison, '54c). There is, however, evidence that their fecundity is low: Dr. Gillian Jacob kindly allows me to state that she has found one homozygote in electrophoretic tests of specimens from 184 pregnant Baganda women and 82 pregnant women from other tribes whose blood showed sickle cells; and there were no homozygotes among the mothers of 261 children with sickle cell anemia reported from the Belgian Congo by Vandepitte ('54). Hence the conclusion (Allison, '54c) that the genetic fertility of the sickle cell homozygote in Africa, as in the United States, is not more than one quarter that of the heterozygote seems to be fully justified.

The sickle cell heterozygote shows a somewhat greater range of variability, in accordance with the rule that the heterozygote tends to be more variable than either homozygote, while of the latter the abnormal is more variable than the normal. The proportion of sickle cell to normal adult hemoglobin varies in different individuals, presumably owing to the relative rates of synthesis of the two pigments, but tends to be constant in any one individual. In 42 heterozygotes from the colored population of the United States, Wells and Itano ('51) found that the frequency distribution curve of the proportion of sickle cell hemoglobin lay between 24 and 45 per cent and appeared to be bimodal (Fig. 1). These and other data were statistically analysed by Neel, Wells and Itano ('51), who reported that there were highly significant differences between the mean values for families and concluded that influences exist, probably at least in part genetic, which are capable of modifying the proportion of abnormal pigment present in an individual heterozygous for the sickle cell gene. From inspection of the data published by Neel and his colleagues it appears highly probable that the modifier or modifiers of the sickle cell gene are autosomal and independent of the gene.

My own observations on 38 heterozygotes from the Luo tribe

in East Africa are included in Figure 1 for comparison. The technique used (filter paper electrophoresis, with dye elution) was different from that used by Wells and Itano (free electrophoresis) so that the absolute values are not strictly comparable; but the variations in both the American and African groups are consistent and reproducible, and lie far beyond variation due to technique alone. The American and African curves resemble one another quite closely; both cover approximately the same range and both appear to be bimodal, although the possibility of further modes cannot be excluded. Dr. Gillian Jacob kindly allows me to state that she has obtained a similar distribution curve, covering a somewhat higher range and possibly showing several modes in addition to the two primary ones, in heterozygotes of the Baganda tribe.

It can therefore be concluded that the proportion of sickle cell hemoglobin formed in heterozygotes varies and is itself under genetic control; the sickle cell gene acts as a switch mechanism determining that some of the hemoglobin formed shall be of the sickle type, while the proportion of sickle cell hemoglobin synthesized is regulated by modifying factors. The variation is not, however, great; heterozygotes with less than 20 percent sickle cell hemoglobin are known (Singer and Fisher, '52) but are rare, as are heterozygotes with more than 50 percent sickle cell hemoglobin. This range seems to be optimal in permitting the selective advantage of the heterozygote to be effective while keeping the proportion of abnormal pigment below that which would bring about the sickling process *in vivo,* with consequent hemolysis and decreased fitness.

The central problem from the point of view of population genetics can now be stated: how can such high heterozygote frequencies—up to 40 percent—be maintained in African tribes despite rapid elimination of genes through death of homozygotes? It has been calculated that to replace the loss of sickle cell genes by mutation alone a mutation rate of about 10^{-1} per gene per generation would be necessary (Allison, '54c). This is of the order of 5,000 times as great as other estimated mutation rates in man, (Haldane, '49), and approximately 60 times as great as

the upper limit of mutation to the sickle cell condition estimated from limited data by Vandepitte, Zeulzer and Neel ('55).
Furthermore, to explain the restricted distribution of the sickle
cell gene such abnormally high mutation rates would have to be
confined not only to one or two races of mankind but to isolated
groups of individuals within these races. Hence it is reasonable
to exclude an increased mutation rate as an explanation of the
remarkably high heterozygote frequencies which are known to
be present.

The occurrence of the sickle cell trait must therefore be regarded as a true polymorphism, and the remarkably constant
upper limit to the heterozygote frequencies observed suggests that
in Africa it is a balanced polymorphism. The stable equilibrium
which this implies could not be produced by reproductive over-
compensation, that is, replacement of children lost through sickle
cell anemia in susceptible families, as suggested by Foy, Kondi,
Timms, Brass and Bushra ('54) ; but it could be achieved through
selective advantage of the heterozygote. There is direct evidence that heterozygotes are at an advantage in Africa since they
suffer from subtertian malaria less frequently and less severely
than normal individuals. That possessors of the sickle cell trait
might be resistant to malaria had been suggested by Brain ('52)
and by Mackey and Vivarelli ('52) ; substantial evidence in support of this view was presented by Allison ('54a), who studied
the parasite rates and densities in children under natural conditions and obtained large differences in the response to artificial
infection of susceptible volunteers with and without the sickle
cell trait. Further observations which seem to establish beyond
reasonable doubt that children with the sickle cell trait are resistant to malaria have recently been published by Raper ('55), who
effectively answers critics of this interpretation. In the age group
of one to three years, which is the age of maximum susceptibility
to and mortality from malaria, Raper found that the *P. falciparum*
rate was significantly lower in the sickle cell trait group than in
those without the trait; parasite counts were very much lower in
sickling than in non-sickling subjects. It is therefore highly probable that in regions where malaria is hyperendemic (i. e. trans-

mission of *Plasmodium falciparum* continues throughout the greater part of the year, so that the population is constantly re-infected and susceptible individuals suffer from severe and pro-longed disease) children who possess the sickle cell trait will tend to survive while some of those without the trait will be eliminated before they acquire immunity to malaria.

It should prove possible eventually to make direct estimates of the fitness of sickle cell heterozygotes in malarious regions. Calculations indicate that the advantage possessed by the hetero-zygote under these conditions must be great. The highest equili-brium frequency of heterozygotes attained in African populations —when maximal heterosis balances elimination of genes through death of homozygotes—appears to be around 40 percent; all fre-quencies up to this limit are observed in East Africa and the limit

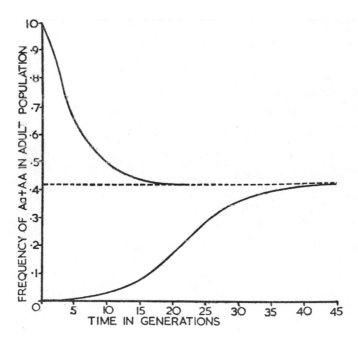

Fig. 2. The change in sickle cell homozygote-heterozygote frequency in the adult population which would occur from a high or a low level when the fitness of the normal homozygote, sickle cell homozygote and heterozygote are 0.95, 1.19 and 0.30 respectively. The interrupted horizontal line represents an equilibrium frequency of 40 per cent heterozygotes.

is reached in several widely separated communities but never exceeded (Allison, '54b). Assuming that three quarters of the homozygotes die without reproducing, an equilibrium frequency of 40 percent heterozygotes implies that the fitness of the heterozygote must be about 1.26 times that of the normal homozygote (Allison, '54c). This is not quite so surprising when it is remembered that the infant mortality is about 200-500 per 1000. With selective forces of this magnitude operating in a population, the rate of increase or decrease of the adult sickle cell carrier frequency from low or high values to the limiting value is shown in Figure 2.

The equilibrium would be stable, of course, only when the population is constantly exposed to subtertian malaria. It would therefore be expected that tribes living in malarious environ-

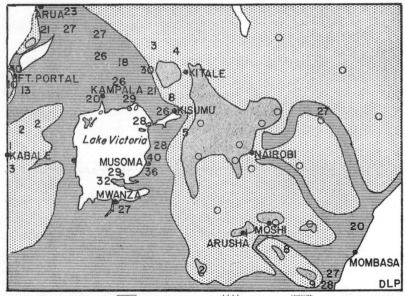

FALCIPARUM MALARIA: ▨HYPERENDEMIC ▦EPIDEMIC ▨NO TRANSMISSION

Fig. 3. Sketch map of East Africa, outlining the regions where subtertian malaria is hyperendemic (i.e., transmitted throughout the greater part of the year), epidemic (i.e., seasonal or present near water) and absent. The observed percentages of indigenous Africans with the sickle cell trait in different localities are superimposed (redrawn from Allison '55, Fig. 4).

ments should have higher sickle cell trait frequencies than those living in environments free from malaria. In East Africa, which forms a convenient testing ground for the hypothesis because of the great diversity of climate, rainfall and malarial severity encountered there, this is indeed the case. In 35 East African tribes from widely different environments the incidence of the sickle cell trait was found to be invariably about 10 percent in the tribes suffering from hyperendemic malaria and less than 10 percent in tribes living in regions where malaria is absent or epidemic: this difference cuts across racial, linguistic and ethnographic barriers (Allison, '54b, see Fig. 3). In general, high trait frequencies are found in Central Africa, where malaria is prevalent, but not in Northern or Southern Africa, where subtertian malaria is less common and is partially replaced by benign tertian malaria. There are, however, in the marginal zones tribes exposed to subtertian malaria of varying degrees of severity who do not have the sickle cell trait or have it in low frequencies; this is true of the Northern Nilotes in the Sudan (Foy, Kondi, Timms and Bushra, '54; Roberts and Lehmann, '55) and of the Zulus of South Africa (Budtz-Olsen and Burgers, '55). Little is known about the past histories of these tribes, who may have entered malarious habitats only a few generations ago; and they may not have acquired, or may only recently have acquired, the sickle cell gene. Even under conditions of maximum heterosis, the increase in frequency of the sickle cell gene in such populations would at first be slow (Fig. 2); later it would be more rapid, falling again as the limit is approached. That the trait is rare or absent in other races exposed to severe subtertian malaria (e. g. in Thailand) is also remarkable, but an explanation for this is suggested below. It is much more significant that high sickle cell trait frequencies do not occur in populations who have not been exposed to subtertian malaria. Thus, the high frequencies of the trait recorded in the aboriginals of South India (Lehmann and Cutbush, '52), in the Greeks of Lake Copais (Choremis, Ikin, Lehmann, Mourant and Zannos, '53) and in some southern Turks (Askoy, '55) all occur in notoriously malarious regions.

The comparatively high incidence of the sickle cell trait ob-

served in the colored population of the United States cannot be
regarded as an exception to this generalization, since there is evidence that the frequency is unstable.   The incidence of the trait
in the slave population was probably at least 22 percent (Allison,
'54c).   Anthropologists estimate that "the average Negro is about
one third white and Indian" which is in accordance with blood
group data (Glass and Li, '53).   Given a population with 22 percent carriers of the sickle cell trait and a one third admixture of
strains having no sickle cell, a trait frequency of 15.4 percent
would be expected.   In fact, the incidence of the sickle cell trait
in United States Negroes is not over 9 percent (Neel, '51).   Hence
a significant fall in the frequency of the trait seems to have
occurred among West Africans living in the United States.   Such
a fall would have taken place in about 12 generations, that is,

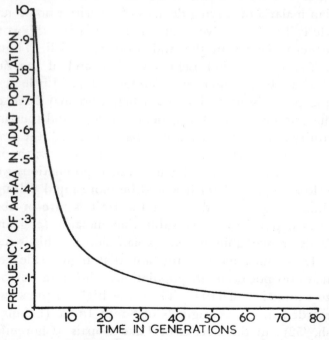

Fig. 4. The change in sickle cell homozygote + homozygote frequency in the
adult population which would occur when the fitness of the sickle cell
homozygote is 0.25 and there is no heterosis, i.e., the fitness of the heterozygote and of the homozygote is 1.0.

300 to 350 years, which fits the historical records of slave importations into the New World satisfactorily (Fig. 4).

If this interpretation is correct, the sickle cell polymorphism in the United States is a transient one, with the level of the sickle cell gene falling in each successive generation. The rate of fall would now be slow and the gene would be expected to persist in the population in low frequencies almost indefinitely, but eventually to be balanced only by recurrent mutation.

EFFECTS OF GENES FOR OTHER ABNORMAL HEMOGLOBINS

One of the remarkable features of the distribution of the sickle cell trait in Africa is the higher maximum frequency attained in East Africa, where several tribes have 40 percent with the trait, than in West Africa, where all the tribes so far observed have trait frequencies below 30 percent. This was, indeed, one of the points which led Lehmann ('54) to conclude that the sickle cell gene had been introduced into Africa from the North-East.

There is no reason to suppose that mortality from malaria is any lower in West Africa than in East Africa. Recently, however, another important factor has come to light. The hemoglobin C trait has been found in 12 percent of Africans from the Gold Coast (Edington and Lehmann, '54) and also in Africans from Ibadan, Nigeria, by Dr. N. A. Barnicot and Mr. J. Garlick. On the other hand, the hemoglobin C gene seems to be absent from Uganda (Jacob, '55), the Sudan and Tanganyika (Roberts and Lehmann, '55) and Kenya (Allison, unpublished). Now, it is known that individuals who are heterozygous for both the sickle cell gene and the hemoglobin C gene sometimes develop a disease similar to, though rather less severe than, sickle cell anemia (Kaplan, Zuelzer and Neel, '51; Smith and Conley, '54). Hence in a population where the two genes are present the sickle cell gene will be eliminated through failure of both sickle cell homozygotes and the double heterozygotes to reproduce, that is, the rate of elimination will be greater than in a population where only the sickle cell gene is present. It follows that if the selective advantage of the sickle heterozygote is the same in both populations, the stable equilibrium frequency, at which heterosis exactly counterbalances elimination, will be reached at a lower level in the population with hemoglobin C than in the population without it. Here, then, is a ready explanation for the lower limiting frequency imposed on the sickle cell gene in West Africa: there is no need to have recourse to hypothetical migration of populations.

Penrose ('55) has recently shown theoretically that three or more alleles will be in equilibrium provided that all homozygotes have a fitness below average, that is, the heterozygotes are at an advantage. A genotype table for a West African population where the sickle cell heterozygote frequency is 30 percent and the hemoglobin C heterozygote frequency is 12 percent was included in the appendix to this paper. The values for the fitness of the sickle cell heterozygote and homozygote agree quite well with those previously calculated for East Africans (Allison, '54c) —1.19 and 0.30 respectively. The fitness of the sickle cell: hemoglobin C double heterozygote is about 0.51; in other words, the individual with sickle cell: hemoglobin C disease would have at least twice as great a chance of reaching reproductive age and bearing children as the individual with homozygous sickle cell anemia. This seems to be a reasonable estimate, and is one which could be confirmed or disproved by direct observations on hemoglobin types in the reproducing population.

That some individuals who are homozygous for the hemoglobin C gene are liable to develop disease is also known (for references see Singer, Chapman, Goldberg, Rubinstein and Rosenblum, '54). It follows that in the West African population the hemoglobin C gene must be eliminated through death of sickle cell: hemoglobin C and homozygous hemoglobin C cases before reproductive age. It is highly probable, therefore, that the polymorphism is balanced through selective advantage of the hemoglobin C heterozygote. If the hemoglobin C homozygote has a fitness of 0.74, . . . the fitness of the hemoglobin C heterozygote would be 1.12. We have no knowledge of any advantage possessed by the hemoglobin C heterozygote, but clearly the possibility of a relationship to malaria should be explored first. The limited available data again suggest that the stability of the equilibrium was destroyed when the West Africans were transferred to the New World. The frequency of the hemoglobin C heterozygotes in the slave population was probably of the order of 10 percent, whereas in the colored population of the United States today it is only 1.8 to 3 percent (Smith and Conley, '53; Schneider, '53).

Similar problems are raised in connection with the polymorphism of the thalassemia gene in Italy, Greece and Thailand and that of the hemoglobin E gene in Thailand. It is now universally accepted that individuals homozygous for the thalassemia gene suffer from a very severe disease which reduces their fitness nearly to zero; in addition, heterozygotes are often mildly anemic. In spite of the great selective disadvantage to the thalassemia gene which this implies, the frequency of heterozygotes in many Italian districts is four percent or higher, reaching 18 percent in the Ferrara region (Bianco, Montalenti, Silvestroni and Siniscalco, '52). It was first suggested by Bianco and her colleagues that the loss of genes might be compensated to some extent by increased fecundity of matings between heterozygotes; later some evidence was obtained that the heterozygotes in Italy have a selective advantage (Montalenti, '54). The figures presented for normals and heterozygotes, however, show an insignificant difference and the advantage is too small to keep the gene frequency equilibrium stable at its present high level in Ferrara. If the fitness of the abnormal homozygote is 0.1 and that of the normal homozygote is 0.95 the fitness of the heterozygote where the heterozygote frequency is stable at 18 percent would be 1.077, that is, the advantage must be of the order of nine percent. The position is thus still far from clear and has been complicated by the discovery that thalassemia is relatively common in Thailand (Minnich, Na-Nakorn, Chongchareonsuk and Kochaseni, '54). In Thailand the thalassemia gene appears to be at an even greater disadvantage than in Italy owing to the reduced fitness of individuals who are doubly heterozygous for this gene as well as for the hemoglobin E gene (Na-Nakorn, Minnich and Chernoff, '55). According to Na-Nakorn and his colleagues, the frequency of hemoglobin E heterozygotes in the Thai population is 12. 5 percent. Since some of those who are homozygous for the hemoglobin E gene also develop disease, the situation is similar to the coexistence of the sickle cell gene and hemoglobin C gene in West Africa, the two abnormal homozygotes as well as those heterozygous for both abnormal genes being at a disadvantage.* The most probable explanation of the fact that the thalassemia gene has become common in two widely separated populations, and for the continued and apparently stable polymorphism of this gene together with the hemoglobin E gene in Thailand, is that both heterozygotes are at an advantage, or have been at an advantage until recently.

In a similar way the thalassemia and sickle cell genes interact to produce a diseased double heterozygote (Silvestroni and Bianco, '46; Powell, Rodarte and Neel, '50; Smith and Conley, '54). Hence if both genes are present in a population, each would tend to check the frequency of the other. It is possible that the relatively low maximum frequencies of the sickle cell trait recorded in Greece (17.8 percent, Choremis, Ikin, Lehmann, Mourant and Zannos, '53) and in Turkey (13.3 percent, Askoy, '55) are due to the known coexistence of the thalassemia gene in these countries; but the populations investigated may not have reached a stable equilibrium in respect of the sickle cell gene frequency under conditions of maximum heterosis.

The apparent rarity of the hemoglobin D and hemoglobin G, H, I, and K genes, on the other hand, may imply that the heterozygotes have little or no advantage, and the same is probably true of another globin abnormality described by Hörlein and Weber ('48), which may be termed hemoglobin M. It has recently been discovered that both sheep and goats have electrophoretically different hemoglobin types (Harris and Warren, '55). If the formation of these hemoglobin types proves to be under independent genetic control, these species must be poly-

---

*Since the thalassemia and hemoglobin E genes are probably not allelic, however, the two situations are not identical genetically.

morphic for the genes concerned. It may then be possible to make a direct experimental analysis of the mechanism by which this polymorphism is maintained.

BLOOD GROUP POLYMORPHISM

For many years it was widely held that the human blood groups were neutral from the point of view of natural selection and that the different frequencies observed in different parts of the world were due to genetic drift (see, for instance, Wright, '40). Fisher and Ford have long maintained that the stability of the blood group polymorphism must in all probability be due to the action of selective agencies (Ford, '45). The discovery that immunization of an Rh-negative (*d/d*) mother by a heterozygous Rh-positive (*D/d*) fetus could produce hemolytic disease of the newborn established beyond doubt that these blood groups have selective value. In this case, selection acts against the heterozygote, which—as Haldane ('42) and Wiener ('42) pointed out— would lead to an unstable equilibrium and eventually bring to a low level the rarer of the two genes, the Rh-negative (*d*) gene. If this is so, the Rh polymorphism in Western Europe is of the transient type. To explain the high frequency of the Rh-negative gene still present, both Haldane and Wiener suggested that the Western Europeans might be descended from the products of intermarriage between a race predominantly Rh-positive (as in the populations of Africa and Asia) and a race predominantly Rh-negative. The subsequent discovery that the Rh-negative (*d*) gene is approximately twice as frequent in the Basques as in other Europeans (Etcheverry, '47; Chalmers, Ikin and Mourant, '48) made this interpretation more plausible, but cannot be accepted as confirmation of it. There is an unresolved difficulty: if one of the Rh genes arose as a mutation from the other, it is theoretically improbable that such a mutant gene, if devoid of selective value and disadvantageous in the heterozygous phase, could have become predominant in certain populations. The alternative view, that the Rh polymorphism is balanced and relatively stable, has been taken by Fisher, Race, and Taylor ('44).

These authors suggested one way in which the intensity of selection against the Rh negative gene through hemolytic disease might be reduced. Where the father is heterozygous in families with hemolytic disease, only half of the children will be affected; the unaffected children will be homozygous Rh-negative, so that even a partial replacement of children lost will help to compensate for the loss of Rh-negative genes. Glass ('50) has some evidence that white Rh-negative, immunized mothers have a higher average number of pregnancies than either Rh-negative non-immunized or Rh-positive mothers. Glass found no such difference in the colored population investigated, and this type of over-compensation would only be expected where there is effective control over family size. It seems very dubious whether such over-compensation was significant in the past and could have operated constantly enough to produce more or less uniform Rh frequencies over the greater part of Western Europe. The loss of Rh negative genes may be partially compensated in other ways. One association which has recently been found is the apparently decreased susceptibility of Rh-negative individuals to squamous carcinoma of the bronchus (McConnell, Clarks, and Downton, '54). However, since deaths from bronchial carcinoma usually take place after reproductive age, the higher mortality among Rh-positive individuals would not confer much selective advantage on the Rh-negative gene.

It is not sufficiently recognized that, however effective such compensation for the loss of Rh negative genes might be, it could not lead to a stable equilibrium and a balanced polymorphism; the best it could do—in the improbable event of its exactly counter-balancing elimination—would be to produce a neutral equilibrium. A stable equilibrium could be produced through the possession of a selective advantage by the heterozygote, which would have to be large so as to overcome the disadvantage in hemolytic disease, or through strong interaction with other genes in the way described above. The heterozygote cannot, unfortunately, be recognized serologically on a wide scale, so that it would be difficult to collect data regarding its selection coefficient. This important investigation should nevertheless be attempted. Only two Rh genes (*D* and *d*) which are most commonly involved in hemolytic disease have so far been considered. The same general principle, selection against the heterozygote, applies equally to immunization by other Rh antigens.

On the other hand, there is some evidence for an interaction between the Rh and other blood groups. In hemolytic disease of the newborn due to Rh immunization, the parents are much more often compatibly mated as regards ABO blood groups, in the sense that the husband could be a donor to his wife, than would be expected (Race and Sanger, '54). And Grubb and Sjöstedt ('55) found in a series of marriages with two or more pregnancies terminating in intrauterine death for unknown reasons a highly significant excess of ABO incompatibility in the mating combination Rh positive: Rh positive but not in other Rh combinations. These findings illustrate the interdependence of different blood group systems in the genesis of disease—which is direct evidence that the selective forces acting on one system of blood group genes will be influenced by the presence or absence of blood group genes belonging to different systems, as they doubtless are by many other genes. Whether these interactions are of sufficient magnitude to be a significant factor in producing a stable equilibrium through the mechanism analysed mathematically by Fisher ('30) remains to be seen.

From what has been said, and from the fact that hemolytic disease of the newborn is sometimes produced by ABO incompatibility (Race and Sanger, '54), it will be clear that the ABO blood group genes, also, can no longer be regarded as devoid of selective value. Other unexpected, and at present inexplicable, associations between the ABO groups and disease have recently come to light. Struthers ('51) compared the ABO groups, in consecutive series of young West Scottish children coming to autopsy, with the groups of the adult population to which the parents belonged. A significant deficiency of group O was found among the infants, especially those with autopsy evidence of bronchopneumonia. More firmly established is the finding that the frequency of group A is greater and the frequency of O is less in patients suffering from cancer of the stomach than in the general population of the locality in which they live (Aird, Bentall and Fraser Roberts, '53). More recently (Aird, Bentall, Mehigan and Fraser Roberts, '54), the ABO groups in three other cancers—colon, rectum and breast—were found not to differ significantly from the population controls. Patients suffering from peptic ulceration, however, showed a higher incidence of group O and a correspondingly lower incidence of the other three groups than the controls; if their series is typical—which it seems to be, judging from confirmatory Norwegian evidence (Westlund and Heistö, '55) —persons of group O are about 35 percent more liable to develop peptic ulceration than persons of the other groups. McConnell, Clarke and Downton ('54) found a barely significant excess of A at the expense of O in patients with oat-cell tumours of the lung but not in other types of lung cancer. And Pike and Dickins ('54) reported a significant excess of women with group O among 541 cases of toxemia of pregnancy compared with the groups of 3651 admissions to a maternity hospital.

Most of the studies of blood groups and disease so far published are, however, rather superficial and the results do not necessarily imply that the associations found are due to pleiotropic effects of the blood group genes. They might equally well be due to other factors, for example, population stratification. In the investigation of Pike and Dickins the question of maternal age and parity, which was not considered, might be very relevant. Nevertheless, the demonstration of significant associations between the incidence of certain blood groups and resistance or susceptibility to a variety of diseases is important, since disease is probably the most potent agent producing natural selection in man. Other selective agents which deserve attention are those affecting fecundity. Here the evidence of a relationship to blood groups is less clear. In a much-quoted paper, Waterhouse and Hogben ('47) asserted that there was a highly significant deficiency of A offspring of the mating of father A times mother O; their conclusions have, however, been criticized on statistical grounds by Bennett and Brandt ('54). No significant deficiency of A newborn children of O mothers could be found among 2000 London mother-infant combinations (Boorman, '50) or

7856 such Australian combinations published by Bryce, Jakobowicz, McArthur and Penrose ('50). The table comparing Japanese
parents and children presented by Matsunuga ('55) shows fewer
O parents than O children and more AB parents than AB children. Similar deficiencies of AB children were found by Boorman and by Bryce and her colleagues. Allen ('53) reviewing
his own and other data, concludes that the fecundity of individuals with different blood groups—that is, the mean number of
offspring—is not equal.

It is therefore probable, though not satisfactorily proven,
that the ABO blood group genes do not appear at random among
the offspring of different matings. Through differences in respect of such features as well as susceptibility to disease, each of
the blood groups would be at an advantage in certain situations
and at a disadvantage in others. But this alone would not establish a stable equilibrium. The search for increased fitness of
the heterozygotes, which would keep the system in equilibrium,
has not yet been intensively pursued. There are, however, some
pointers: the increased susceptibility of persons with group O to
peptic ulcer and perhaps toxemia of pregnancy during reproductive age can be quoted as an instance of selection against one
homozygote; and the excess of AB mothers in the series cited
could be attributable to increased fitness of one heterozygote.

The great majority of human populations possess all three
antigens, which suggests that the polymorphism is balanced. However, the frequencies are far from uniform: in fact, they show
quite wide variations over relatively small distances. Mourant
('54) suggests that the ABO groups may be adaptive, in the sense
that they are subject to environmental selection, whereas the
remarkably uniform frequencies of most blood group genes over
large areas of continental dimensions seems to imply a long-term
stability not closely dependent on the varied external conditions
provided by such an area. The evidence from distribution of the
blood groups seems to be equivocal, however. In some instances
populations of different racial origins living in the same region
have the same ABO blood groups, as in the high B frequencies
of Mongolians and Caucasians in Central Asia, whereas other

populations known to have the same origin but living in different regions retain very similar blood group frequencies, for example, the gypsies quoted by Mourant.

Mourant also draws attention to the widespread distribution of ABO antigens and closely related substances among living organisms, and quotes evidence that part at least of the Rh and MN antigen systems seems to have been derived from an early primate stock. The very persistance of these antigens suggests that they may not be devoid of selective value; and once a population had become polymorphic in respect of such characters it might as a whole gain a versatility in resistance to disease advantageous for survival under unfavourable conditions.

A further instance of polymorphism in man which may be very ancient is that of the taste-deficiency gene, t, which has a frequency of about 53 percent in Englishmen and 19.5 percent in East Africans (Allison, '51). Fisher, Ford and Huxley ('39) found that chimpanzees show definite differences in taste threshold for phenylthiocarbamide, as do humans. These authors concluded that our ancestors may have possessed both T and t genes in common with the ancestors of the anthropoids. In view of the apparent stability of the polymorphism, they believed that it was balanced by unknown selective forces—possibly an advantage possessed by the heterozygote. There is a somewhat suggestive relationship between the chemical structure of phenylthiocarbamide and that of certain antithyroid substances occurring in natural foods such as cabbages and turnips (Astwood, Greer and Ettlinger, '49) ; and Harris, Kalmus and Trotter ('49) obtained evidence suggesting that non-tasters are more liable to develop nodular goiter than tasters.

COMMENTS

All human populations are polymorphic for blood group genes and many are known to be polymorphic for genes controlling hemoglobin synthesis as well. Since all the latter are at a disadvantage when homozygous, it is probable that their polymorphism is due to heterosis, there being direct evidence that this is so in the case of the sickle cell gene. These conditions may be exceptional in the magnitude of the selective forces involved, but perhaps not in the principle by which polymorphism is maintained. Heterosis appears to be common in natural populations: it has recently become clear that wild populations of *Drosophila* contain numerous genes or gene complexes which are deleterious when homozygous; the majority of these are neutral or disadvantageous when heterozygous, but a substantial proportion of them produce heterozygotes which are fitter than normal (Stern, Carson, Kinst, Novitski and Uphoff, '52; Cordeiro and Dobzhansky, '54). These investigations, together with those of Lerner ('50) and others on domestic animals, indicate that heterosis is an important mechanism maintaining variability in populations of sexually reproducing and normally outbreeding species.

Sheppard ('53) has offered a plausible explanation for the evolution of polymorphism through dominance-modification. Genes usually, and perhaps always, have multiple effects, it is unlikely that more than one effect of each gene will be advantageous. Through selection of the gene complex the advantageous effect will tend to become dominant and the disadvantageous effects recessive. The heterozygote will then possess only advantageous characters while the homozygote will have some that are advantageous and many that are not. Hence the heterozygotes will be favoured and polymorphism will develop.

The interaction of the genes for which man is known to be polymorphic deserves closer consideration. In the case of the genes controlling hemoglobin synthesis it seems that interaction is always disadvantageous: individuals who are heterozygous for any two abnormal genes tend to be diseased. This is known to be the case with the sickle cell and thalassemia gene (Silvestroni and Bianco, '46; Powell, Rodarte and Neel, '50), the sickle cell and hemoglobin C genes (Kaplan, Zuelzer and Neel, '51; Smith and Conley, '54), the sickle cell and hemoglobin D genes (Itano, '51) the sickle cell and hemoglobin E genes (Spaet,'55), the thalassemia and hemoglobin E genes (Na-Nakorn, Minnich and Chernoff, '55) and the thalassemia and hemoglobin C genes (Zuelzer and Kaplan, '54; Singer, Kraus, Singer, Rubinstein and

Goldberg,'54) . Hence the presence of two such genes in any population will reduce the limiting frequency of both, as appears to be the case in West Africa. Furthermore, if any one of these genes is already common in a population, it will be difficult for any other to spread. New mutants will be subject initially not only to the full force of random survival but also to elimination in the double heterozygous condition. This may help to explain why the sickle cell gene is not found in malarious countries like Thailand, where the hemoglobin E and thalassemia genes are already established.

Reference has been made to the relationship of the ABO blood groups to hemolytic disease caused by Rh immunization and to the non-random distribution of ABO and Rh groups in matings resulting in intrauterine death. These findings illustrate the interdependence of several blood group systems in the genesis of disease.

If this type of interaction is of sufficient magnitude, it might play a part in the stabilization of the blood group gene frequencies. It might also have another interesting consequence. Sheppard ('53b) has drawn attention to the fact that in many different groups of animals exhibiting extreme polymorphism, the genes concerned have been shown to be subject to strong selection, the direction and intensity of which varies from one gene combination to another. Such genes are often found to be closely linked. From the frequent association between polymorphism, strong selection and close linkage, Sheppard concludes that there is a causal connexion between them and suggests that the linkage has been evolved. There is evidence that if a species is polymorphic for two pair of closely linked genes and if the genes have different selective values in different combinations, linkage between them is likely to increase as a result of natural selection. Sheppard suggests that if the genes are initially on different chromosomes, any translocation which moves them onto the same chromosome will be advantageous, so that genes which alter one another's selection coefficient will tend to accumulate in one or a few linkage groups, the speed at which this process would take place depending in part on the intensity of selection. It would be of great interest to know whether the linked blood group genes in man (e. g. *M, N, S,* Henshaw and Hunter) interact in any way.

It might therefore be expected that genes controlling a polymorphism would often be so closely linked as to form a "super-gene." Crossing over would occur between the constituent loci so rarely that these super-genes would easily be confused with multiple allelomorphs. This has actually happened in the case of the Rh super-gene in man, and it may well be true of other blood group systems (e. g. the ABO system) and even the genes controlling abnormal hemoglobin synthesis as well. If super-genes have been created through increasing linkage, it is to be expected that the process might not always be complete. This may well be the case with the Henshaw gene, which is closely linked to the *M N S* genes in West Africa but apparently not so closely associated with them in East Africa (Allison, Ikin and Mourant, '55).

All the genes which have been considered in this paper produce discrete effects. They have been deliberately chosen for investigation because their genetics are known, the genotypes are easily identified and the selective forces acting on them were expected to be of sufficient magnitude to be easily detectable. Polymorphic genes are especially subject to rapid evolution through changes in the balance of selective forces by which the polymorphism is stabilized, A substantial beginning has been made in demonstrating the nature and magnitude of the selective agencies which affect the frequencies of some of these genes in human populations and in estimating the rate at which change in the genetic constitution of such populations—that is to say, evolution—might be expected to take place. However, it is probable that these sharply discontinuous characters represent a rather special class of genetic variants in man and that most important human characters are under multifactorial control. This seems to be true, for instance of the genes affecting stature and bodily proportions, skin, eye and hair colour, intelligence, metabolism and resistance to most diseases.

The evidence given above and that from other species of

animals quoted by Sheppard ('53 a and b) indicates that some genes at least have high selection coefficients. If changes controlled by single genes are subject to such heavy selection pressure, the selective value of alterations of the same order of magnitude under multifactorial control should be as large. Nevertheless, characters under multifactorial control are easily susceptible to gradual evolution, and they may be difficult to investigate for this reason.

ACKNOWLEDGMENTS

I am indebted to Prof. L. S. Penrose and Dr. E. B. Ford for criticizing this paper in manuscript and to Mrs. S. Maynard Smith for the calculations which are presented in the appendix. She has also kindly allowed me to use as Figures 2 and 4 curves originally presented in her appendix to Allison ('54c). This work has been financed in part by a grant from the Colonial Development and Welfare Fund recommended by the Colonial Medical Research Committee.

REFERENCES

Aird, I., Bentall, H. H., and Fraser Roberts, J. A.: Relationship between cancer of the stomach and the ABO blood groups, *Brit. M. J., 1*:779-780, 1953.

Aird, I., Bentall, H. H., Mehigan, J. A., and Fraser Roberts, J. A.: The blood groups in relation to peptic ulceration and carcinoma of the colon, rectum, breast and bronchus, *Brit. M. J., 2*:315-321, 1954.

Allen, T. M.: ABO blood groups and human fertility, *Brit. J. Prev. & Social Med., 7*:220-226, 1953.

Allison, A. C.: A note on taste-blindness in Kenya Africans and Arabs, *Man, 5*:119-120, 1951.

Allison, A. C.: Protection afforded by sickle cell trait against subtertian malarial infection, *Brit. M. J., 1*:290-292, 1954a.

Allison, A. C.: The distribution of the sickle cell trait in East Africa and elsewhere, and its apparent relationship to the incidence of subtertian malaria, *Tr. Roy. Soc. Trop. Med. & Hyg., 48*:312-318, 1954b.

Allison, A. C.: Notes on sickle cell polymorphism, *Ann. Human Genet., 19*:39-57, 1954c.

Allison, A. C.: Notation for human hemoglobin types and genes controlling their synthesis, *Science, 122*:640-641, 1955.

Allison, A. C., Ikin, E. W., and Mourant, A. E.: Further observations on blood groups in East African Tribes, *J. Roy Anthropol. Inst., 84*:158-162, 1954.

Askoy, M.: Sickle cell trait in South Turkey, *Lancet, 1*:589-590, 1955.

Astwood, E. B., Greer, M. A., and Ettlinger, M. G.: 1-5-vinyl-2-thiooxazolidone, an antithyroid compound from yellow turnip and from *Brassica* seeds, *J. Biol. Chem., 181*:121-130, 1949.

Bennett, J. H. and Brandt, J.: Some more exact tests of significance for O-A maternal-foetal incompatibility, *Ann. Eugen. Lond., 18*: 302-310, 1954.

Bianco, I., Montalenti, G., Silvestroni, E., and Siniscalco, M.: Further data on the genetics of microcythaemia or thalassemia minor and Cooley's disease or thalassemia major, *Ann. Eugen. Lond., 16*:299-315, 1952.

Boorman, K. E.: An analysis of blood types and clinical conditions of 2,000 consecutive mothers and infants, *Ann. Eugen. Lond., 15*:120-134, 1950.

Bryce, L. M., Jakobowicz, R., McArthur, N., and Penrose, L. S.: Blood group frequencies in a mother and infant sample of the Australian population, *Ann. Eugen. Lond., 15*:271-275, 1950.

Budtz-Olsen, O. E., and Burgers, A. C. J.: The sickle-cell trait in the South African Bantu, *South African M. J., 29*:109-110, 1955.

Chalmers, J. N., Ikin, E. W., and Mourant, A. E.: Basque blood groups, *Nature, 162*:27, 1948.

Choremis, C., Ikin, E. W., Lehmann, H., Mourant, A. E., and Zannos, I.: Sickle cell trait and blood-groups in Greece, *Lancet, 2*:909-911, 1953.

Cordeiro. A. R. and Dobzhansky, Th.: Combining ability of certain chromosomes in Drosophila willistoni and invalidation of the "wildtype" concept, *Am. Nat., 88*:75-88, 1954.

Edington, G. M.: Sickle cell anemia in the Accra district of the Gold Coast, *Brit. M. J., 2*:957-959, 1953.

Edington, G. M., and Lehmann, H.: A case of sickle cell hemoglobin C disease and a survey of hemoglobin C incidence in West Africa, *Tr. Roy. Soc. Trop. Med. & Hyg., 48*:332, 1954a.

Edington, G. M., and Lehmann, H.: A new hemoglobin found in a

West African, *Lancet*, 2:173-174, 1954b.

Etcheverry, M. A.:   El factor Rh en personas de ascendencia Iberica e Italica residentes en la Argentina, *La Semana Medica, 2802*:500-512, 1947.

Fisher, R. A.:   *The Genetical Theory of Natural Selection*, London, Oxford, 1930.

Fisher, R. A., Ford, E. B., and Huxley, J. S.:   Taste-testing the anthropoid apes, *Nature, 144*:750 751, 1939.

Fisher, R. A., Race, R. R., and Taylor, G. L.:   Mutation and the rhesus reaction, *Nature, 162*:27, 1944.

Ford, E. B.:   Polymorphism and taxonomy, in *The New Systematics*, J. S. Huxley (ed.), London, Oxford, 1940.

Ford, E. B.:   Polymorphism, *Biol. Rev., 20*:73-88, 1945.

Foy, H., Kondi, A., Timms, G. L., Brass, W., and Bushra, F.:   The variability of sickle cell rates in the tribes of Kenya and the southern Sahara, *Brit. M. J., 1*:294-297, 1954.

Glass, B.:   The action of selection on the principal Rh alleles, *Am. J. Human Genet., 2*:269-278, 1950.

Glass, B., and Li, C. C.:   The dynamics of racial intermixture—an analysis based on the American Negro, *Am. J. Human Genet., 5*:1-20, 1953.

Grubb, R. and Sjöstedt, S: Blood groups in abortion and sterility, *Am. J. Human Genet., 19*:183-194, 1955.

Haldane, J. B. S.:   Selection against heterozygosis in man, *Ann. Eugen. Lond., 11*:333-340, 1942.

Haldane, J. B. S.:   The rate of mutation of human genes, *Proc. VII Int. Cong. Genet.* :267-273, 1949.

Harris, H., Kalmus, H., and Trotter, W. R.:   Taste sensitivity to phenylthiourea in goitre and diabetes, *Lancet, 2*:1038-1039, 1949.

Harris, H. and Warren, F. L.:   Occurrence of electrophoretically distinct hemoglobin in ruminants, *Biochem. J., 60*:29, 1955.

Hörlein, H., and Weber, C.:   Ueber chronische familiäre Methäemoglobinämie und eine neue Modifikation des Methäemoglobins, *Deutsche med. Wchnschr., 73*:746-762, 1948.

Itano, H. A.:   A third abnormal hemoglobin associated with hereditary hemolytic anemia, *Proc. Nat. Acad. Sc. Wash., 37*:775-784, 1951.

Itano, H. A.:   Human hemoglobin, *Science, 117*:89-94, 1953.

Jacob, G. F.:   A survey for hemoglobins C and D in Uganda, *Brit. M. J., 1*:521-522, 1955.

Kaplan, E., Zuelzer, W. W., and Neel, J. V.:   A new inherited abnormality of hemoglobin and its interaction with sickle cell hemoglobin, *Blood,* 6:1240-1259, 1951.

Lambotte-Legrand, J., and Lambotte-Legrand, C.: L'anémie a hématies falciformes chez l'enfant indigène du Bas-Congo. *Mem. Inst. R. Col. Belge., Mem., 19*:93, 1951.

Lehmann, H.: Distribution of the sickle cell gene, *Eugen. Rev., 46*: 3-23, 1954.

Lehmann, H., and Cutbush, M.: Sickle cell trait in southern India, *Brit. M. J., 1*:404-406, 1952.

Lerner, I. M.: *Population Genetics and Animal Improvement,* London, Cambridge University Press, 1950.

McConnell, R. B., Clarke, C. A., and Downton, F.: Blood groups in carcinoma of the lung, *Brit. M. J., 1*:323-325, 1954.

Mackey, J. P., and Vivarelli, F.: *Annual report of the Tanganyika Medical Laboratory,* 1952.

Matsunuga, E.: Intra-uterine selection by the ABO incompatibility of mother and foetus. *Am. J. Human Genet., 7*:66-71, 1954.

Minnich, V., Na-Nakorn, Supa, Chongchareonsuk, S., and Kochaseni, S.: Mediterranean anemia. A study of thirty-two cases in Thailand, *Blood, 9*:1-23, 1954.

Montalenti, C.: The genetics of microcythaemia, *Caryologia, suppl.* :554-563, 1954.

Mourant, A. E.: *The Distribution of the Human Blood Groups,* Oxford, Blackwell, 1954.

Na-Nakorn, Supa, Minnich, V., and Chernoff, A. L.: Studies on hemoglobin E; incidence of hemoglobin E in Thailand, *J. Lab. & Clin. Med., 47*:490-498, 1956.

Neel, J. V.: The inheritance of sickle cell anemia, *Science, 110*:64-66, 1949.

Neel, J. V.: The population genetics of two inherited blood dyscrasias in man, *Cold Spring Harbor Symposia on Quantitative Biology, 15*: 141-158, Cold Spring Harbor, The Biological Laboratory, 1951.

Neel, J. V.: Data pertaining to the population dynamics of sickle cell disease, *Am. J. Human Genet., 5*:154-167, 1953.

Neel, J. V., Wells, I. C., and Itano, H. A.: Familial differences in the proportion of abnormal hemoglobin present in the sickle cell trait, *J. Clin. Invest., 30*:1120-1124, 1951.

Pauling, L., Itano, H. A., Singer, S. J., and Wells, I. C.: Sickle cell anemia, a molecular disease, *Science, 110*:543-548, 1949.

Penrose, L. S.: The meaning of "fitness" in human populations, *Ann.*

Eugen. Lond., 14:301-303, 1949.

Penrose, L. S.: Short and long term influences of various factors on the frequency of genes which affect the characteristics of a population, *Proc. World Population Conf. Rome Meeting 53,* 1954.

Penrose, L. S.: Personal communication, 1955.

Pike, A., and Dickins, A. M.: ABO blood groups and toxaemia of pregnancy, *Brit. M. J., 1*:321-323, 1954.

Powell, W. N., Rodarte, J. C., and Neel, J. V.: The occurrence in a family of Sicilian ancestry of the traits for both sickling and thalassemia, *Blood, 10*:887-897, 1950.

Race, R. R., and Sanger, R.: *Blood Groups in Man,* Oxford, Blackwell, 1954.

Ranney, H. M.: Observations on the inheritance of sickle cell hemoglobin and hemoglobin C, *J. Clin. Invest., 33*:1634-1641, 1954.

Raper, A. B.: Sickle cell disease in Africa and America—a comparison, *J. Trop. Med., 53*:49-53, 1950.

Raper, A. B.: Malaria and the sickling trait, *Brit. M. J., 1*:1186-1189, 1955.

Rich, A.: Studies on the hemoglobin of Cooley's anemia and Cooley's trait, *Proc. Nat. Acad. Sc. Wash., 38*:187-192, 1952.

Roberts, D. F., and Lehmann, H.: A search for abnormal hemoglobins in some southern Sudanese peoples, *Brit. M. J., 1*:519-521, 1955.

Schneider, R. G.: Paper electrophoresis of hemoglobin as a practical method of differentiating various types of sickle cell disease and of hemoglobin "C" trait, *Texas Rep. Biol. & Med., 11*:352-356, 1953.

Sheppard, P. M.: Polymorphism and population studies, *Symp. Soc. Exp. Biol., 7*:274-289, 1953a.

Sheppard, P. M.: Polymorphism, linkage and the blood groups, *Am. Nat., 87*:283-294, 1953b.

Silvestroni, E., and Bianco, I.: Una nuova entita nosologia: "la malattia micro-drepanocitica," *Haematologica, 29*:455-488, 1946.

Singer, K., Chapman, A. Z., Goldberg, S., Rubinstein, H. M., and Rosenblum, S. A.: Studies on abnormal hemoglobins. IX. Pure (homozygous) hemoglobin C disease, *Blood, 9*:1023-1031, 1954.

Singer, K., Chernoff, A. I., and Singer, L.: Idem. I. Their demonstration by means of alkali denaturation, *Blood, 6*:412-428, 1951.

Singer, K., Kraus, A. P., Singer, L., Rubinstein, H. M., and Goldberg, S. R.: Idem. X. Thalassemia-hemoglobin C disease. A new syndrome presumably due to the combination of the genes for thalassemia and hemoglobin C, *Blood, 9*:1047-1054, 1954.

Singer, K., and Fisher, B.: Idem. V. The distribution of type 5 (sickle cell) hemoglobin and type F (alkali resistant) hemoglobin within the red cell population in sickle cell anemia, *Blood, 7*:1216-1226, 1952.

Smith, E. W., and Conley, C. L.: Filter paper electrophoresis of human hemoglobin with special reference to the clinical significance of hemoglobin C, *Bull. Johns Hopkins Hosp., 93*:94-109, 1953.

Smith, E. W., and Conley, C. L.: Clinical features of the genetic variants of sickle cell disease, *Bull. Johns Hopkins Hosp., 94*:289-318, 1954.

Spaet, T. H.: Personal communication, 1955.

Stern, C., Carson, G., Kinst, M., Novitski, E., and Uphoff, D.: The viability of heterozygotes for lethals, *Genetics, 37*:413-449, 1952.

Struthers, D.: ABO groups of infants and children dying in the West of Scotland (1949-1951), *Brit. J. Soc. Med., 5*:223-228, 1951.

Vandepitte, J. M.: Aspects quantitatifs et génétiques de la sicklanémie à Léopoldville, *Ann. Soc. Belge de Med. Trop., 34*:501-516, 1954.

Vandepitte, J. M., Zuelzer, W. W., Neel, J. V., and Colaert, J.: Evidence concerning the inadequacy of mutation as an explanation of the frequency of the sickle cell gene in the Belgian Congo, *Blood, 10*:341-350, 1955.

Waterhouse, J. A. H., and Hogben, L.: Incompatibility of mother and foetus with respect to isoagglutinin a and its antibody, *Brit. J. Soc. Med., 1*:1-17, 1947.

Welbourn, H., and Raper, A. B.: Sickle cell anemia in Uganda, *Brit. M. J., corr. 1*:1440, 1954.

Wells, I. C., and Itano, H. A.: Ratio of sickle cell anemia hemoglobin to normal hemoglobin in sicklemics, *J. Biol. Chem., 188*:65-74, 1951.

Westlund, K., and Heistö, H.: Blood groups in relation to peptic ulceration, *Brit. M. J., 1*:847, 1955.

Weiner, A. S.: The Rh factor and racial origins, *Science, 96*:407-408, 1942.

Wright, S.: The statistical consequences of Mendelian heredity in relation to speciation. In: *The New Systematics*, J. S. Huxley (ed.), London, Oxford, 1940.

Zuelzer, W. W., and Kaplan, E.: Thalassemia-hemoglobin C disease. A new syndrome presumably due to the combination of the genes for thalassemia and hemoglobin C, *Blood, 9*:1047-1054, 1954.

IX. ADMIXTURE AND RACE

Of the various evolutionary mechanisms involved in the formation of human races, only admixture (or "hybridization") was both accepted and commonly investigated from 1850 to 1950. Generations of human experience attested to the frequency of mixture between micro-races, between local races and between geographical races. There could be no doubt that admixture was an important race-forming mechanism and there was no doubt that admixtures of various kinds had been going on for millenia.

Some of the earliest studies on admixture in man were conducted simply to test then-popular notions that the products of admixture were less fertile, less viable or less capable than their more homozygous ancestors. Later, after the phenomenon of heterosis (or hybrid vigour) was discovered by plant geneticists, still other attempts were made to discover examples of heterosis in man. Again, in the early days of human genetics, "hybrid" populations were analyzed in the hope of finding human traits that segregated out in simple Mendelian fashion.

One of the major purposes of studying admixture in man was to find general principles that could be used to reconstruct the genetic history of populations exhibiting considerable polymorphism, presumably because of ancient admixture. As mentioned previously, the variability of the Polynesians was interpreted as indicating multiple origins, and the existence of Caucasoid-like, Negroid-like and Mongoloid-like individuals among the Polynesians was considered proof of a true hybrid origin.

Many of these earlier studies of race-crossing can be criticized as being genetically naive. The selection of polygenic traits such as skin color, yielded results compatible with the incorrect theory of blending inheritance. The identification of "types" in a population once a basic operational approach, may be attributed to chance combinations and need not be indicative of the ancestral groups that entered into admixture.*

The most recent studies of admixture have centered attention on monogenic traits, particularly the human blood groups. Working with such simply-inherited phenomena, students of human genetics have drawn rather interesting conclusions. On the basis of blood-group frequencies, for example, it is unlikely that there is any appreciable proportion of Amerindian genes in the American colored population. The use of the gene-frequency method has provided much better estimates of the extent and direction of admixture in known hybrid populations as shown in the following articles.

While it is obvious that the ABO, MN, Rh, Kell, Kidd and Lutheran factors can make for exceptional accuracy in analyses of recent admixture, attempts to reconstruct the racial history of ancient hybrid populations are still subject to error. Drift, for example, must be excluded, largely by restricting studies to relatively large populations. Natural selection must be ruled out, something that is by no means easy to do. If the frequency of B is 15% in a hybrid population, it may indicate incorporation of equal numbers of high-B and low-B ancestors. Alternatively, it may be due to a loss of B, due to natural selection, or an increase in B, again due to natural selection.

Thus, the study of admixture in man is still largely limited to known populations of recent formation. Inferences as to the original ancestry of old, presumably hybrid populations must be made with caution. In particular, *admixture* should not be the only hypothesis entertained in considering population polymorphism.

ADDITIONAL READINGS

Stuckert, R. P.: African ancestry of the white American population, *Ohio J. Sc.,* *58*:155-160, 1958.

Glass, B. and Li, C. C.: The dynamics of racial intermixture—an analysis based on the American Negro, *Am. J. Human Genet.,* 5:1-20, 1953.

---

*For further discussion of this point see Hunt, E. E. Jr., *American Anthropologist*, *61*:64-87, 1959.

The Dynamics of Racial Intermixture in the American Negro — Some Anthropological Considerations

Reprinted from *American Journal of Human Genetics*, Vol. 7, No. 4, pp. 361-367 (1955).

By D. F. ROBERTS

The recent development, by Drs. Bentley Glass and C. C. Li ('53), of a method making use of gene frequencies for the study of the dynamics of race mixture is a welcome contribution to the genetic aspects of anthropological research. By the application of this method, the authors estimate the average rate of gene flow into the American Negro per generation from the White population, assuming ten generations of intermixture, to be .0358; the accumulated amount of White admixture in their American Negro sample is calculated to be 30.6. The following note endeavours to amplify their conclusions in the light of information more recently available.

The use in their communication of gene frequencies pertaining to South African Bantu, East Africans and Sudanese was satisfactory for demonstration of the statistical model; Glass and Li had of necessity to include these in their calculations on account of the paucity of data then to hand. Acceptance of the gene flow values so obtained however implies that it is immaterial whence the African parental population gene frequencies are derived. That there is a "high degree of uniformity in the distribution of the Rh and MNS groups throughout tropical Africa" does not mean that Rh chromosome frequencies are constant throughout Negro Africa, but only that the overall pattern is generally similar. Thus in every sample yet investigated from Africa south of the Sahara, chromosome cDe is the most frequent, yet its calculated frequency varies between .34 and .82; cde is the second most frequent in more than 85% of samples, yet its value varies from .13 to .28. On the other hand frequencies of the genes of the MN blood group system do tend to be less variable, and much of the variation observed from sample to sample could be explained as random effects in sampling, though there is a slight tendency for the M frequency to increase from west to east. Statistically significant differences occur in the ABO frequencies, which in East Africa for example serve to distinguish the major ethnic subdivisions of the peoples. By reason of these variations, for computations involving actual blood group frequencies, such as are required by Glass and Li's method, it is obvious that in addition to the question of choice of characters to discriminate most clearly between the parental populations, attention has to be given to the choice of population whose gene frequencies are to represent the African parental contribution.

The extensive researches of Herskowits ('28, '33, '42) showed that the provenance of the Negro slaves in the U. S. A. was of more limited area than had been earlier thought. A few were derived from Madagascar and east coast localities, but the large majority originated from the western regions of Africa. The coastlands and a broad belt of territory behind them, in places several hundred miles in depth, extending from Gambia in the north to Angola in the south, provided the bulk of the American slaves. There was a shift in supply from area to area throughout the slaving period, and it is impossible to estimate the proportions of the different African peoples who contributed to the American Negro genetic constitution. Nevertheless the problem relates to an essentially western African population. It is from peoples occupying this zone that the gene frequencies should be drawn for the African parental population in the study of American Negro hybridization.

Relevant to the problem are comprehensive Rh data for four samples from different parts of Nigeria (Chalmers, Ikin and Mourant, '53) and two from the Gold Coast, for Ashanti and Ewe (Armattoe, Ikin and Mourant, '53), examined at the Blood Group Reference Laboratory, London, together with a second for the Ewe (Armattoe, '51) referred to by Glass and Li; two samples from the lower Congo (Lambotte-Legrand, '50) give simple Rh positive and negative data. Information on the MN blood group system is given for all except the two Congo samples, the

TABLE 1

Average Rates of Gene Flow per Generation, Assuming Ten Generations
of Intermixture, from the American White into the American
Negro Population as Represented by Six Samples

African Sample Used	American Negro Sample								
	Baltimore[6]		Washington[7]		Ohio[8] and Southern	New York[9]		New York[10]	Michigan(?)[11]
	Estimate 1[12]	Estimate 2[13]	Estimate 1[12]	Estimate 2[13]		Estimate 1[14]	Estimate 2[15]		
R⁰ (Rh blood group system)									
Ewe[1]	.0214	.0215	.0208	.0209					
Ewe[2]	.0078	.0078	.0072	.0072					
Ashanti[2]	.0235	.0236	.0228	.0229					
S. W. Nigeria[3]	.0312	.0314	.0306	.0307					
S. E. Nigeria[3]	.0244	.0245	.0237	.0239					
Jos Plateau[3]	.0253	.0254	.0246	.0248					
N. Nigeria[3]	.0199	.0200	.0191	.0194					
T (PTC taste)									
W. Africa[4]					.0384				
R¹ (Rh blood group system)									
Ewe[1]	.0219	.0210	.0208	.0198					
Ewe[2]	.0192	.0184	.0183	.0174					
Ashanti[2]	.0087	.0083	.0076	.0073					
S. W. Nigeria[3]	.0271	.0260	.0262	.0250					
S. E. Nigeria[3]	.0303	.0288	.0293	.0280					
Jos Plateau[3]	.0398	.0383	.0388	.0373					
N. Nigeria[3]	.0154	.0147	.0143	.0137					
Jk^b (Kidd blood group system)									
W. Africa[5]						.0221	.0215		
S (MNS blood group system)									
S. W. Nigeria[3]								.0183	.0246
S. E. Nigeria[3]								.0237	.0300
Jos plateau[3]								———	.0041
N. Nigeria[3]								.0112	.0175

[1]Armattoe 1951 (gene frequencies calculated by Glass and Li 1953, Table 3).
[2]Armattoe, Ikin, and Mourant 1953.
[3]Chalmers, Ikin, and Mourant 1953.
[4]Included in results of Barnicot 1950.
[5]Ikin and Mourant 1952.
[6]Glass and Li 1953.
[7]Moore 1955.
[8]Lee 1934, using American White gene frequency of Snyder 1932.
[9]Rosenfield, Vogel, Gibbel, Ohno, and Haber 1953.
[10]Miller, Rosenfield, and Vogel 1951.
[11]Neel and Hanig 1951, using American White gene frequencies of Wiener, Di Diego, and Sokol, 1953.
[12]Using American White gene frequencies of Unger, Weinberg, and Lefkon 1946.
[13]Using American White gene frequencies of Wiener 1945.
[14]Using American White gene frequencies of Allen, Diamond, and Niedziela 1951.
[15]Using American White gene frequencies of Rosenfield, Vogel, Gibbel, Ohno, and Haber 1953.

Ss subdivisions being included among the Nigerian data. Data for the ABO system are to hand for more than a dozen relevant samples, while several studies have been made, mainly on composite samples from West Africa, of the less widely investigated blood groups. Altogether there are now available frequencies of some twenty genes or gene combinations which allow comparisons of western Africans, American Negroes and American Whites.

From these data the gene flow rate into the American Negro has been recalculated, assuming ten generations of intermixture. In the Rh calculations allowance was made where possible for the fact that where no D^u tests are done possessors of the D^u gene may be classified as d (Mourant, '54).

Table 1 shows the estimates of average geneflow rate obtained from the five genes or chromosomes that give the clearest discrimination between the parental populations—discrimination being assessed in terms of the minimum interval between the frequencies obtained in samples of the parental groups. The five characters are arranged in descending order of their discriminatory value. It is interesting that the trend of these estimates is considerably below those found by Glass and Li, the modal value of gene flow rate now occurring between .02 and .025. Plotting of 200 positive estimates obtained from seventeen genes or chromosomes, of which more than half are of little discriminatory value, gives a similar mode, though the range is considerably greater. The amount of White admixture (Table 2) is likewise lower than previous estimates, the modal value, for the five characters given in Table 1, lying between 18 and 22%. The estimate derived from the phenylthiocarbamide taste gene (T) probably may not be as reliable as its position in the table seems to suggest since the West African sample on which it is based, that of Barnicot ('50), comprised only 57 individuals. The gene frequencies used in the computations and the size of sample from which they were derived are given in Table 3.

These figures for gene flow rate and intermixture must again be regarded as provisional. In addition to the difficulties noted by Glass and Li, there is no possibility of weighting the African frequencies to compensate for the different propor-

TABLE 2

PERCENTAGE OF WHITE ADMIXTURE IN THE AMERICAN NEGRO SAMPLES OF TABLE 1

African Sample Used	American Negro Sample								
	Baltimore		Washington		Ohio and Southern	New York		New York	Michigan(?)
	Estimate 1	Estimate 2	Estimate 1	Estimate 2		Estimate 1	Estimate 2		
R⁰									
Ewe	19.46	19.58	18.88	18.99					
Ewe	7.53	7.57	6.86	6.90					
Ashanti	21.14	21.26	20.57	20.68					
S. W. Nigeria	27.17	27.32	26.66	26.80					
S. E. Nigeria	21.88	22.00	21.31	21.43					
Jos Plateau	22.59	22.71	22.04	22.16					
N. Nigeria	18.19	18.30	17.61	17.72					
T									
W. Africa					32.41				
R¹									
Ewe	19.83	19.05	18.95	18.21					
Ewe	17.67	16.95	16.77	16.09					
Ashanti	8.34	7.96	7.33	7.01					
S. W. Nigeria	24.03	23.14	23.20	22.34					
S. E. Nigeria	26.47	25.51	25.67	24.74					
Jos Plateau	33.41	32.31	32.69	31.62					
N. Nigeria	14.33	13.72	13.40	12.84					
Jkᵇ									
W. Africa						20.00	19.56		
S									
S. W. Nigeria								16.90	22.07
S. E. Nigeria								21.34	26.23
Jos Plateau								———	4.04
N. Nigeria								10.61	16.17

tions of these peoples who were transported to the U. S. A. The estimates obtained for the gene flow rate from data relating to small local samples of American Negroes should not be taken as representative of the whole American Negro population. It appears doubtful to assume that there has been no change

TABLE 3

Gene Frequencies from Which the Estimates in
Tables 1 and 2 Were Calculated

African			*American Negro*			*American White*		
Sample	*Sample size*	*Gene frequency*	*Sample*	*Sample size*	*Gene frequency*	*Sample*	*Sample size*	*Gene frequency*
R[0]								
Ewe[1]	853	.547	Baltimore[6]	907	.446	New York[12]	7317	.028
Ewe[2]	161	.480	Washington[7]	937	.449	New York[13]	1000	.031
Ashanti[2]	113	.558						
S. W. Nigeria[3]	145	.602						
S. E. Nigeria[3]	106	.563						
Jos plateau[3]	124	.568						
N. Nigeria[3]	165	.539						
T								
W. Africa[4]	57	.813	Ohio and Southern[8]	3156	.697	Ohio[14]	3643	.455
R[1]								
Ewe[1]	853	.077	Baltimore[6]	907	.145	New York[12]	7317	.420
Ewe[2]	161	.086	Washington[7]	937	.142	New York[13]	1000	.434
Ashanti[2]	113	.120						
S. W. Nigeria[3]	145	.058						
S. E. Nigeria[3]	106	.046						
Jos Plateau[3]	124	.007						
N. Nigeria[3]	165	.099						
Jk[b]								
W. Africa[5]	85	.217	New York[9]	305	.269	Boston[15]	189	.477
						New York[16]	726	.483
S								
S. W. Nigeria[3]	112	.124	New York[10]	580	.160	New York[17]	394	.337
S. E. Nigeria[3]	57	.112	Michigan[11]	96	.171			
Jos Plateau[3]	123	.164						
N. Nigeria[3]	159	.139						

[1]Armattoe 1951 (gene frequencies calculated by Glass and Li 1953, Table 3).
[2]Armattoe, Ikin, and Mourant 1953.
[3]Chalmers, Ikin, and Mourant 1953.
[4]Included in results of Barnicot 1950.
[5]Ikin and Mourant 1952.
[6]Glass and Li 1953.
[7]Moore 1955.
[8]Lee 1934.
[9]Rosenfield, Vogel, Gibbel, Ohno, and Haber 1953.
[10]Miller, Rosenfield, and Vogel 1951.
[11]Neel and Hanig 1951.
[12]Unger, Weinberg, and Lefkon 1946.
[13]Wiener 1945.
[14]Snyder 1932.
[15]Allen, Diamond, and Niedziela 1951.
[16]Rosenfield, Vogel, Gibbel, Ohno, and Haber 1953.
[17]Wiener, Di Diego, and Sokol 1953.

in the gene frequencies of the populations concerned.   Glass
and Li have noted the possibility of different selective forces
under African and American conditions.   Historical facts have
also to be taken into account.   For example, concerning the
White population, the pattern of immigration into the U. S. A.
within the last century shows how the proportions of immigrants
contributed by different regions of Europe has varied, with consequent fluctuation in gene frequencies of the White parental
population.   There should also be considered the tendency for
particular European groups to settle in particular regions of the
U. S. A., especially in the earlier days, with consequent restriction of potential hybridization to only part of the white population.   Such effects however on the genes listed in the table may
well have been slight.

Finally the assumption is made that the American Negro is
the product of hybridization between two, and only two, parental
populations, an assumption noted with reference to the American Indian by Stern ('53).   In Meier's ('49) sample, 69% of his
Mississippi born Negroes were recorded as having some American Indian ancestry, while in Herskowits' ('30) sample, mainly
from the mid Atlantic and southeastern states, 27% were so recorded.   None of the few American Indian tribes whose serology
has as yet been investigated in detail is likely to have made an
important contribution to the American Negro hybrid, and known
regional differences in blood group frequency among Indian
tribes preclude accurate estimates of the gene frequencies which
Indians of the South and East must have contributed.   However
the general pattern of gene frequency, as regards the characters
listed in the table, may perhaps be inferred from what is known
for Indians of the Plains and the South West.   Only for gene T
does the frequency found in the American Indian resemble that
of the African—and it has been pointed out above that the estimate
of intermixture here derived from this character may not be very
reliable.   Otherwise, as regards frequencies of R^0, R', Jk^b, and
S, the American Indian tends to be much more similar to the
European than to the African; in each does the hybrid frequency
fall intermediately between the African figure on the one hand

and those of the European and American Indian on the other. That is to say that for these characters the shift in gene frequency of the American Negro away from that of the African is due to the combined effect of European and Indian admixture, each reinforcing not counteracting the other. It therefore appears that the above estimates of the European contribution to the American Negro gene-pool may be too high, by a greater or lesser degree proportional to the magnitude of the Indian contribution.

SUMMARY

The average gene flow rate per generation from the American White population into the American Negro population has been recalculated using data from western Africa, the region whence the majority of the Negro slaves were derived, to represent the African parental population. The modal value for gene flow rate assuming ten generations of intermixture falls between .02 and .025, while the amount of accumulated White admixture is estimated as about 20%. That these estimates are provisional has been stressed.

REFERENCES

For the numerous publications on which are based the general statements in the text concerning gene frequencies, the reader is referred to the invaluable compilation of Mourant ('54) listed below.

Allen, F. H., Diamond, L. K. and Niedziela, B.: A new blood-group antigen, *Nature, 167*:482, 1951.

Armattoe, R. E. G.: ABO and Rh blood types among the Ewes of West Africa, *Am. J. Phys. Anthropol., N.S. 9*:371-373, 1951.

Armattoe, R. E. G., Ikin, E. W. and Mourant, A. E.: The ABO, Rh and MN blood groups of the Ewe and the Ashanti of the Gold Coast, *West African M. J.,* 2:89-93, 1953.

Barnicot, N. A.: Taste deficiency for phenylthiourea in African Negroes and Chinese, *Ann. Eugen., Lond., 15*:248-254, 1950.

Chalmers, J. N. M., Ikin, E. W. and Mourant, A. E.: The ABO, MNS and Rh blood groups of the Nigerians, *Ann. Eugen., Lond., 17*:168-176, 1953.

Glass, B. and Li, C. C.:   The dynamics of racial intermixture—an analysis based on the American Negro, *Am. J. Human Genet.*, 5:1-20, 1953.

Herskovits, M. J.:   *The American Negro: A Study in Racial Crossing,* New York, Knopf, 1928.

Herskovits, M. J.:   *The Anthropometry of the American Negro,* New York, Columbia University Press, 1930.

Herskovits, M. J.:   On the provenience of New World Negroes, *Social Forces, 12*:252-262, 1933.

Herskovits, M. J.:   *The Myth of the Negro Past,* New York, Harper, 1942.

Ikin, E. W. and Mourant, A. E.:   The frequency of the Kidd blood-group antigen in Africans, *Man, 52*:21, 1952.

Lambotte-Legrand, J. and Lambotte-Legrand, C.:   Repartition des groupes sanguins des types A, B, O et Rh chex les indigenes du Bas-Congo, *Ann. Soc. Belge Med. Trop., 30*:547-552, 1950.

Lee, B. F.:   A genetic analysis of taste deficiency in the American Negro, *Ohio J. Sc., 34*:337-342, 1934.

Meier, A.:   A study of the racial ancestry of the Mississippi college Negro, *Am. J. Phys. Anthropol., N. S.* 7:227-240, 1949.

Miller, E. B., Rosenfield, R. E. and Vogel, P.:   On the incidence of some of the new blood agglutinogens in Chinese and Negroes, *Am. J. Phys. Anthropol., N. S. 9*:115-126, 1951.

Moore, R. E.:   Distribution of blood factors, ABO, MN and Rh in a group of American Negroes, *Am. J. Phys. Anthropol., N. S. 13*:121-128, 1955.

Mourant, A. E.:   *The Distribution of the Human Blood Groups,* Oxford, Blackwell, 1954.

Neel, J. V. and Hanig, M. M.:   The inheritance and frequency of the MNS factor in the American Negro, *Genetics, 36*:84-92, 1951.

Rosenfield, R. E., Vogel, P., Gibbel, N., Ohno, G. and Haber, G.:   Anti Jk[a]: three new examples of the isoantibody.   Frequency of the factor in Caucasians, Negroes and Chinese of New York City, *Am. J. Clin. Path., 23*:1222-1225, 1953.

Snyder, L. H.:   The inheritance of taste deficiency, *Ohio J. Sc., 32*: 436-440, 1932.

Stern, C.:   Modal estimates of the frequency of white and near white segregants in the American Negro, *Acta Genet. Statist. Med., 4*:281-298, 1953.

Unger, L. J., Weinberg, M. and Lefkon, M.:   The Rh factor as applied to the operation of blood banks, *Am. J. Clin. Path., 16*:498-505, 1946.

Wiener, A. S.: The Rh blood types and some of their applications, *Am. J. Clin. Path., 15*:106-121, 1945.

Wiener, A. S., DiDiego, N. and Sokol, S.: Studies on the heredity of the human blood groups. I. The M-N types, *Acta Genet. Med. et Gemel., 2*:391-397, 1953.

On the Unlikelihood of Significant Admixture of Genes from the North American Indians in the Present Composition of the Negroes of the United States

Reprinted from *American Journal of Human Genetics,* Vol. 7, No. 4, pp. 368-385 (1955).

By Bentley Glass

Glass and Li ('53), in their first effort to examine the dynamics of racial intermixture, deliberately oversimplified the interplay of factors responsible for the present status of the North American Negro, in order to construct a model that in principle would exemplify the effects of gene flow between populations. Two aspects of their simplified model have received a certain amount of criticism. In the first place, although they implicitly recognized that the great majority of the slaves brought to North America were derived from West Africa, yet, in the absence of data on the frequencies of certain blood groups among West African natives, they utilized frequencies from Bantu (MN; Rh), from East African tribes (Rh; PTC taste capacity), and from the Sudan (PTC taste capacity). This was done in the hope that PTC taste capacity, like the Rh and MNS blood groups, would, in Mourant's words, prove to reveal a "high degree of uniformity in the distribution . . . throughout tropical Africa" (pers. commun.). Now that Chalmers, Ikin, and Mourant ('53) have published data on four geographical groups of Nigerians, and Armattoe, Ikin, and Mourant ('53) have supplied further data on the Ewe and Ashanti of the Gold Coast, it seems desirable to recheck the original calculations in order to see whether the estimates of the amount of White admixture in the North American Negro and the gene flow per generation were seriously in error.

In the second place, Stern ('53) and others (Sturtevant, pers. commun.) have remarked on the failure in our original

234

treatment to take into account the considerable amount of genetic admixture between the American Indians and the North American Negro populations. Herskovits ('30) and Meier ('49) have been cited to indicate the very high proportion of Negro college students who claim some American Indian ancestry. Stern has justly criticized the generality and validity of these data. They may possibly apply better to the Mississippi Valley region than to the Eastern United States. More important is the fact that a very few American Indian ancestors seven to ten generations back might have numerous descendants in the North American Negro population of the present day. Clearly, the number of persons who claim to have at least one American Indian ancestor yields no clue whatsoever to the amount of gene flow from the Indian into the Negro population, particularly during the more recent generations.

The recent publication of the blood group frequencies of the Chippewa Indians of Northern Minnesota, by Matson, Koch, and Levine ('54), supplies somewhat better data for estimating the American Indian contribution to the North American Negro gene pool than previously existed, although obviously if we had data on the blood group frequencies of the Cherokees or the Iroquois, these would be even better. The Chippewas themselves almost certainly never intermingled with the North American Negroes to any great extent, if at all; and the allele frequencies among the Chippewas can only be taken as substitutes for those of the more eastern and southern tribes. These are in most cases now so broken up and so intermixed with White genetic elements that it may never be possible to find a reliable sample of the original Indian tribes. The Chippewas at least indicate the chief features of the Eastern and Southern tribes better than the Southwestern tribes (Navaho, Apache, Pueblo Indians) would be likely to do; and the classification of the Chippewas into "pure," "greater than 3/4" "less than 3/4" enables one, as with no other set of data, to use in the calculations values approximating those of the aboriginal American Indians.

The central, crucial estimate in these calculations is that of the frequency of the R^0 (cDe) allele, because of the tremendous difference between its frequencies in the West African and the White populations. It is also of special importance that the R^0 frequencies in the Whites (0.028) and Amerindians (0.000) scarcely differ at all. The R^0 frequencies can therefore be utilized to calculate the total genetic change between the West African and the North American Negroes, *irrespective of the relative magnitudes of the contributions to the hybrid population made by Whites and Amerindians.* Hence it is possible to test the problematical contribution of the Amerindians by first calculating expectancies for each gene on the basis of the hypothesis that all the shift in the R^0 frequency from the West African value to the North American Negro value has been produced by admixture with the White population, and then checking these expectancies against the actual frequencies observed in the North American Negro population. Several situations arise: (a) when W. African and White frequencies are the same and the Amerindian frequency is different; (b) when the White and Amerindian frequencies deviate from the W. African frequencies in the same direction but to a different degree; and (c) when the White and Amerindian frequencies deviate from the W. African frequency in opposed directions.

A REESTIMATION OF THE GENE FLOW BETWEEN N. AMERICAN WHITE AND NEGRO POPULATIONS

The former estimate of the frequency of the R^0 allele among African Negroes was 0.630 (Glass and Li, '53), derived from the value for the East Africans given by Donegani, Ibrahim, Ikin, and Mourant ('50). This value was selected simply because it was intermediate between the value for the South African Bantu, 0.633 (Shapiro, '51) and that for the Ewe of the Gold Coast, 0.593 (Armattoe, '50). It may seem that the latter value, the only one available from West Africa at the time, ought to have been used in making the estimate; but the marked deviations from other African Negro values in the $R1$ (*CDe*) and R^2 (*cDE*) values in Armattoe's data for the Ewe made us somewhat distrustful of his determinations (see Glass and Li, Table 3). We would have

TABLE 1

ESTIMATION OF THE AMOUNT OF GENETIC ADMIXTURE IN AND GENE FLOW
INTO THE NORTH AMERICAN NEGROES, CALCULATED FROM
THE FREQUENCIES OF CHROMOSOME

R^o (cDe)

W. African Negroes	$D + D^u$	D	U. S. White		Amerindian	
S. Nigeria (2)*	.6004	.5820	New York City (1)	.0279	Chippewa (1)	.0000
N. Nigeria (2)	.6090	.5532				
Nigeria (4)	.6047	.5676				
Ewe (1)	.5478	.4795				
Ashanti (1)	.6244	.5576				
W. Africa (6)	.5985	.5512				

U. S. Negroes
Baltimore (1) .4381
Average (4) .4332

$$Admixture = 1.00 - \frac{q_k - Q}{q - Q}$$

	Lower estimate	Higher estimate
$D + D^u$	$1.00 - \dfrac{.4381 - .0279}{.5985 - .0279} = 28.1\%$	$or \quad 1.00 - \dfrac{.4332 - .0279}{.5985 - .0279} = 28.97\%$
D	$1.00 \quad \dfrac{.4381 - .0279}{.5512 - .0279} = 21.62\%$	$or \quad 1.00 - \dfrac{.4332 - .0279}{.5512 - .0279} = 22.55\%$

Gene Flow

	$D + D^u$	D
m —	.0325 or .0336	.0241 or .0252

Data from following sources: *Nigeria*, (SW — 145; SE — 106; Jos Plateau — 124; N — 165) Chalmers, Ikin, and Mourant, 1953 (M); *Ewe* (161), Armattoe, Ikin, and Mourant, 1953 (M); *Ashanti* (113), Armattoe, Ikin, and Mourant, 1953 (M); *U. S. White* (7317), Unger, Weinberg, and Lefkon, 1946 (M); *Chippewa* (161), Matson, Koch, and Levine, 1954; *Baltimore Negroes* (907), Glass and Li, 1953 (M); *New York Negroes,* (135) Levine, 1945 (M); (231) Wiener et al., 1944; (284) Wiener and Gordon, 1952 (M). Chromosome frequencies are those calculated by Mourant (1954) by the method of maximum likelihood, or are averages derived from them by the methods described in the text. The numbers in parentheses given with the sources of data in this and the following tables are the numbers of individuals in the respective series. [M, Mourant, 1954]

*In this and the following tables the numbers in parentheses are the numbers of separate series used in the respective estimates.

done well to use his R^0 value, since it turns out to be almost exactly right.

In the present calculations there arises the problem of what to do with the D^u frequency. In serological testing D^u sometimes reacts as D, sometimes as d, depending on the antiserum used. Mourant ('54) proposes that D^u be reckoned as equivalent to d in series where no test for D^u was performed. But on the other hand, there is evidence that D^u has arisen chiefly, if not entirely, at the expense of D. Since it is not clear at what time in the past this has taken place and since the frequency of D^u varies considerably, from 0.00% to 11.27%, among the Nigerians, it might be better to base the estimate on the total of $D + D^u$. Unfortunately, there is at present no evidence regarding the frequency of D^u among the North American Negroes. Consequently the best that can be done is to make the estimate both ways, so as to set upper and lower limits to the estimate of gene flow based on R^0. It is also uncertain whether it would be better to assume that the slaves came mainly from the coastal areas of West Africa, from the interior, or from both equally. If D and D^u are combined, the total would not be sensibly different for Southern and Northern Nigeria; but if D^u is excluded the value for Southern Nigeria is higher than for Northern Nigeria (see Table 1). Again, if D and D^u are combined, the value for the Ashanti is higher and that for the Ewe is lower than the average for the four parts of Nigeria; but if D^u is excluded, the Ashanti value is slightly lower than the value for all Nigeria, and the Ewe value is very much below. It is clear that the values show much better agreement when D and D^u are totalled than when D is taken alone.

Another problem is how best to average the values for different areas when the samples are different in size. If the samples were drawn from a homogeneous population, then the average should be weighted according to the respective sizes of the contributory samples. Thus, in the previous study (Glass and Li, '53) the samples of North American Negroes from New York City (2 series) and from Baltimore (1 series) did not prove to be significantly different from one another and the R^0 frequency was therefore calculated by combining the three samples. In

West Africa the tribes are clearly heterogeneous. Sample size must therefore be ignored unless it is proportional to population in each and every tribe. There being no assurance that this is the case, it seems better to treat each sampled tribe or area as a unit, adding the calculated frequencies for each sampled population and dividing by the number of such populations. Inasmuch as the sample size for the six available West African populations ranged only from 106 to 167, there is little error in considering them as equal. It would be far more important to know the actual provenience of the slaves taken to North America, but it seems impossible to do better than to sample as wide a range of populations from West Africa as possible, from Gambia in the north to Angola in the south (Herskovits, '28, '33, '42). In time, the data to refine the present estimates should be available.

Certain other values in making the estimates have been altered. The R^0 frequency for the U. S. Whites remains the same, for although several more series of Rh tests on U. S. Whites have been reported, none compare in extensiveness with the great series of Unger *et al.* ('46) and the other series are in reasonable agreement with it. Wiener has reported two series of New York City Whites, in one of which the R^0 frequency was .0309 (N = 1468) and in the other .0260 (N = 743), and Levine has reported one with a frequency of .0335 (N = 335). The average of all four series is .0284, not significantly different from the large series alone. The series of Minnesota Whites included by Matson *et al.* in the study of the Chippewa Indians seems to be so far out of line with other Whites, even from Scandinavia, whence many of the Minnesotans are derived, that it has seemed best to ignore them in these calculations.

In reexamining the data from the series of New York City Negroes published by Wiener, Belkin, and Sonn ('44), and comparing these with the data given in Table 21 of Mourant ('54), a source of considerable confusion was uncovered. Mourant cites Wiener, Sonn, and Belkin ('43), Wiener, Sonn, and Belkin ('44), and *ibid.*, in three successive rows of the table. These might be taken as three independent samples of the U. S. Negro population. However, they are not so, for the two papers include essentially the same individuals, as the original papers state. The final report on these individuals is contained in Wiener, Belkin, and Sonn ('44), in which a footnote to Table 3 states that it includes, together with a few additional bloods, the data reported in Wiener, Sonn, and Belkin ('44). The final report, like the second paper which was used by Mourant, breaks up the data into two series, in which the numbers of individuals were respectively 94 and 137, or a total of 231, after excluding two cases of atypical reaction. Glass and Li ('53) used the frequencies of the Rh sub-types as cited by Potter ('47) from the final report. But Potter undertook to combine the two series, and in so doing recorded a wrong total; and thus all the frequencies she calculated were in error. From the report by Wiener, Belkin, and Sonn I have reestimated the gene frequencies and have applied Bernstein's correction, which the authors failed to do. The revised values are as follows: No. 231; R^1 (*CDe*), 0.1706; R^2 (*cDE*), 0.1618; R^0 (*cDe*), 0.3589; r' (*Cde*), 0.0217; r'' (*cdE*), 0.0069. These revised values have been used in all the calculations of this paper in which reference is made to Wiener *et al.* ('44).

An additional U. S. Negro series is now available (Wiener, Gordon, and Cohen, '52), with an R^0 frequency of 0.4675 (N = 284). The series by Miller, Rosenfield, and Vogel ('51) has not been used because those authors state that they specifically selected subjects for darkness of skin. It is therefore not surprising that they found the highest R^0 frequency of all, namely 0.4850. Such data cannot be used to characterize the whole U. S. Negro population, as socially defined.

Table 1 reveals that the reduction of the frequency of R^0 from 0.630 to 0.600 (if D and D^u are combined) slightly reduces the previous estimate of the amount of white admixture in the North American Negro gene pool; and that if D alone is used the estimated admixture is reduced very considerably, being lowered from 30 percent to 22 or 23 percent. The estimated gene flow per generation is correspondingly reduced. The lower and upper limits of estimate are .0241 and .0336 per generation, rather than .0358 (Glass and Li, '53).

There are three other genes the frequencies of which are

TABLE 2

AMOUNT OF GENETIC ADMIXTURE IN THE NORTH AMERICAN NEGRO
CALCULATED FROM THE FREQUENCIES OF THE
S AND MS BLOOD GROUP GENES

S

W. African Negro			*U. S. White*		*Amerindian*	
S. Nigeria	(2)	.1176				
N. Nigeria	(2)	.1512				
Nigeria	(4)	.1344	New York (1)	.3374	Chippewa (1)	.3416

*Expectancy:**	$D + D^u$	.1915 — .1933
	D	.1783 — .1802

*Observed:**
U. S. Negroes (1)   .1708

Admixture: 17.92%

MS

W. African Negro			*U. S. White*		*Amerindian*	
S. Nigeria	(2)	.0803				
N. Nigeria	(2)	.0899				
Nigeria	(4)	.0851	New York (1)	.2524	Chippewa (1)	.2829

*Expectancy:**	$D + D^u$	.1320 — .1336
	D	.1213 — .1229

*Observed:**
U. S. Negro (1)   .0933

Admixture: 4.9%

Data from following sources: *Nigeria* (451), Chalmers, Ikin, and Mourant, 1953 (M); *U. S. White* (394), Wiener, Di Diego, and Sokol, 1953 (M); *Chippewa* (161), Matson, Koch, and Levine, 1954; *U. S. Negroes,* Mich. (96), Neel and Hanig, 1951 (M). [M, Mourant, 1954]

*This and the following tables are so arranged that the respective positions of the expectancies and observed (U. S. Negro) values indicate roughly their relative positions on a scale delimited by the gene frequencies in the W. African Negro and U. S. White. Thus it can be seen at a glance from the present table that the observed frequencies do not depart from those of the W. African Negro quite as much as would be expected on the basis of the R^o frequencies.

approximately the same in the North American Indian and the U. S. White, and which can therefore be used to check the overall admixture of foreign genes with the original heritage of the American slaves. These are S and the MS combination at the MNS locus, and the K/k alleles of the Kell blood groups. Table 2 demonstrates that the S allele in the aggregate ($MS + NS$) yields an estimate of 17.92% of admixture; but when the MS combination alone is used, the admixture is found to be only 4.9%. The latter value is so far below all other estimates that we may be sure it is unreliable, and this throws doubt on the estimate based on S as well. It is not difficult to determine the sources of unreliability here. Of the two available series of tests reporting the distribution of MNS in the North American Negroes, the larger is that compiled by Miller, Rosenfield, and Vogel ('51), which must unfortunately be discarded for the present purposes, for the reason already given. The remaining series (Neel and Hanig, '51) numbers only 96 individuals, so that the experimental error is high. The only available U. S. Negro series for the Kell antigens is that of Miller *et al.*, so that for the present we must forego its use. In any case, the range between the frequency in West African Negroes (.0000-.0088, 2 series) and the frequencies of U. S. Whites (.0599, 2 series) and American Indians (.0776, Chippewas) is at the lower limit of usefulness.

For purposes of comparing the amounts of admixture calculated from different gene frequencies, an expectancy for the frequency in the U. S. Negro is calculated in each case from the R^o data. This is done by multiplying the difference between the frequencies in the West African Negroes and the U. S. Whites by the amount of admixture calculated for the R^o gene (28.1% — 27.4% for $D + D^u$; 21.6% — 20.8% for D). For example, for S, one finds $.3374 - .1344 = .2030$. 28.1% of this $= .0571$, which added to .1344 gives .1915, the upper limit of the expectancy if the parameter $D + D^u$ is used.

A situation analogous to that in which the U. S. White and Indian frequencies are alike is that wherein the gene frequencies in the American Indian and the West African Negro populations are nearly identical, whereas the frequency in the U. S. White population is quite different. In this situation, too, no genetic introgression from the American Indian into the U. S. Negro population would be detectable, and all the difference between the West African and U. S. Negro populations would be attributable to admixture with the White population. This relationship is exemplified by the Kidd blood group alleles, Jk^a/Jk^b (Table 3).

TABLE 3

THE KIDD (Jk^a) BLOOD GROUP FREQUENCIES

W. African Negro	Amerindian		U. S. White
Nigeria (1) .783	Blood (1) Obs.	.722	(2) .518
	Corr.	.770	

Expectancy:	$D + D^u$	.709 — .706	
	D	.726 — .723	

Observed:
U. S. Negro — New York (1)   .7315

Admixture: 19.4%

Sources of data: W. *Africans* (85), Ikin and Mourant, 1952; *Blood* (194), Chown and Lewis, 1953 (M); U. S. *White* (Boston, 189), Allen, Diamond, and Niedziela, 1951 (M); (New York, 726), Rosenfield, Vogel, Gibbel, Ohno, and Haber, 1953 (M); U. S. *Negro* (New York, 305), Rosenfield et al. 1953 (M). [M, Mourant, 1954]

No data for the Chippewas are available for the Kidd antigens, but Chown and Lewis ('53) have reported series of tests of the Blood and Blackfoot Indians. The former series included 194 individuals. Chown and Lewis, on the basis of the assumed absence of *B* and *cde* from pure Indians and the frequency of these genes in the Bloods, estimated that approximately one-sixth of the present genes in the tribe are of White origin; and thus arrived at an estimate of .77 for the gene frequency of Jk^a. But there is in any case a very strong objection to using data from the Blood and Blackfoot tribes in such studies as the present one. The Blood and Blackfoot are among the American Indian tribes possessing the highest known frequencies in the world of *A*

(.64), and in this respect they depart radically from the more eastern Indian tribes, whose frequency of A (see Snyder, '26) is low and ranges from a maximum of .151 down to .035. For example, the Bloods are markedly different in their frequency of A from the Chippewas (.088). Consequently, until something is known of the frequency of the Kidd alleles in other American Indian tribes, the comparison with the Bloods may be entirely misleading. The data for Africans reported by Ikin and Mourant ('53) include, among 120 tested individuals, 20 who were from Kenya (Luo). These have been subtracted so as to give a purely Nigerian (Jos Plateau and S. Nigerian) sample. The data for the U. S. Negro are those of Rosenfield, Vogel, Gibbel, Ohno, and Haber ('53). As in apparently all of the studies by Rosenfield and his collaborators on the U. S. Negroes, individuals were selected for their dark skin color. These data therefore fail to provide suitable material for studying the degree of foreign admixture in the total U. S. Negro population. At the same time, as Table 3 clearly shows, the amount of admixture in these selected individuals is very considerable and in fact approaches very closely the amount predicted from the R^0 frequencies when D alone is used for the estimation and D^u is excluded from consideration. From general genetic considerations, this agreement is what would be expected unless certain genes for dark skin color were very closely linked with the particular blood group loci being studied and the racial intermixture had been limited to a couple of generations. Otherwise segregation and recombination of loci would occur, and the selection of individuals on the basis of one genetic trait would not afford a good index to their "racial purity" in respect to other genetic traits. However, if the skin color differences between Negroes and Whites rest, as Stern ('53) has estimated, upon 4 to 6 loci, then linkage could have a small, if not precisely calculable, effect upon the blood group frequencies. Moreover, the U. S. Negro is assuredly not a panmictic population, but a heterogeneous population with real differences in frequency of admixture. Consequently, the darker an individual's skin color the greater the chance that the rest of his genotype approximates the original West African constitution. Such appears to be shown by the fact that in most instances the data for the U. S. Negro gathered by Rosenfield and his co-workers (see Miller, Rosenfield, and Vogel, '51) yield frequencies somewhat closer to those of the West African Negro than do the other, more randomly sampled, series of data for the U. S. Negro. It is indeed difficult to see what group the Negroes in the series of Rosenfield *et al.* represent, except themselves alone. They clearly do not represent either the West African Negroes or the generality of U. S. Negroes.

CASES WHEREIN THE ENTIRE SHIFT IN GENE FREQUENCY WOULD BE ATTRIBUTABLE TO GENETIC ADMIXTURE OF AMERINDIANS AND NEGROES

In certain cases the allelic frequencies in the West African Negroes and the North American Whites are identical or exceedingly similar. Whenever that is the case, and whenever at the same time the allelic frequency in the North American Indians is quite different, any significant observed difference between the West African Negroes and the North American Negroes must be attributable wholly to non-White, i. e., to Amerindian, admixture. Two blood group genes fall into this category, namely, O of the ABO blood group system and M of the MN blood group system. In the former instance, the American Indian exceeds the West African Negro by 23.18% and in the latter instance by 34.2%.

For the ABO blood groups there are, in addition to the recent data for the Chippewa, two other available series in which an effort was made to separate pure from mixed Indians. These series are those for the Cherokees (Snyder, '26) and Sioux (Matson and Schrader, '33). It should be noted that the Cherokee series has not been entered as such in Boyd's compilation of blood group data ('39); for Boyd entered only the values for the entire series, of 250 individuals, mixed and pure combined. However, Snyder stated in the text of his paper that 110 of the 250 were known from "records and the personal knowledge of the physician" to be pure and that, among these, 93.6 percent were of

TABLE 4

COMPARISONS OF GENE FREQUENCIES IN CASES WHEREIN THE W. AFRICAN NEGRO AND
U. S. WHITE FREQUENCIES ARE NEARLY IDENTICAL AND THE N. AMERICAN
INDIAN FREQUENCY IS QUITE DIFFERENT

O

W. African Negro		*U. S. White*		*Amerindian*	
Nigeria (4)	.730	New York City (1)		Chippewa (1)	.936
			.674	Cherokee (1)	.9675
Other W. African (5)	.673	N. Car.? (1)		Sioux (1)	.947
Average (9)	.704			Aver. (3)	.950

Expectancy:
$D + D^u$ .696 — .695
D .698 — .697

Observed:
U. S. Negro (3)   .679

M

W. African Negro		*U. S. White*		*Amerindian*	
Ewe (2)	.568	New York City (3) .540		Chippewa (1) .718	
Ashanti (1)	.438				
Nigeria (4)	.460				
W. Africa (6)	.476				

Expectancy:
$D + D^u$ .494 — .495
D .490

Observed:
U. S. Negro (5)   .489

Sources of data:

O. *W. African Negro:* (2251) Yoruba, Sierra Leone, Fr. Guinea, Senegal, Ewe (B; G and L); Nigeria (542), Chalmers, et al., 1953 (M). *U. S. White:* New York (10,000), Tiber (B; G and L); N. Car.? (20,000) Snyder (B; G and L). *Amer. Indian:* Chippewa (161), Matson, et al., 1954; Cherokee (110), Snyder, 1926; Sioux (48), Matson and Schrader, (B). *U. S. Negro:* Baltimore (605), Glass and Li, 1953; N. Car.? (500), Snyder (B; G and L); New York City (730), Landsteiner and Levine (B; G and L).

M. *W. African Negro:* Ewe (853), Armattoe, 1951 (M); Ewe (161), Armattoe et al., 1953 (M); Ashanti (113), Armattoe et al., 1953 (M); Nigeria (500) Chalmers et al., 1953 (M). *U. S. White:* Combined (6129), Wiener, 1943; New York City (582), Wiener et al., 1944 (M); New York City (954), Wiener, et al., 1953 (M). *Amer. Indian:* Chippewa (161), Matson et al., 1954. *U. S. Negro:* Baltimore (580), Glass and Li (M); New York City, combined (278), Wiener, 1943 (M); New York (227) Wiener et al., 1945 (M); Michigan (96), Neel and Hanig, 1951 (M). [B, Boyd, 1939; G and L, Glass and Li, 1953; M, Mourant, 1954]

Group I (O), whereas among those known to be mixed the proportion was 59.3 percent. Unfortunately, the frequencies of groups A and B among the 110 pure Cherokees were not given. The data on the Sioux, from Matson and Schrader, are equally valuable for the present purpose, because the Sioux and Cherokees—particularly the latter—represent much better than the Chippewas the Indian tribes which may have had an opportunity to intermix in some degree with the North American Negroes. For the Sioux, fortunately, the frequencies of all the ABO groups are given. It is important, in considering the validity of the use in the present study of the Chippewas to represent the American Indians with whom the Negroes might have interbred, that Chippewas, Cherokees, and Sioux, all three, agree extremely closely in all of those comparisons which can be made between them in these limited data.

Table 4 demonstrates that in neither of these exceptionally favorable cases for detecting the introgression of an American Indian element into the U. S. Negro is there any sign of a significant admixture.

CASES WHERE BOTH WHITE AND AMERINDIAN GENE FREQUENCIES DEPART FROM THE WEST AFRICAN IN THE SAME DIRECTION, BUT THE AMERINDIAN TO A SMALLER DEGREE

When this situation obtains, the effect of any signficant amount of gene flow from the American Indian into the U. S. Negro population would tend to reduce the divergence of the latter from the West African frequencies below the expectancy calculated upon the assumption that all significant admixture of U. S. Negroes was with the U. S. White population. This may be termed a case of "supplementary action, diminished by Amerindian effect." Two cases of this relationship exist, R^1 of the Rh alleles and P. In the former the difference between the frequencies in the W. African Negro and the U. S. White is 35.11%, between the Amerindian and White 8.36%. Thus the working range is large, but the difference to be expected in the event of

TABLE 5

COMPARISONS OF GENE FREQUENCIES IN CASES WHEREIN THE SERIATION IS
W. AFRICAN NEGRO, N. AMERICAN INDIAN, AND U. S. WHITE
(Supplementary Action, Diminished by Amerindian Effect)

$R1$

W. African Negro		*Amerindian*		*U. S. White*	
Ewe (1)	.0858	Chippewa (1)	.3367	New York City (3)	.4203
Ashanti (1)	.1195				
Nigeria (4)	.0500				
Average (6)	.0692				

Expectancy:

$D + D^u$	.1675 — .1705
D	.145 — .148

Observed:

U. S. Negro (3)	.1582

P

W. African Negro		*Amerindian*		*U. S. White*	
Nigeria (2)	.7803	Chippewa	.6069	New York City (2)	.5225
				Minnesota (1)	.5745
				Average (3)	.5420

Expectancy:

$D + D^u$	.713 — .712
D	.728 — .726

Observed:

U. S. Negro (2)	.847(!)

Sources of data:

$R1$. *W. African Negro:* Ewe (161), Armattoe et al., 1953 (M); Ashanti (113), Armattoe et al., 1953 (M); Nigeria (540), Chalmers et al., 1953 (M); *Amer. Indian:*
Chippewa (161), Matson et al., 1954. *U. S. White:* New York City (7317), Unger
et al., 1946 (M); N.Y.C. (1071), Wiener and Gordon, 1949 (M); N.Y.C. (1468),
Wiener et al., 1945 (M). *U. S. Negro:* N.Y.C. (231), Wiener et al., 1944; N.Y.C.
(135) Levine, 1945 (G and L; M); Baltimore (907), Glass and Li, 1953 (M).

P. *W. African Negro:* Nigeria (114), Barnicot and Lawler, 1953 (M); Nigeria (29),
Chalmers et al., 1953 (M). *Amer. Indian:* Chippewa (161), Matson et al., 1954.
U. S. White: N.Y.C. (265), Landsteiner and Levine, 1929 (M); N.Y.C. (237),
Wiener and Unger, 1944 (M); Minnesota (300), Matson et al., 1954. *U. S. Negro:*
N.Y.C. (267), Landsteiner and Levine, 1929 (M); N.Y.C. (73) Wiener and Unger,
1944 (M). [M, Mourant, 1954]

even a very large Amerindian admixture would be slight. As for *P*, the difference between the frequencies in the U. S. White and W. African Negro is 23.83%, but between the American Indian and White only 6.49%; so that the minimizing effect to be expected in case there is any significant American Indian admixture would be even less apparent than in the instance of the R^1 frequencies.

Table 5 presents the analysis of the available data. Clearly there is no evidence of any significant amount of Indian admixture in the R^1 frequencies, if the expectancy is based on *D* alone; and even if based on $D + D^u$, the diminution in the observed frequency is less than 1 percent, which must be considerably below the limit of experimental error.

In regard to *P*, an anomalous situation exists, for the mean frequency reported in the N. American Negroes is actually greater than the frequency reported in the W. African Negroes, although it would be expected, on the basis of all the other evidence as to the amount of genetic modification of the N. American Negro, to be less. [In only one series has a lower value than that in the W. African Negroes been reported, and that, strangely enough, in one of the studies by Miller *et al.* (cited from Mourant, '54) in which presumably the group was selected for dark skin color. The two series by Miller *et al.* have been excluded from the tabulation, but would not modify the conclusions if averaged in.] Consequently, the values reported for the frequencies of *P* must be regarded as unreliable in some or all series, and cannot be used in answering the present problem. It is indeed well known among serological workers (Levine, pers. commun.) that antisera for *P* are quite variable and that reliable comparisons between different groups of individuals cannot be made unless all of them were typed with the same antiserum.

CASES WHEREIN BOTH WHITE AND AMERINDIAN GENE FREQUENCIES DEPART FROM THE WEST AFRICAN IN THE SAME DIRECTION, BUT THE AMERINDIAN TO A GREATER DEGREE

In this situation, the effect of a significant amount of gene flow from the American Indian into the N. American Negro population would tend to increase the divergence of the latter from the West African frequencies so as to attain values greater than the expectancies calculated upon the assumption of gene flow into the Negro population from the U. S. White population alone. This might be called "supplementary action, enhanced by Amerindian effect."

Three genes, B of the ABO system, R^2 of the Rh system, and Ns of the MNS system, exhibit this relationship. In the case of B, the difference in gene frequency between the highest and lowest of the three base populations, the West African and the N. American Indian, is quite small, being only 15.13%. The U. S. White frequency is, however, almost exactly intermediate between the W. African and the American Indian, so that if the genetic introgression from the Indian population into the U. S. Negro population has been considerable, it might be detected. R^2 presents a highly favorable case for casting light on the present problem. The difference between W. Africans and Indians amounts to 44.42%, and the frequency in the U. S. Whites differs only by 6.4% from that in the West Africans. Consequently even a small genetic introgression from the American Indian into the U. S. Negro might be expected to raise the observed R^2 frequency above the expectancy calculated on the basis of White admixture alone.

Ns, like MS, yields anomalous results. Whereas the amount of genetic admixture calculated from MS is only 4.9% (Table 2), it is 60.6% for Ns, if it be assumed that all admixture was with Whites, and 49.2% if all admixture was with Indians. In other words, for some reason the MS combination is more frequent and the Ns combination less frequent than would be expected.

Table 6 presents the analysis based on B, R^2, and Ns. Clearly if Ns is excluded as being anomalous, there is again no

TABLE 6

COMPARISONS OF GENE FREQUENCIES IN CASES WHEREIN THE SERIATION IS
W. AFRICAN NEGRO, U. S. WHITE, AND N. AMERICAN INDIAN
(Supplementary Action, Enhanced by Amerindian Effect)

R^2

W. African Negro		*U. S. White*		*Amerindian*	
Ewe (1)	.0528	New York City (3)	.1499	Chippewa (1)	.5303
Ashanti (1)	.0265				
Nigeria (4)	.1093				

W. Africa (6)	.0861

Expectancy:

$D + D^u$	.1040 — .1045
D	.0999 — .1005

Observed:

U. S. Negro (4)	.1088

B

W. African Negro		*U. S. White*		*Amerindian*	
Nigeria (4)	.1278	New York City (1)	} .078	Chippewa (1)	.000
Other W. African (5)	.174	N. Car. (?) (1)		Sioux (1)	.000

W. African Negro				*Amerindian*	
Average (9)	.1513			Average (2)	.000

Expectancy:

$D + D^u$	.1307 — .1301
D	.1355 — .1348

Observed:

U. S. Negro (3)	.139

Ns

W. African Negro		*U. S. White*		*Amerindian*	
Nigeria (4)	.4901	New York City (1)	.3529	Chippewa (1)	.2208

Expectancy:

$D + D^u$	.4515 — .4503
D	.4605 — .4591

Observed:

U. S. Negro (1)	.4068

Sources of data:

R^2. *W. African Negro:* Ewe (161), Armattoe et al., 1953 (M) Ashanti (113), Armattoe et al., 1953 (M); Nigeria (540), Chalmers et al., 1953 (M). *U. S. White:* N.Y.C. (7317) Unger et al., 1946 (M); N.Y.C. (1468) Wiener et al., 1945 (M); N.Y.C. (1071), Wiener and Gordon, 1949 (M). *Amer. Indian:* Chippewa (161), Matson et al., 1954. *U. S. Negro:* Baltimore (907), Glass and Li (M); N.Y.C. (135), Levine, 1945 (M); N.Y.C. (231), Wiener et al., 1944; N.Y.C. (284), Wiener et al., 1952 (M).

B. *W. African Negro:* (2251) Yoruba, Sierra Leone, Fr. Guinea, Senegal, Ewe (G and L); Nigeria (542), Chalmers et al., 1953 (M). *U. S. White:* N.Y.C. (10,000), Tiber (G and L); N. Car.-? (20,000), Snyder (G and L). *Amer. Indian:* Chippewa (161), Matson et al., 1954; Sioux (48), Matson and Schrader (B). *U. S. Negro:* Baltimore (605), Glass and Li, 1953; N. Car. (500), Snyder (G and L; B); N.Y.C. (730), Landsteiner and Levine (G and L; B).

Ns. *W. African Negro:* Nigeria (451), Chalmers et al., 1953 (M). *U. S. White:* N.Y.C. (394), Wiener et al., 1953 (M). *Amer. Indian:* Chippewa (161), Matson et al., 1954. *U. S. Negro:* Mich. (96), Neel and Hanig, 1951 (M). [B, Boyd, 1939; G and L, Glass and Li, 1953; M, Mourant, 1954]

indication of any detectable shift in gene frequencies attributable to American Indian admixture.

CASES WHEREIN WHITE AND AMERINDIAN GENE FREQUENCIES DEPART FROM THE WEST AFRICAN IN OPPOSITE DIRECTIONS

The final group of cases comprises those which might be denominated cases of "competitive" or "opposed" action, because in them the influence of any genetic admixture between the American Negro and Indian populations would have the effect of reducing the shift from the original W. African frequencies toward those of the U. S. White population. Into this category fall *A* of the ABO system, *r* of the Rh system, and *MS* of the MNS system.

In the case of *A*, the gene frequency in the U. S. White population is 10.0% greater than in the W. African Negroes, and the gene frequency in the N. American Indians is 8.7% lower than that in the W. African Negroes. Although the range of differences is not great, the symmetry is such that any pronounced admixture of the American Indian should be apparent. It is significant that this is another of the few cases in which there are data for "pure" Indians of other tribes than the Chippewa.

In the case of *r*, the range is much greater than for *A*, the difference in gene frequency between U. S. White and W. African Negro being 17.1% and between W. African Negro and Amerindian being 21.1%. Once again, the symmetrical distribution of these differences around the W. African Negro frequency, in the middle, makes the data of particular value in answering our question.

Table 7 reveals that neither the *A* frequencies nor the *r* frequencies yield the slightest indication of any effect of Amerindian admixture.

Ms, like the preceding MNS examples, behaves anomalously. At first sight it might seem that this similarity could rest upon a general excess of *s* and deficiency of *S* in relation to expectation, as shown to exist in Table 2. Actually, the situation is more in-

TABLE 7

COMPARISON OF GENE FREQUENCIES IN CASES WHEREIN THE SERIATION IS U. S. WHITE,
W. AFRICAN NEGRO, AND N. AMERICAN INDIAN — OPPOSITIONAL CASES

	A	
U. S. White	*W. African Negro*	*Amerindian*
New York City (1) ⎫	W. Africa (5)　.153	Chippewa (1)　.0642
⎬ .248		
N. Car. ? (1) ⎭	Nigeria (4)　.1423	
	W. Africa (9)　.1484	

Expectancy:
$D + D^u$　　　.1769 — .1754
D　　　　　.1708 — .1699

Observed:
U. S. Negro (3)　.1875

	r	
U. S. White	*W. African Negro*	*Amerindian*
New York City (2)　.3842	Nigeria (4)　.2005	Chippewa (1)　.0000
	Ewe (1)　.2348	
	Ashanti (1)　.2296	
	W. Africa (6)　.2111	

Expectancy:
$D + D^u$　　　.2612 — .2597
D　　　　　.2502 — .2485

Observed:
U. S. Negro (4)　.2637

	Ms	
U. S. White	*W. African Negro*	*Amerindian*
New York City (1)　.3098	Nigeria (4)　.3755	Chippewa (1)　.4376

Expectancy:
$D + D^u$　　　.3564 — .3570
D　　　　　.3607 — .3613

Observed:
U. S. Negro (1)　.4068

Sources of data:
   A.　U. S. White: N.Y.C. (10,000), Tiber (B; G and L); N. Car.? (20,000), Snyder (B; G and L). *W. African Negro:* (2251) Yoruba, Sierra Leone, Fr. Guinea, Senegal, Ewe (G and L); Nigeria (542), Chalmers et al., 1953 (M). *Amer. Indian:* Chippewa (161), Matson et al., 1954. *U. S. Negro:* Baltimore (605), Glass and Li, 1953; N. Car. (500), Snyder (B; G and L); N.Y.C. (730), Landsteiner and Levine (B; G and L).
   r.　U. S. White: N.Y.C. (7317), Unger et al., 1946 (M); N.Y.C. (1071), Wiener and Gordon, 1949 (M). *W. African Negro:* Nigeria (540), Chalmers et al., 1953 (M), Ewe (161), Armattoe et al., 1953 (M); Ashanti (113), Armattoe et al., 1953 (M). *Amer. Indian:* Chippewa (161), Matson et al., 1954. *U. S. Negro:* Baltimore (907), Glass and Li, 1953 (M); N.Y.C. (231), Wiener et al., 1944; N.Y.C. (135), Levine, 1945 (M); N.Y.C. (284), Wiener et al., 1952 (M).
   Ms.　U. S. White: N.Y.C. (394), Wiener et al., 1953 (M). *W. African Negro:* Nigeria (451), Chalmers et al., 1953 (M). *Amer. Indian:* Chippewa (161), Matson et al., 1954. *U. S. Negro:* Mich. (96), Neel and Hanig, 1951 (M). [B, Boyd, 1939; G and L, Glass and Li, 1953; M, Mourant, 1954]

volved than this, for Table 6 indicates that there is a deficiency of *Ns*, which is offset by the excess over expectation of the *Ms* shown in Table 7. No explanation can be advanced for these anomalies at the present time; but it may be pointed out that the data of Miller *et al.*, although excluded from the present computation for the reason previously given, agree with the data of Neel and Hanig very closely. Here is evidently a puzzling situation which only the further study of MNS frequencies in the respective populations can resolve.

DISCUSSION

The answer to the question whether there is any genetic evidence of a significant amount of gene flow from the Amerindian into the U. S. Negro population is clearly in the negative. Excluding the dubious *S-s* frequencies, the *A*, *B*, *O*, R^1, R^2, *r*, and *MN* frequencies alike indicate no significant shifts in the respective directions to be expected if admixture with the N. American Indian had been considerable. The *A* and *r* cases are particularly conclusive, because in both those cases the effects of the admixture of White and Indian genes would be vectorially opposed to one another, and the range of differences in gene frequency is very great (25% to 38% respectively).

It should not be concluded, of course, that the result of this analysis means that no Indian genes have entered the N. American Negro gene pool. It means only that the effect must be regarded as of very minor magnitude, probably not over the present limits of experimental error in determining gene frequencies in the respective populations. Nor ought one to conclude that because the Negro gene pool has relatively few American Indian genes, the converse is likewise true. That would by no means follow; for the American Indian populations being so much smaller and the tribes so much more isolated in mating than the American Negro population, it may well be that in certain Indian tribes the proportion of genes derived from Negroes is considerable. In fact, the conclusions reached in the present analysis merely reflect what a judgment *a priori* might have decided. For escaped

Negro slaves in colonial times would have left descendants among any Indian tribes with whom they took refuge and intermarried; but those descendants would have remained in the socially defined "Indian" population for the most part. In order that genes from the American Indian population might enter the Negro gene pool, such hybrid individuals would have to forsake their Indian homes and relatives, migrate into some Negro community, and there become accepted as "Negro." It seems far less likely that Indian braves would have mated with Negro women who remained within the Negro community than that admixture was mainly through Negro males who escaped from slavery and found refuge among the Indians. Consequently the Indians were far more exposed to introgression of Negro genes than were Negroes to the introgression of Indian genes.

Why, then, have the anthropologists and sociologists, following Herskovits and Meier, generally assumed that the U. S. Negro has so considerable an admixture of genes from the North American Indians? It seems very probable that the misconception is due to a failure to appreciate the necessary consequences of the Mendelian, that is, particulate, nature of heredity. An Indian ancestor, four or five generations removed, might indeed have a large number of descendants at the present day. It is not so immediately apparent that his contribution to the Negro gene pool is limited quantitatively to that initial set of genes present in each one of his functioning gametes that produced a hybrid offspring. Because of the Mendelian mechanism, the genes in each such original gamete simply become distributed more and more widely among the descendants. In a stable population no introduced gene would increase in number, except by chance or the effects of natural selection, since an F_1 hybrid, or heterozygote, is by the rules of probability expected to produce, among every two offspring, only one carrier of the gene, and like the parent a heterozygote. In a population increasing in size the proportion of the introduced genes to the native genes would remain the same, as long as the reproductive fertility of the hybrid and non-hybrid individuals was the same. For example, if the population in the first generation subsequent to hybridization consisted of 100,000 persons, among whom 10 were hybrids, the net contribution of foreign genes to the gene pool is simply 0.005%, no matter how many individuals might eventually, generations later, be descended from the 10 hybrids. Consequently, unless the introduction of genes from the Indian population took place when the Negro population was very small, or unless the actual number of F_1 hybrids at some later date formed a significant portion of the population, say above 1.0%, and this was repeated over several generations, the contribution of the American Indians to the U. S. Negro gene pool would be too small to detect in the presence of the experimental and statistical errors of several percent now incurred in our determinations of blood group frequencies.

ACKNOWLEDGMENTS

The author would like to acknowledge the assistance of Mr. Timothy Merz in helping to collect and analyze the data; and the valuable criticisms and suggestions of Dr. C. C. Li in the preparation of the manuscript. The opinions expressed are, however, entirely the responsibility of the author.

SUMMARY

1. Recent data published on the frequencies of various blood groups among the West African Negroes make it possible to revise the original estimates made by Glass and Li (53) of the amount of foreign admixture now present in the U. S. Negro population, and of the average amount of gene flow per generation required to account for it. The frequency of R^o (cDe) being taken as .5985 ($D + D^u$) or .5512 (D alone), the new estimate of the amount of admixture in the U. S. Negro population is 28.1-28.97% (based on $D + D^u$) or 21.62-22.55% (based on D alone). The revised estimates of the gene flow per generation are respectively .0325-.0336 or .0241-.0252.

2. By calculating expectancies based on the frequencies of R^o, and upon the assumption that all foreign admixture with the U. S. Negroes was derived from the White population, it has

proved possible to test the hypothesis that there has been a significant American Indian contribution to the U. S. Negro gene pool. The data for A, B, O, R^1, R^2, r, and MN agree in denying the hypothesis. The data derived from the A and r frequencies are particularly conclusive.

3. Anomalies in the available data for P and S (MNS system) are pointed out. These anomalies made it necessary to exclude them from use in the present considerations.

REFERENCES

Allen, F. H., Jr., Diamond, L. K. and Niedziela, B.: A new blood-group antigen, *Nature, 167*:482, 1951.

Armattoe, R. E. G.: The significance and distribution of blood group and rhesus factor among the Ewes, *Med. World,* Aug. 25, 1950.

Armattoe, R. E. G.: ABO and Rh blood types among the Ewes of West Africa, *Am. J. Phys. Anthropol., N. S. 9*:371-373, 1951.

Armattoe, R. E. G., Ikin, E. W. and Mourant, A. E.: The ABO, Rh and MN blood groups of the Ewe and the Ashanti of the Gold Coast, *West African M. J.,* 2:89-93, 1953.

Barnicot, N. A. and Lawler, S. D.: A study of the *Lewis, Kell, Lutheran* and *P* blood group systems and the *ABH* secretion in West African negroes, *Am. J. Phys. Anthropol., N. S.,* 11:83-90, 1953.

Boyd, W. C.: Blood groups, *Tabul. Biol.,* 17:113-240, 1939.

Chalmers, J. N. M., Ikin, E. W. and Mourant, A. E.: The *ABO, MNS* and *Rh* blood groups of the Nigerians, *Ann. Eugen.,* 17:168-176, 1953.

Chown, B. and Lewis, M.: The *ABO, MNSs, P, Rh, Lutheran, Kell, Lewis, Duffy* and *Kidd* blood groups and the secretor status of the Blackfoot Indians of Alberta, Canada, *Am. J. Phys. Anthropol., N. S.,* 11:369-383, 1953.

Donegani, J. A., Ibrahim, K. A., Ikin, E. W. and Mourant, A. E.: The blood groups of the people of Egypt, *Heredity,* 4:377-382, 1950.

Glass, B. and Li, C. C.: The dynamics of racial intermixture—an analysis based on the American negro, *Am. J. Hum. Genet.,* 5:1-20, 1953.

Herskovits, M. J.: *The American Negro; A Study in Racial Crossing,* New York, Knopf, 1928.

Herskovits, M. J.: *The Anthropometry of the American Negro,*

Columbia University Contributions to Anthropology 11, New York, Columbia University Press, 1930.

Herskovits, M. J.:   On the provenience of New World Negroes, *Soc. Forces, 12*:247-267, 1933.

Herskovits, M. J.:   *The Myth of the Negro Past,* New York, Harper, 1941.

Ikin, E. W. and Mourant, A. E.:   The frequency of the Kidd blood-group antigen in Africans, *Man, 52*:21, 1952.

Landsteiner, K. and Levine, P.:   On the racial distribution of some agglutinable structures of human blood, *J. Immunol., 16*:123-131, 1925.

Levine, P.:   Anti-Hr sera, *Nature, 156*:18, 1945.

Matson, G. A., Koch, E. A. and Levine, P: A study of the hereditary blood factors among the Chippewa Indians of Minnesota, *Am. J. Phys. Anthropol., N. S. 12*:413-426, 1954.

Matson, G. A. and Schrader, H. F.:   Blood grouping among the "Blackfeet" and "Blood" tribes of American Indians, *J. Immunol., 25*:155-163, 1933.

Meier, A.:   A study of the racial ancestry of the Mississippi college negro, *Am. J. Phys. Anthropol., N. S. 7*:227-239, 1949.

Miller, E. B., Rosenfield, R. E. and Vogel, P.:   On the incidence of some of the new blood agglutinogens in Chinese and Negroes, *Am. J. Phys. Anthropol., N. S. 9*:115-126, 1951.

Mourant, A. E.:   *The Distribution of the Human Blood Groups,* Springfield, Thomas, 1954.

Neel, J. V. and Hanig, M. M.:   The inheritance and frequency of the MNS factors in the American Negro, *Genetics, 36*:84-92, 1951.

Potter, E. L.:   *Rh . . . Its Relations to Congenital Hemolytic Disease and to Intragroup Transfusion Reactions,* Chicago, Year Book Publishers, 1947.

Rosenfield, R. E., Vogel, P., Gibbel, N., Ohno, G. and Haber, G.:   Anti Jk[a]; three new examples of the isoantibody. Frequency of the factor in Caucasians, Negroes and Chinese of New York City, *Am. J. Clin. Path., 23*:1222-1225, 1953.

Shapiro, M.:   The ABO, MN, P and Rh blood group systems in the South African Bantu, *South African M. J., 25*:165-170, 1951.

Snyder, L. H.:   Human blood groups: their inheritance and racial significance, *Am. J. Phys. Anthropol., 9*:233-263, 1926.

Stern, C.:   Model estimates of the frequency of White and near-White segregants in the American Negro, *Acta Genet. Statist. Med., 4*:281-

298, 1953.

Unger, L. J., Weinberg, M. and Lefkon, M.: The *Rh* factor as applied to the operation of blood banks, *Am. J. Clin. Path., 16*:498-505, 1946.

Wiener, A. S.: *Blood Groups and Transfusion*, Springfield, Thomsa, 1943.

Wiener, A. S., Belkin, R. B. and Sonn, E. B.: Distribution of the A_1-A_2-B-O, M-N, and Rh blood factors among Negroes of New York City, *Am. J. Phys. Anthropol., N. S., 2*:187-194, 1944.

Wiener, A. S., DiDiego, N. and Sokol, S.: Studies on the heredity of the human blood groups. I. The M-N types, *Acta Genet. Med. et Gemel., 2*:391-398, 1953.

Wiener, A. S. and Gordon, E. B.: Studies on the blood factor *Rh, Am. J. Clin. Path., 19*:621-629, 1949.

Wiener, A. S., Gordon, E. B. and Cohen, L.: A new rare *Rhesus* agglutinogen, *Am. J. Human Genet., 4*:363-372, 1952.

Wiener, A. S., Sonn., E. B. and Belkin, R. B.: Heredity and distribution of the *Rh* blood types, *Proc. Soc. Exper. Biol. & Med., 54*:238-240, 1943.

Wiener, A. S., Sonn, E. B. and Belkin, R. B.: Heredity of the *Rh* blood types, *J. Exper. Med., 79*:235-253, 1944.

Wiener, A. S., Sonn, E. B. and Belkin, R. B.: Distribution and heredity of the human blood properties *A, B, M, N, P*, and *Rh, J. Immunol., 50*:341-348, 1945.

Wiener, A. S. and Unger, L. J.: Isoimmunization to factor *P* by blood transfusion, *Am. J. Clin. Path., 14*:616-618, 1944.

Wiener, A. S., Unger, L. J. and Sonn, E. B.: New data on the distribution of the *Rh* blood types, *Proc. Soc. Exp. Biol. & Med., 58*:89-92, 1945.

X. EXPERIMENTAL STUDIES ON RACE

The fact that human races have evolved in geographically-separate and climatically distinct sections of the globe immediately suggests the possibility of local adaptations. It is a reasonable guess that the Polar Eskimos are cold-adapted, that Indonesians can grow satisfactorily on a low caloric intake, or that the Tuareg and Bedouin have a superior water economy. Moreover, it is possible to test many of these hypotheses, using experimental methods.

Naturally, careful distinction must be made between genetic adaptations and physiological adaptations. Cold-climate dwellers are better adapted to cold climates than residents of St. Augustine, Florida because they live in cold climates. Therefore, in experimental studies it is important to allow a sufficient time for physiologic adaptation to take place. Pitting Harvard athletes against Negro sharecroppers without acclimatization hardly constitutes a valid test of racial differences in physiology.

For lack of evidence, it is commonly assumed that the vitamin and amino-acid requirement of all races is the same. In all probability racial differences do occur, especially with respect to vitamin C. Again, one may question whether the cystine and methionine requirements of all races are the same when some races had to live on diets deficient in sulfur-containing amino acids. Just as the volume of the sacral canal differs in Negroes and whites (requiring different amounts of caudal anesthesia), anatomical differences between races may be paralleled by differences in physiologic requirements.

Good experimental studies are possible in comparing races, but great care must be taken to avoid culturally-mediated differences. For example, Chinese-European divergences in urinary amino acid excretion patterns may still be due to differential food selection, even within the standard dietary provided by the University of Michigan Union. Superior fitness indices of American colored draftees may merely reflect better physical conditioning and more experience with manual tasks.

Experimental studies on race can be conducted, and are a most important antidote to purely speculative assumptions. No science has progressed far, until speculation was replaced by the laboratory and by the experimental approach. Nevertheless, investigation of race-differences calls for considerable sophistication, not only in biology and physiology, but also in social anthropology. The weight-corrected, load-carrying capacity of Koreans may exceed that of Americans at the 1% level of confidence, without the difference being genetic at all. Grip-strength of European males may exceed that of "natives" if experience and motivation, in an assemblage of aborigines collected for testing, are lacking.

ADDITIONAL READINGS

Barnicot, N. A.: The experimental approach to physical anthropology, in Roberts, D. F. and Wiener, J. S.: *The Scope of Physical Anthropology*, New York, Wenner-Gren Foundation for Anthropological Research, 1958.

Garn, S. M.: Cultural factors affecting the study of human biology, *Human Biol., 26*:71-79, 1954.

Sutton, H. E. and Clark, P. J.: A biochemical study of Chinese and Caucasoids, *Am. J. Phys. Anthropol., N. S., 13*:53-66, 1955.

Baker, P. T.: Racial differences in heat tolerance, *Am. J. Phys. Anthropol., N. S., 16*:287-306, 1959.

Brown, G. M.: Cold acclimatization in Eskimo, *Arctic, 7*:343-353, 1954.

The Effect of Chronic Exposure to Cold on Temperature and Blood Flow of the Hand

Reprinted with deletion of two figures from *Journal of Applied Physiology*, Vol. 5, No. 5, pp. 221-227 (1953).

By G. Malcolm Brown *and* John Page

Various authors have studied the blood flow of the hand at different ambient temperatures and with the hand at different local temperatures. Spealman ('45), Freeman, Shaw and Snyder ('36), Abramson, Zazeela and Marrus ('39), and Forster, Ferris, Jr. and Day ('46) have determined the effect of short exposure to low ambient temperatures on hand blood flow. We know of no published data concerning the effect of chronic exposure to low ambient temperatures on hand blood flow. It is the purpose of this paper to present observations on hand temperature as well as hand blood flow in a group accustomed to low ambient temperatures and to compare these with a control group.

METHOD

The group accustomed to low ambient temperatures consisted of 22 healthy male Eskimos on Southampton Island, Northwest Territories; their ages varied from 18 to 40 years. The observations in this group were carried out in July and August of 1949 and 1950 when the outdoor temperatures ranged from 30° to 67° F. The average room temperature of the Eskimo dwellings during July was found to be about 20° C. The subjects chosen were all men who lived the native life of hunting and fishing during the summer and hunting and trapping during the winter. Their dwellings were the usual tent, shack or igloo.

The control data were collected by repeating the experiments in September and October of 1951 on 37 young, healthy men attending Queen's University, Kingston, Ontario. The temperatures in Kingston during those months were roughly similar to those on Southampton Island during July and August.

All experiments were conducted at a mean room temperature of 20° ± 0.5°C. and a relative humidity from 50 to 60 per cent. The amount of clothing that was comfortable for the Eskimo was worn by both groups, with the exception that the Eskimo wore seal skin muklucks while the control group wore oxfords. This clothing consisted of a woolen shirt and trousers. The subjects were studied in a fasting state.

The experimental method was patterned after the investigation of temperature and blood flow in the forearm by Barcroft and Edholm ('43, '46). Direct hand blood flow measurements were made with a Lewis-Grant ('25) type of venous occlusion plethysmograph. Temperatures were measured by means of thermocouples. Blood pressures were recorded with a sphygmomanometer.

The left wrist and forearm were shaved and a plethysmographic cuff of suitable size was applied. The superficial veins were marked out so that the thermocouple junctions would not be placed near them. A rectal thermocouple was introduced approximately 6 inches into the rectum. The subject then lay on a couch, his trunk and head being elevated to a 30° angle.

At the end of a 30-minute rest period thermojunctions were attached to the thenar eminence, the dorsum of the hand and to the dorsal aspects of the distal phalanges of the first, third and fifth fingers. The plethysmograph was fastened into position and raised to heart level. The appropriate venous occluding pressure was determined for each subject and the experiments were begun 10 to 15 minutes after the rest period. Hand blood flow and temperature measurements were made every 2½ minutes during the first half hour and every 5 minutes thereafter. Pulse and blood pressure were recorded every 5 minutes during the first half-hour and every 10 minutes thereafter. Two groups of experiments were carried out: a) Hand blood flow and temperature in room air at 20° C.; the plethysmograph was not ventilated. b) Hand blood flow in water-baths at 5° to 45° C. Except for the experiments in the 5° C. water-bath, the observations were made over a 2-hour period.

RESULTS

Studies Conducted in Room Air at 20° C. The Eskimos were comfortable throughout the 2-hour experiments while the majority of the control group stated that they felt cool. The hand blood flow over a 2-hour period, the average of the five skin temperatures, and the rectal temperature are shown in Figure 1. The average hand blood flow and the average skin temperature over the entire 2-hour period are shown for both groups in Table 1. As can be seen, the hand blood flow and temperature of the

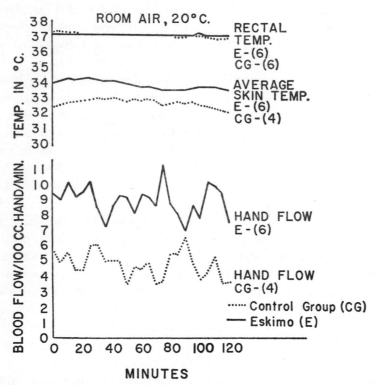

Fig. 1. Rectal temperature, hand temperature, and hand blood flow over a 2-hour period in room air at 20° C. in both the control group and the Eskimo group. Skin temperatures are the average of simultaneous readings from five different sites (redrawn from Brown and Page '52, Fig. 1).

TABLE 1

AVERAGE HAND BLOOD FLOW AND SKIN TEMPERATURE IN ESKIMO
AND CONTROL GROUP IN ROOM AIR AT 20° C

	Hand Blood Flow			Hand Temperature		
	No. of Subj.	No. of Obser.	Hand Blood Flow & S.E.*	No. of Subj.	No. of Obser. on 5 Areas of Hand	Temp of Hand in °C
Control group	5	122	4.7 ± 0.19	5	611	32.8
Eskimo	6	148	8.6 ± 0.43	6	750	33.8

* In cc/100 cc. of tissue/minute.

TABLE 2

EFFECT OF DIFFERENT WATER-BATH TEMPERATURES ON HAND BLOOD FLOW

Bath Temp., °C	Control Group			Eskimo		
	No. of Subj.	No. of Obser.	Hand Blood Flow* and S.E.	No. of Subj.	No. of Obser.	Hand Blood Flow* and S.E.
45.0	3	75	19.7 ± 0.68			
42.5	4	100	16.7 ± 0.47	2	50	18.5 ± 0.64
38.0	4	100	9.2 ± 0.44			
35.0	4	100	6.1 ± 0.42	2	50	10.3 ± 0.68
33.0				5	124	8.6 ± 0.31
32.0	4	100	4.5 ± 0.30			
30.0	4	98	3.8 ± 0.23	4	92	7.1 ± 0.43
20.0	4	96	0.8 ± 0.07	5	121	3.3 ± 0.20
10.0	5	123	1.0 ± 0.05	5	121	3.7 ± 0.26
5.0	3	57	2.9 ± 0.12	3	84	4.1 ± 0.11

* In cc/100 cc. of tissue/minute.

Eskimo were greater than those of the control group. In both groups, the blood flow and temperature decreased slightly over the 2 hours. A greater degree of fluctuation occurred in the blood flow in the Eskimo subjects. The rectal temperature of the Eskimo remained constant while that of the control group decreased 0.4° C. on the average during the 2-hour period.

Studies on Hand Blood Flow at Different Water-Bath Temperatures 5-20° C. Hand blood flows were observed within 45 to 60 seconds following immersion of the hand and forearm. In the 20° C. water-bath, the blood flow of the control group was quickly and markedly reduced while that of the Eskimo fell more slowly. At 5° and 10° C. marked reduction occurred rapidly in both groups. At all bath temperatures in this range the rate of reduction in average hand blood flow was less in the Eskimo.

At 5° C., the blood flow of the Eskimo achieved a steady state within 15 minutes while 30 to 40 minutes were required at 10° and 20° C. In all baths from 5° to 20° C., the control group attained equilibrium within 10 minutes. When equilibrium had been achieved, there was in only one case a variation of more than 1 cc. in the subsequent determinations of individual blood flows. In the 5° C. water-bath, in one Eskimo a high blood flow occurred 90 minutes after immersion. It was an isolated reading and we are unable to account for it; it may have been an artefact. At the conclusion of observation in the 5° C. water-baths, loud noises and painful stimuli failed to alter blood flow.

At any time during the period of observation at these temperatures, the hand blood flow of the Eskimo was greater than that of the control group. The blood flow at 5° C. was greater than that at 10° and 20° C. in both groups, but this effect was more marked in the control group. Figure 2 shows the average hand blood flows at these temperatures throughout the 2-hour period.

30-35° C. In both groups studied, no appreciable alteration in blood flow occurred upon immersion in the 30° to 35° C. water-baths. A steady state was achieved within 10 minutes in all individuals. The frequency and magnitude of fluctuations in hand blood flow increased as the temperature of the water in-

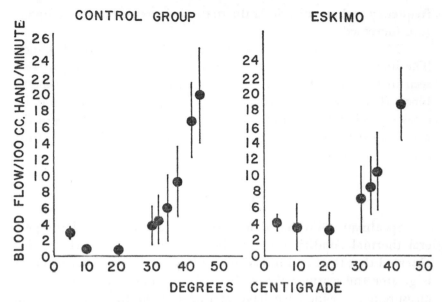

Fig. 2. Average hand blood flow at various hand water-bath temperatures in Eskimo and in the control group, with standard deviations. *Each point* is the mean value of all hand blood flow measurements made at that particular water-bath temperature over a 2-hour period, except in the case of the control group at 5° C. when the period was 1½ hours (redrawn from Brown and Page '52, Fig. 4).

creased. The degree of fluctuation was greater in the Eskimo.

The volume of hand blood flow increased as the temperature of the water-bath increased (Fig. 2). In this range of bath temperature the blood flow of the Eskimo was greater than that of the control group. At 30° to 33° C., the average blood flows in both groups decreased slightly over the 2-hour period. At 35° C., the Eskimo blood flow remained fairly constant while that of the control group decreased slightly. The volume and pattern of hand blood flow in both groups in water-baths at 32° and 33° C. closely resembled that in room air at 20° C.

38-45° C. Increased hand blood flow occurred immediately in all control group subjects and the increase was greater at the higher temperatures. A fairly constant pattern was achieved within 30 to 50 minutes. The volume of the blood flow and the frequency and magnitude of fluctuations increased as the temperature increased.

The hand blood flow was studied at 42.5° C. in the Eskimos. The increase in blood flow upon immersion was similar to that seen in the control group. However, the subsequent volume of blood flow was greater than that of the control group and increased gradually over the 2-hour period. The blood flows of the Eskimos fluctuated more at this temperature than did those of the control group.

DISCUSSION

Spealman ('45) has demonstrated the influence of the general thermal condition of the body on hand blood flow. He observed that the hand blood flow at any given water temperature is greater the warmer the body. The results of the blood flow measurements which we have carried out on the Eskimo at an ambient temperature of 20° C. are similar to those obtained by other workers who have studied the effect of hand temperature on the hand blood flow in man in temperature climates at an ambient temperature of 24° to 27° C. (Spealman '45, Abramson, Zazeela and Marrus '39, Abramson and Fierst, '42). The blood flow and temperature measurments in our control group are in accordance with those made by other workers at similar ambient temperatures on similar subjects (Spealman '45, Killian and Oclassen '38). At their usual summer temperature, the Eskimo has a higher hand blood flow at various water-bath temperatures than does the white man used to a temperate climate; and the results of our studies at one ambient temperature, taken with Spealman's results, suggest that at a given water-bath temperature he has also a higher hand blood flow at various ambient temperatures.

It is to be noted that not only is the hand blood flow greater at low temperatures in the Eskimo than in the white man but also that there is a more precipitous drop in the white man to low levels immediately following exposure to cold. This indicates a greater ability on the part of the Eskimo to maintain hand blood flow for short periods of exposure.

Abramson, Zazeela and Marrus ('39) in comparing hand blood flow measurements at 32° and 45° C. observed that average hand blood flows showed less difference between subjects at 45° than at 32° C. In addition they found that spontaneous changes in the base line usually observed at 32° C. were practically absent at 45° C. They concluded from these observations that minimal fluctuation occurs in hand blood flow at 45° C . We have found, however, in every individual of both groups studied that the frequency and magnitude of fluctuation in successive observations of blood flow was maximal at 42.5° to 45° C. A similar increase in the frequency and magnitude of fluctuations in forearm blood flow at high bath temperatures has been reported by Barcroft and Edholm ('43), and also noted by ourselves.

We have not been able to find any published data concerning the length of time required for the hand blood flow to equilibrate at various water-bath temperatures. The length of time allowed by different workers for the hand blood flow to adjust to a water-bath has varied from 15 minutes (Freeman '35) to 120 minutes (Spealman '45). In all baths between 5° to 35° C., the hand blood flow of the control group subjects reached a steady state within 10 minutes following immersion whereas 30 to 50 minutes were required at the 38° to 45° C. range. The hand blood flow of the Eskimo was slower in equilibrating in the cold and very warm baths.

The vasodilatation which occurs in the skin in response to extreme local cooling was attributed by Lewis ('30) to a local axon reflex. The role of the arteriovenous anastomoses in this response was demonstrated by Grant ('30), Grant and Bland ('31), Grant, Bland and Camp ('32). Increased blood flow in response to extreme local cooling has been demonstrated plethysmographically in the fingers (Greenfield and Shepherd '50) and in the hand (Spealman '45). The failure of additional and distant noxious stimuli to alter the response in our experiments suggests a local mechanism for this vasodilatation, but the observation of Spealman ('45) that the volume of hand blood flow was influenced by the general thermal condition of the body even in extremely cold baths, is against this being the only mechanism.

Our studies are in accordance with Spealman's observation. We feel that this reaction although it has a local and perhaps chemical basis, as suggested by Lewis, is also influenced by the thermal condition of the body.

It has often been remarked that the Eskimos are better able to work with their bare hands in the cold than are white men. There are certainly many factors concerned in this and perhaps not the least is a remarkable tolerance of discomfort on their part. It seems to us, however, that the increased hand blood flow which we have demonstrated has importance in this regard, and this increased blood flow with the increase in hand temperature may explain the relatively enhanced kinaesthetic sensibility and ability to perform fine movements which have been demonstrated by Mackworth ('49) in persons chronically exposed to the cold. Hunter and Whillans ('51) have shown that in the cat, exposure of the knee joint to low ambient temperatures is associated with an important increase in the force required to start movement at the joint, and suggested that an increase in the viscosity of synovial fluid and decrease in the flexibility of the joint capsule and tendons are factors which may be responsible. Increased blood flow and temperature would diminish the degree of these changes. There may be other factors such as the difference in the composition of adipose tissue which play a part.

SUMMARY

A comparative study on hand blood flow and temperature has been carried out on Eskimos in the Canadian Eastern Arctic and on medical students living in a temperate climate. One of the effects of chronic exposure of the individual to cold is a reduction in the ambient temperature required for comfort. At this low ambient temperature, the hand blood flow of the Eskimo is twice that of the white man and the skin temperature of his hand is greater. At any given water-bath temperature, the hand blood flow of the Eskimo is greater. The volume of the hand blood flow of the Eskimo changes more slowly in response to local cold. The degree of spontaneous fluctuation in hand blood flow is greater in the Eskimo and increases in both groups as the local temperature of the hand increases. The alterations which occur in the hand blood flow following chronic exposure to cold would appear to enhance hand function in the cold.

Acknowledgement is gratefully made of the assistance provided by Mr. Gordon Bird and Dr. John Green who, along with the authors, were members of the Queen's University Arctic Expeditions 1949 and 1950.

REFERENCES

Spealman, C. R.: Effect of ambient air temperature and of hand temperature on blood flow in hands, *Am. J. Physiol., 145*:218-222, 1945.

Freeman, N. E., Shaw, J. L. and Snyder, J. C.: Peripheral blood flow in surgical shock; reduction in circulation through hand resulting from pain, fear, cold, and asphyxia, with quantitative measurements of volume flow of blood in clinical cases of surgical shock, *J. Clin. Invest., 15*:651-664, 1936.

Abramson, D. I., Zazeela, H. and Marrus, J.: Plethysmographic studies of peripheral blood flow in man; physiologic factors affecting resting blood flow in extremities, *Am. Heart J., 17*:206-217, 1939.

Forster, R. E., Ferris, Jr., B. G. and Day, R.: Relationship between total heat exchange and blood flow in hand at various ambient temperatures, *Am. J. Physiol., 146*:600-609, 1946.

Barcroft, H. and Edholm, O. G.: Effect of temperature on blood flow and deep temperature in human forearm, *J. Physiol., 102*:5-20, 1943.

Barcroft, H. and Edholm, O. G.: Temperature and blood flow in human forearm, *J. Physiol., 104*:366-376, 1946.

Lewis, T. and Grant, R.: Reactive hyperaemia in man, *Heart, 12*: 73-120, 1925.

Abramson, D. I. and Fierst, S. M.: Resting blood flow and peripheral vascular responses in hypertensive subjects, *Am. Heart J., 23*:84-98, 1942.

Killian, J. A. and Oclassen, C. A.: Comparative effects of water baths and mustard baths at varying temperatures on rate of peripheral blood flow in man, *Am. Heart J., 15*:425-433, 1938.

Freeman, N. E.: Effect of temperature on rate of blood flow in normal and in sympathectomized hand, *Am. J. Physiol., 113*:384-398, 1935.

Lewis, T.: Observations upon reactions of vessels of human skin to cold, *Heart, 15*:177-208, 1930.

Grant, R. T.: Observations on direct communications between arteries and veins in rabbit's ear, *Heart, 15*:281-303, 1930.

Grant, R. T. and Bland, E. F.: Observations on arteriovenous anastomoses in human skin and in bird's foot with special reference to reaction to cold, *Heart, 15*:385-407, 1931.

Grant, R. T., Bland, E. F. and Camp, P. D.: Observations on vessels and nerves of rabbit's ear with special reference to reaction to cold, *Heart, 16*:69-101, 1932.

Greenfield, A. D. M. and Shepherd, J. T.: Quantitative study of response to cold of circulation through fingers of normal subjects, *Clin. Sc., 9*:323-347, 1950.

Mackworth, N. H.: Personal communication, 1949.

Hunter, J. and Whillans, M. G.: Study of effect of cold on joint temperature and mobility, *Canad. J. M. Sc., 29*:255-262, 1951.

Racial Variations to a Standardized Cold Stress

Reprinted from *Journal of Applied Physiology*, Vol. 12, No. 1, pp. 9-12 (1958).

By Thomas Adams *and* Benjamin G. Covino

The reports of cold injury among combat personnel in Korea (Orr, '51-'52) and in recent Army winter maneuvers (Weiner, Ellenhorn, Chamovitz, Eskind, Mirel, Berg, Staffeld, and Vissotsky, '52) suggest a possible physiological difference in the response of various racial and ethnic groups to a severe cold stress. Meehan ('55) initially observed a racial difference in the digital vascular response to cold during ice water immersion of the hand. His results indicated a greater vascular tone and an absence of finger temperature cycling (hunting response) among Negro subjects as compared to Caucasian and Eskimo test personnel. From these observations, he suggested a true physiological basis for the greater incidence of cold injury observed among Negroes. In the light of these reports, this investigation was initiated in an effort to separate inherent racial or ethnic characteristics from other factors which predispose to cold injury.

Preliminary studies (Adams and Rennie, '57) conducted on clothed Negro and Caucasian volunteers revealed further differences in peripheral cooling rates, whole body cooling and metabolic rates between these two racial groups during exposure to an air temperature of $-10°$ C. This present study attempted to illustrate more clearly the basis for these observed differences by subjecting nude individuals to an air temperature of $17°$ C.

METHODS

Seven Negro and seven Caucasian subjects were randomly selected from the Army personnel stationed at Ladd Air Force Base, Alaska. Six Eskimo subjects were obtained from Anaktuvuk Pass, a small, isolated inland village in the Brooks Range of northern Alaska. All experimental observations were made during the months of July and August 1956, in order to avoid the possible complication of cold acclimatization.

On the day of each cold room exposure, the subject reported to the laboratory in a fasted state. In order to de-emphasize the effect of fasting as a separate stress, each individual was given a small, known caloric amount of food prior to actually entering the cold room. A rectal thermocouple was inserted and 16 skin thermocouples were attached as previously described (Adams and Rennie, '57). Copper electrodes were placed on the chest, upper arm and thigh for electromyographic recordings. The subject was then covered with two woolen blankets and carried into the cold chamber which was set at 17° C. After control values were obtained for 30 minutes, the blankets were removed and a 2-hour cold exposure period began. With the exception of the control measurements, each subject was exposed in the cold room clad only in cotton shorts and resting supine on a wire mesh cot which was suspended in the middle of the room.

Average skin temperatures were recorded according to the method of Hardy and DuBois ('38). Rectal, skin and room temperatures were recorded continuously on Brown-Honeywell recording potentiometers; these instruments were calibrated to within 0.1° C. with a National Bureau of Standards thermometer before, during and following the cold room exposures.

Metabolic rate determinations were accomplished during the control and experimental periods by measuring expired air volumes, an aliquot sample of which was continually directed through a Beckman Oxygen Analyzer. Actual calculation of this measure followed the method proposed by Weir ('49). Electromyographic tracings were recorded on a Gilson 8-channel electromyograph. All measurements were collected in duplicate and the methods and temperatures integrated for 5-minute intervals throughout the control and exposure periods.

RESULTS

As shown in Figure 1, no statistical difference (*P* greater than 0.05) can be observed in the measures of average skin or rectal temperatures between the Negro and Caucasian groups, during either the control period or the 2-hour exposure following the removal of the blankets from the resting subject. An absolute temperature difference does exist, however, between the Eskimo and the other two groups in this measure. This group maintained their higher core and shell temperatures throughout the entire exposure period (Fig. 1).

The Eskimo personnel also exhibited a significantly higher metabolic rate (50 Cal/hr/m²) during the control period than either the Negro (38 Cal/hr/m²) or Caucasian (40 Cal/hr/m²) groups (*P* greater than 0.05) (Fig. 2). There is no statistical difference between the control metabolic measurements for the Negro and Caucasian subjects. Both the Eskimo and Cauca-

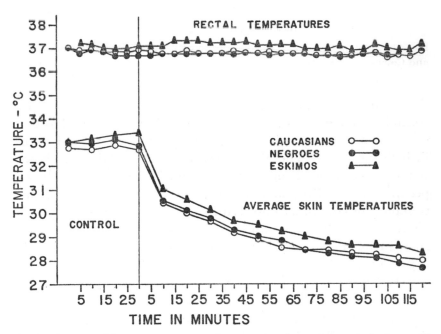

Fig. 1. Average skin temperatures and mean rectal temperatures during cold room exposure (redrawn from Adams and Covino '58, Fig. 1).

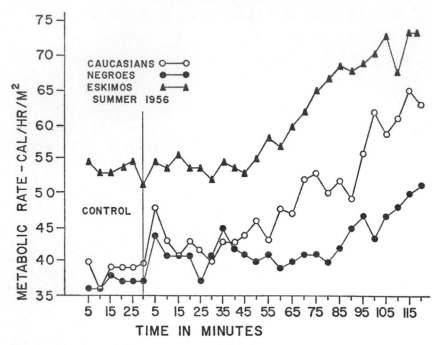

Fig. 2.   Mean metabolic rate during cold room exposure (redrawn from Adams and Covino '58, Fig. 2).

sian groups showed a significant rise in heat production over the control values after 55 minutes of the cold exposure (*P* less than 0.05).   The average rise in metabolic rate was 22 Cal/hr/m² in both instances.   The Negro groups, however, failed to show a significantly elevated metabolic rate until 85 minutes in the exposure period.   Even at this time, the augmented heat production did not equal that observed in either of the two groups.   In all three groups, the significant increase in metabolic rate occurred coincidentally with the onset of shivering as indicated by electromyographic tracings.

Following the removal of the blanket from the resting subject at the end of the control period, there was an immediate rise in heat production of approximately 8 Cal/hr/m² in all three groups.   This increase is not permanent and the level soon returns to that approximating the control values (Fig. 2) .

Figure 3 illustrates the relationship of the average metabolic rate determinations and the average skin temperature measurements. This figure indicates that the Eskimo and Caucasian subjects began to increase their metabolic rates at a considerably higher average skin temperature than did the Negro group. As noted in Figure 2, the Eskimo subjects maintained a higher level of heat production throughout the test, compared to the other two groups. Both the Caucasian and Eskimo groups shivered when the average skin temperatures were approximately 29.5° C., whereas the Negro subjects continued to cool to an average skin temperature of 28° C. before the onset of shivering and the consequent increase in heat production occurred. As a result of the differences in the levels of heat production and surface tem-

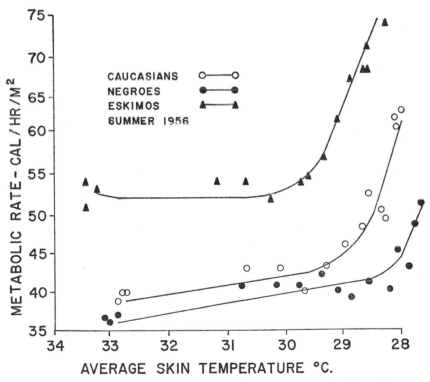

Fig. 3. Mean metabolic rate vs. average skin temperature during cold room exposure (redrawn from Adams and Covino '58, Fig. 3).

peratures, the upper absolute level of heat production attained and the comparative increase over the control level for each group is different at the termination of the test (Fig. 3).

DISCUSSION

As a result of the comparatively warmer exposure temperatures used in this study, no difference in finger temperature or extremity cooling rates was observed between the groups tested, as compared to earlier reports (Meehan, '55; Adams and Rennie, '57). Starting from statistically the same average skin temperature levels of 33° C. during the control period, the Negro and Caucasian subjects both cool at the same rate throughout the cold exposure to 28° C. at the end of the test. There is no statistical difference between the data for these groups in this measure at any point in the test. A difference in thermal state between these groups is apparently not a factor modifying temperature or metabolic responses of these two groups in this design.

The significantly elevated metabolic rates observed in the Eskimo group undoubtedly account for the ability of this group to maintain higher average skin and rectal temperatures prior to and during the cold exposure. Brown *et al.* ('54) and Rodahl ('52) have also reported similar high values for metabolic rates among Canadian and Alaskan Eskimos, and believe that the high specific dynamic action of the native diet probably accounts, in part, for this increased level of heat production.

It is interesting to note that, although the Eskimo possesses a higher metabolic rate and elevated shell and core temperatures than the Caucasian, the pattern of response of these two groups to a standardized cold stress is the same as indicated by the shivering and metabolic response reported here. There apparently exists no true physiological difference between the basic responses of the Eskimo and Caucasian to cold. The seemingly greater tolerance of the Eskimo to cold under field conditions is probably related to dietary, psychological, clothing, acclimatization and other physiologically extraneous factors.

The Negro subjects, on the other hand, beginning from

statistically the same temperature and heat production levels as the Caucasian subjects (Blaisdell, '51) did not increase their metabolic rate levels until relatively late in the exposure (85 min.), and reach a considerably more precarious state of thermal balance before increasing heat production. The failure of the Negro group to increase heat production as soon as or as quantitatively high as the other two groups is indicative of an increased susceptibility to cold injury. This confirms previous findings of the differential responses of clothed Negroes and Caucasian subjects to severe cold (Adams and Rennie, '57).

The additional heat produced following the onset of shivering in any group is not reflected in the measure of average skin and rectal temperature, due to the nature of this measure and the skin temperature areas sampled to produce this parameter. However, warmer hand, feet, finger and toe temperatures have been observed correlative to the Eskimo-Caucasian response in comparison to the Negro group (Adams and Rennie, '57). The amount of additional heat afforded the shivering individual can be accounted for by the increased convective heat loss associated with shivering and by the warmer, more actively heat radiating extremities.

The lower average skin temperatures reached by the Negro group prior to the onset of shivering and subsequent increase in heat production further evidences a physiological difference between this group and the others tested in a response to severe cold.

In addition to the increased digital vascular tone of the Negro reported earlier (Meehan, '55; Adams and Rennie, '57), this evidence further indicates a decreased metabolic response and suggests an elevated shivering threshold in this group compared to the others tested. It is suggested, on the basis of these observations, that real physiological differences in the response to cold do exist between these racial groups, and that the direction of this response would favor increased cold injury among Negro personnel exposed to a cold stress (Orr, '51-'52).

REFERENCES

Orr, K. D. and Fainer, D. C.: *Cold Injuries in Korea During Winter of 1950-51,* Army Medical Research Laboratory, Proj. No. 6-64-12-028, Rep. No. 113, Fort Knox, Ky., 1951-52.

Weiner, D., Ellenhorn, M. J., Chamovitz, D., Eskind, I., Mirel, E., Berg, W., Staffeld, S. E., and Vissotsky, H. J.: *Cold Agglutinens and Frost Bite,* Army Medical Research Laboratory, Proj. No. 6-64-12-028, Rep. No. 90, Fort Knox, Ky., 1952.

Meehan, J. P.: *Individual and Racial Variations in Vascular Response to Cold Stimulus,* Proj. No. 7-7953, Rep. No. 1, Arctic Aeromedical Laboratory, APO 731, Seattle, Wash. (Ladd AFB, Alaska), 1955.

Adams, T. and Rennie, D. W.: *The Comparative Tolerance of Negroes and Caucasians to a Standardized Cold Stress as Indicated by Body Temperature and Metabolic Rate,* Tech. Rep. No. 57-20, Arctic Aeromedical Laboratory, APO 731, Seattle, Wash. (Ladd AFB, Alaska), 1955.

Hardy, J. D. and DuBois, E. F.: Technic of measuring radiation and convection, *J. Nutrition, 15*:461-475, 1938.

Weir, J. B. de V.: New methods for calculating metabolic rate with special reference to protein metabolism, *J. Physiol., 109*:1-9, 1949.

Brown, G. M., Bird, G. S., Boag, L. M., Delahaye, D. J., Green, J. E., Hatcher, J. D. and Page, J.: Blood volume and basal metabolic rate of Eskimos, *Metabolism, 3*:247-254, 1954.

Rodahl, K.: Basal metabolism of Eskimo, *J. Nutrition, 48*:359-368, 1952.

Blaisdell, R. K.: *Effect of Body Thermal State on Cold-Induced Cyclic Vasodilation in the Finger,* Environmental Protection Section, OQMG, MPD, Rep. No. 117, Lawrence, Mass., 1951.

SUBJECT INDEX